great cover
(R. Kent)

3·75

WFC

Men and Volts

EDISON CONCEIVES THE ELECTRIC LIGHT

MEN and VOLTS

The Story of
General Electric

By

John Winthrop Hammond

PHILADELPHIA   LONDON

J. B. Lippincott Company

NEW YORK

Contents

CONTENTS

[PART THREE]
Electric Transportation, Motors, the Transmission of Power

[PART FOUR]
The Period of Expansion and Consolidation

[PART FIVE]
The Formation of the General Electric Company

[PART SIX]
The Development of Big Generating Units, Beginning of Hydroelectric Projects, Expansion of Systems through Transmission

CONTENTS

Preface

JOHN WINTHROP HAMMOND spent more than three years in collecting the historical material for this volume. In 1922, when he started this work, many of the pioneers of the electrical industry were still living, and he was able to get the story from their own lips. Hammond had the temperament of the true historian; he waded through records, he tracked traditional stories to their sources. And because he saw the epic of electricity in terms of men, the story he wrote was a human one. To him, this history was a labor of love.

John Hammond died in 1934. The three hundred thousand word manuscript which he had prepared was later edited and condensed to approximately its present dimensions by Arthur Pound, well-known writer on industrial subjects. With a few minor changes, it is here presented.

Because Hammond's manuscript closed with the year 1922, a brief Epilogue has been added, highlighting the major achievements of the succeeding years. In addition, there has been included as an Appendix the statement presented before the Temporary National Economic Committee by Owen D. Young, Honorary Chairman of the Board.

This volume is published as a record of the amazing accomplishments of those pioneers of the electrical industry who, in the face of almost insurmountable difficulties, harnessed the gigantic force of electricity and put it to work to serve mankind. But the drama of the progress of electricity is a never-ending one; it goes forward today with an ever-changing cast. May this record of the courageous work of the pioneers serve as an inspiration to the men and women who carry on their work today!

Prologue

To PEER INTO THE FUTURE—to be allowed for one precious moment to see the world as it will be sixty years from now—what wouldn't any of us give to see the marvels yet undreamed of that will mark the year 2000? And even could we, by some strange happenstance, see for a fleeting moment the wonders of that day, would we believe what we saw? Probably not, for the world of sixty years hence will be as different from today as today is different from the world of sixty years ago.

The world of sixty years ago—1880—some can still remember it. No electric lights, except in the hands of a few ridiculed experimenters; no electric streetcars, except in the minds of a few "addled visionaries"; no electricity at all, except in a few isolated applications that had not yet penetrated the consciousness of the laity. Yet in the years to follow, the experimenters, the visionaries, the men of science were to create a world as unbelievable to the people of that day as the imaginings of a Jules Verne. And even they could not foresee the vast changes that their work would bring.

We, who today enjoy the comforts, the conveniences, the

high living standards that they created for us, see but the outer shell of a grand and intricately woven matrix, into the creation of which has been spent the genius of three generations. To most of us, the world of today is the world of all-time—of yesterday, today, tomorrow. We cannot peer ahead —we are intolerant of the struggles of the past. And yet, if we but realize it, to stand at our present vantage point and follow step by step the weird discoveries of the pioneers is as fascinating a journey as the mind of man can hope to take. And having taken it, the world of today will never again be to us the world of all-time—it becomes rather a position achieved by the diligence of those who have gone before; a foundation upon which we too must build to that unknown destiny that holds the fate of man.

With the past to inspire us, no goal is too difficult, no objective too high, no idea too visionary to command our efforts. No matter how large or how small the part we play, each is essential in the scheme of things. Ours is the torch to carry forward, that the world of tomorrow may be an even better world in which to live.

In this volume, the pioneer period of General Electric's history is related in detail—the history of the last two decades all too briefly. But someday, when time has added the perspective so essential in preparing a historical narrative, the story of those two decades must be told, for it was in these years that many of the efforts of the pioneers were brought to fruition. And in this period, too, were sown the seeds that will mature to create the wonders of the world to come.

PHILIP D. REED, *Chairman*
CHARLES E. WILSON, *President*
General Electric Company

[PART ONE]

The Creative Period of the Arc Light

and the Incandescent Light

1

Planters of the Acorn

AMERICAN LIFE AT THE BEGINNING OF 1876 appears to our twentieth-century eye a simple, unhurried existence. Horse-cars jangled leisurely through the principal streets of the larger cities. Multitudes of horses furnished their motive power, at the expense of immense stables and many grooms. The life of these horses was rigorous, and on the average they lived only about three years. In 1886, according to an estimate published at that time, the 500 horse railways operating in the United States utilized 120,000 horses for 25,000 cars, or more than four horses to a car.

In these conveyances business men of the seventies rode to store or office. In the wintertime passengers' feet were embedded in hay or straw, with which the floors were carpeted for the sake of warmth.

As evening approached, lamplighters made their rounds through the city streets. Many were Civil War veterans, and the "lame lamplighter" became almost a proverbial figure. The lamps made small, yellow spots of illumination in the darkness, dotting the gloomy streets in double lines. They burned with a certain amount of flicker from air currents in

3

the square glass chambers. A high wind was apt to extinguish them. In thrifty cities the lamps were turned out on nights of the full moon.

This was the era of the reciprocating steam engine. Wherever power in large volume was required, there the reciprocating engine was to be found. The engines were bulky and towering—a bewildering spectacle of intricate parts in noisy motion.

Gas companies flourished, though they were targets of public criticism. The young clerk courted his sweetheart by gas-light. One of the perennial jokes of the day was built upon the romantic practice of turning down the gas in the front room while Sally entertained her beau. In most houses, however, it was an almost daily chore to fill the kerosene lamps, trim wicks and keep the glass chimneys washed.

New York in 1876 was a city of ground-scrapers. Few buildings rose higher than five stories, and in downtown Manhattan there were quaint brick structures with a Dutch air about them. Fulton Street, going down to the old Fulton Ferry, was the suburban outlet, where twice a day crowds surged in the great American "rush-hour." In the nation's manufacturing plants lines of shafting turned hour after hour and a maze of belts whirred ceaselessly; in the back country, mountain streams tumbled impetuously toward the sea, unharnessed, unmolested.

Eighteen seventy-six was America's centennial year, and it's Centennial Exposition was destined to open a new gateway, on which might well have been carved a proverb after the manner of Solomon: "It is the glory of God to conceal a thing; but the honor of man to search it out." Through that gateway lay the Electrical Era.

The prophets of that age smiled in condescension when its pioneers dared to assert that the future belonged to the mysterious force with which Ben Franklin, more than a century before, had played. People might listen; but soon they shrugged skeptical shoulders and turned to the other wonders of the Centennial Exposition, marking the end of a century of existence for the United States of America.

The Exposition, like all such displays, was chiefly a record of things done. It was concerned with history, not with prophecy. Nonetheless, there was a real prophet present, not of flesh and blood, but a thing of iron and copper; not a man with ringing voice, but a man-made machine, whispering a new language. That prophet was the electric dynamo.

There were two types of dynamos represented at the Exposition; the Gramme and the Wallace, one Belgian and one American. Small and unobtrusive, each supplied current to a single arc lamp. One of them, connected to a second dynamo, drove a small pump.

"What curiosities!" spectators remarked, held for a moment by the dazzle of bluish light. Then they passed on, to lavish their admiration upon the huge Corliss steam engine. This gigantic machine overshadowed everything in Machinery Hall. Thirty feet high, the world's greatest prime mover, and wonder of the exposition, it was capable of producing one thousand horsepower of mechanical energy!

The mighty engine was daily applauded, the little electric dynamos quickly forgotten. Purring quietly in their corners, they gave no intimation that they would one day compel the steam giant to bow its head in defeat. Even before the Exposition closed, the principle of electricity yoked for service had established itself. Inventive minds kept prodding it into more tangible reality. These were the successors of Davy, of Faraday, of Henry. And in the work of four of them is to be found the acorn that became the oak. Each of these four was a pioneer; each struggled courageously to introduce a startling innovation. They were men of imagination and faith, whom doubt and criticism did not daunt.

Charles Francis Brush in the year of the Exposition was fashioning an electric dynamo which created illumination through the agency of arc lamps. Elihu Thomson and James John Wood were soon to fashion dynamos of their own, each of distinct design. The fourth of these pioneers was Thomas Alva Edison.

None of these four men had an inkling that his activities would be of value to the others. Practical dreamers though they were, each with his own theories, his own workshop, and his own financial supporters, there is no intimation that any one of them foresaw the tidal currents which in hardly more than fifteen years were to sweep them into a single powerful organization.

The gates to a new era began to swing open under the pressure of new ideas.

2

A Light in the West

OLD "UNCLE" BALDWIN, so the story goes, had come to Cleveland in 1877 to see the sights. One of the most amazing things he observed was a light of peculiar brilliance blazing at the door of a little shop.

"That's a wonderful light, wonderful!" the old fellow murmured to a young man who stood in the doorway.

"That, sir," the young man told him, "is the light of the future—electricity. Some day you'll see it light the entire world."

Charles F. Brush, who at the age of twenty-eight had successfully brought out his electric dynamo and arc lamp, was the young man in the little shop.

When Brush graduated from the University of Michigan, he was thoroughly familiar with the principles of electricity as then understood and with the several dynamos which had appeared. The most important of these were the "ring armature" dynamo, devised by Pacinotti, an Italian, and later introduced anew by Gramme, a Belgian, whose name it bore; and the "drum armature" type, invented by Alteneck of the German Siemens-Halske Company, and generally designated as the Siemens dynamo.

7

Brush believed that he could improve upon them both. Five years after graduation he had worked out the design of his dynamo. He could have prepared working drawings at a moment's notice, but he doubted if there would be a market in America for such a machine.

Geo. W. Stockly was at this time Vice President and Manager of the Cleveland Telegraph Supply Company, manufacturer of telegraph instruments, electric bells, and fire alarm systems, where Brush worked. Once Brush chanced to remark to Stockly that he could build a more efficient dynamo. Stockly caught at the idea, offered Brush the shop facilities of the Telegraph Supply Company, and agreed that if the dynamo proved successful, his company would undertake its manufacture. This was the encouragement Brush needed.

He went to his country home near Wickliffe and set to work. When toward the end of the summer of 1876 he drove to the door of Stockly's office in a buggy, there was on the seat beside him a machine that looked no larger than a model, hand-built throughout except for iron castings furnished by the Telegraph Supply Company.

The machine was taken into the company's shop and connected to an arc lamp. The shaft of the armature was belted to the main shaft of the shop. It was a tense moment when the engine started. Brush with his dynamo stood at the limit of electrical knowledge. Was he to pass a boundary? The lamp, shining steadily, signalled his advance in dispelling some of the darkness that lay beyond.

Brush had fulfilled his promise to Stockly, but he still needed an arc lamp to go with his dynamo. In that period there were not many lamps to be found and none of those tested gave the results that Brush desired. Finally he undertook to design one of his own.

In Brush's arc lamp automatic action permitted the proper regulation of the arc without the touch of human hands. The mechanism was ingenious but simple. Working entirely by magnetic control, it kept the carbons always a certain distance apart, the arc always at a given length.

Two years later Brush completed his memorable invention of a series arc lamp with regulating shunt coil. This invention, which enabled him to introduce arc lighting from central stations as a commercial venture, marked the birth of that industry. Neat and compact in appearance, the new arc lamp included a short-circuiting device, the function of which was to carry the current around any disabled lamp to the others in the series, thus keeping the circuit unbroken.

Ambition growing with success, Brush turned again to his dynamo, a one-light machine, with an armature only nine inches in diameter. Having achieved a series lamp, it was inevitable that Brush should seek to build a larger dynamo, his goal being a sixteen-light machine, which would give him the basis of a practical electric lighting system.

Then began a period of designing and experimenting during which the Telegraph Supply Company furnished financial backing in such amount that the directors of the company became apprehensive. A majority of them protested to Manager Stockly that Brush was working in a field without a future. They insisted that it would be better for the company to confine itself to its "legitimate business." Fortunately for future generations, Stockly quieted the fears of his directors for a year or so.

In the winter of 1876–77, the company entered into a formal agreement with Brush whereby they received the sole right to manufacture and sell the Brush system under any patents the latter might obtain. Patents were issued to Brush the following April for his arc dynamo, and in the fall for his arc lamp. Other patents followed, including one for a dynamo to operate at constant voltage, used first for electroplating, later for incandescent lighting. As yet the world of commerce, industry, and trade knew little of these inventions. In 1877, however, two of Brush's small-size dynamos and two of his lamps came suddenly into prominence among several contemporary machines that were tested by the Franklin Institute of Philadelphia. The committee which studied these machines was composed of two men, Professors Edwin J. Houston and Elihu Thomson.

Thomas A. Edison   Elihu Thomson

Charles F. Brush   James J. Wood

THE FOUR PIONEERS OF ELECTRIC LIGHTING

These photographs were taken about 1880, shortly after Edison invented the
incandescent lamp.

THE FIRST DYNAMO BUILT BY CHARLES F. BRUSH

PRIMITIVE, BUT EFFICIENT
A dynamo built by Thomson in 1878.

3

Miniature Moons

At the age of 11 Elihu Thomson had fashioned his first electrical device, an old-fashioned frictional machine, its revolving element consisting of a wine bottle with a hole knocked in the bottom. With it the lad charged a small Leyden jar and proceeded to demonstrate by inflicting a shock upon his incredulous father. Parental amusement spurred young Elihu to build a larger Leyden battery of five jars. When the elder Thomson touched this reservoir of electricity, he received a shock that nearly threw him off his feet. After that Elihu's experiments were viewed with respect from a distance.

At the close of a brilliant high school career, Thomson was familiar with most of the branches of mechanics, and his incessantly active mind had approached the limits of contemporary electrical knowledge. Professional advancement kept pace with his scientific development. At eighteen he was made Assistant Professor of Chemistry at the Boys' Central High School of Philadelphia, a school of exceptionally high standing, and five years later, in 1876, he succeeded to the full professorship of chemistry and mechanics.

Before he was twenty-four, Thomson was invited by the
Franklin Institute to deliver a course of five public lectures
on electricity. Though young for such an honor, he seized
the opportunity eagerly. Contemporary textbooks described
electricity as being of two forms, static and dynamic.
Through research Thomson had discovered error in the
definition. It was the purpose of his lectures not only to
prove the error but to establish his own theory in place of
the old.

For five meetings he packed the auditorium and held an
audience spellbound. During one lecture he exhibited a
small direct-current dynamo of his own design and construction, which created sufficient current to light an arc lamp on
the platform. An astonished audience viewed the unfamiliar
phenomenon in utter silence. By sheer accident in the course
of another experiment he discovered the principle of electrical resistance welding. When the series was concluded,
Elihu Thomson had become a person of standing in the
scientific world, for he had shown that electricity, instead of
being two forces, was inherently the same throughout nature.

Shortly after Thomson's lectures the Franklin Institute
undertook the first measurement of the output of an electrical dynamo. Desiring to purchase a dynamo, the Institute
conducted scientific tests of several types of machines then
available. Several months were consumed in testing a
Gramme dynamo, two Brush dynamos, and two Wallace
dynamos by Professors Houston and Thomson, colleagues
at the Boys' Central High.

It was no easy task which these men had undertaken, for
electrical measuring facilities in those days were crude. But
Thomson and Houston did their work so well that their
results were studied by scientists for years to come. The

Gramme dynamo made the best record—an efficiency of 38 per cent! The two Brush dynamos had respective efficiencies of 31 and 27 per cent. But it was found that the Brush machines yielded the most powerful current and hence produced the best light. For this reason, the two professors recommended that the Institute purchase a Brush dynamo. In this disinterested manner did Thomson first come into contact with Charles F. Brush and his work.

Then occurred an event which greatly stimulated Thomson's thinking—the first Brush arc lamps were installed in Philadelphia at the store of John Wanamaker. Five Brush dynamos were put to work, each supplying current to four arc lamps in the windows of the store. These lights became one of the wonders of 1878. People gathered in throngs on the sidewalk to examine them. For weeks they were talked about and a contemporary writer called them "miniature moons on carbon points, held captive in glass globes."

Inspection of these developments convinced Thomson that the field of electrical activity had an unlimited future. Within a year he had justified his expectations by the performance of one of the most remarkable electrical experiments of the period. In the lecture hall of the Franklin Institute, before a small group of spectators, Thomson exhibited a revolutionary dynamo and two arc lamps which he and Professor Houston had made. While friends were exclaiming over this exhibition and the genius of the man who had prepared it, Thomson was drawn by a chance encounter into the field of electrical manufacture.

Enthusiasm for photography frequently brought Thomson to the studio of a commercial photographer in Philadelphia, Thomas H. McCollin. One day McCollin invited his cousin, George S. Garrett, up from Garrettsford, Pennsylvania, to witness a demonstration of Thomson's dynamo, induction coils, and vibrating arc lamp.

During the demonstration Thomson remarked, "I can build a better machine than this; one that will run any number of lights you want." Garrett was enthusiastic. "Let's build a four-lighter," he suggested. "I'll stand the expense."

It was virtually an offer to Thomson to enter the business of building an arc-lighting system for market. He called upon his associate, Prof. Houston. Almost overnight they prepared drawings, engaged a pattern-maker, and arranged with the Harrison Machine Shop to do the machine work. Thomson himself put the electrical windings on the new dynamo. The inventor himself did not realize the possibilities of this dynamo until he watched it in operation.

In the oven room of the Fuller Bakery in Philadelphia, Garrett was permitted to install the Thomson-Houston dynamo and its four arc lamps for all-night illumination of the bakeshop's operations. It was the beginning of summer, and the oven room registered a temperature of 140 degrees Fahrenheit. The heat was so terrific that Houston could stand it for only a short time. He worried about his colleague, who stayed in the oven room until late every night. But nothing could deter Thomson, who laughed at Houston's protests, reinforced himself with a pitcher of ice water and continued his vigil.

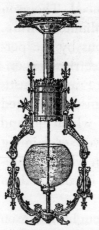

THE ARC LAMP DEVISED BY CHARLES F. BRUSH

The hot spell passed. Garrett, pleased with the results of the Fuller Bakery tests, asked for a machine that would operate more arc lamps. Thomson set to work immediately. Changing the circuit connections of the dynamo enabled it to supply eight arc lamps instead of four. The machine was successfully tested just as it came from the shop; and several Brush arc lamps were borrowed to fill out the circuit, for Thomson had no supply of his own.

Now came discovery which was to reward long hours of experiment. Thomson switched one of the lamps out of the circuit while the dynamo was running. He knew what would happen. The moment one lamp was cut out, the balance of the circuit was upset. Thomson stepped to the dynamo and changed the position of the metal brushes that were picking current off the whirring commutator until he had restored the current entering the circuit. He found that if he adjusted the brushes properly each time, he could turn off all of the lamps, one after the other, and the current would stay constant. Instantly he saw the possibility of automatic control, and set about designing a regulator. Its superiority lay in the fact that individual lamps could be switched off or on at will without upsetting the circuit. Other systems either introduced a large section of iron wire to set up a substitute resistance, or more commonly, maintained a reserve bank of lamps at the power station, one of which had to be switched in by an attendant every time a lamp in the working circuit was switched out.

There was a fire one night in John H. Gardner's brewery, where the second installation of the Thomson-Houston system was located. Several lamps were disabled, yet the circuit was un-

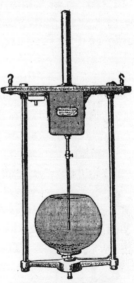

THE ARC LAMP INVENTED BY PROFESSORS THOMSON AND HOUSTON

impaired. The automatic regulator kept the other lamps operating normally and lighted the rescue of all the horses from the burning stable. One of the firemen, after seeing the arc lamps drenched with water, exclaimed, "What the dickens kind of a light is that? You pour water on her and she won't go out!"

Garrett and Thomson had survived an emergency, and upon the success of their system they now began to build a thriving business. For the moment, however, let us leave them and examine contemporary developments.

4

One of the Four

THE SHOP FOREMAN of the Brady Manufacturing Company
of Brooklyn was James J. Wood, an intelligent and observant
young man of twenty-one. He was good-natured and oblig-
ing, and so thoroughly likable that he was known to everyone as "Jimmy." Some of his subordinates in the shop never
knew his last name. Yet young Jimmy Wood was destined to
take his place with Brush, Thomson, and Edison as one of
the four outstanding pioneers in applying electricity to common use.

Jimmy Wood had determined to build a dynamo that
would reduce heat losses, and that would weigh well below
the average of dynamos then in use, which was around six
hundred pounds. He had no money, but his employer, James
Brady, promised to manufacture the proposed dynamo if
Wood would allow him a half-interest in the patent. To this
the latter agreed. When the dynamo was finished, in May
1879, it was, like Brush's, hardly larger than a model. It
weighed 87 pounds; its armature was only eight inches in
diameter and two and one-half feet in length. A trifle more
than one horsepower would operate it.

Officials of the Fuller Electrical Company were dumbfounded by the achicvement, and not until a reputable electrical engineer tested it would they credit what this young
man had done.

Then came action. They paid Wood and Brady ten thousand dollars for the patent rights. They renamed their organization the Fuller-Wood Company, with Wood's dynamo as

DYNAMO, 1879 MODEL
Built by Jimmy Wood

their chief stock-in-trade. Soon it was being sold, installed,
and operated in a wide-spreading territory.

Level-headed even after this sudden turn of fortune
Jimmy Wood proceeded to improve his already efficient machine. He knew that his original dynamo had weaknesses
which could be avoided. Accordingly his commercial dynamo, developed immediately, was built for higher voltage
and for series-circuit work. Any tendency of the machine to

EDISON'S MENLO PARK LABORATORY IN THE '70'S

The laboratory is the long building with the porch. In the foreground is the office building; the building at an angle is the "glass house" where experimental lamp bulbs were blown; at right angles to the laboratory in the rear is the machine shop; the experimental railway can be seen at the right.

BIRTHPLACE OF THE INCANDESCENT LAMP

Edison's Menlo Park Laboratory, showing the lamp used in the first public demonstration on pole in foreground.

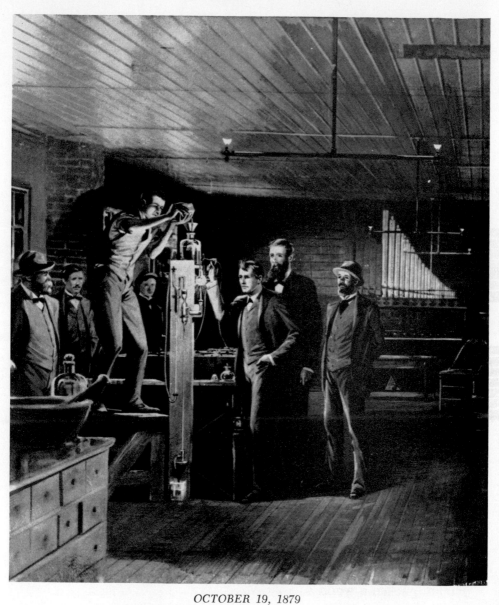

OCTOBER 19, 1879

Artist's reconstruction of the scene in the Menlo Park laboratory when the first successful lamp was turned on.

emit flashes, or to "spark" at the point where the brushes were in contact with the commutator was avoided. Wood's dynamo showed no sparking; it ran with little noise; it was utterly simple. When ready for the market it weighed 120 pounds.

Like Thomson, Wood devised an automatic regulator, which included the use of two brushes under each magnetic pole. These brushes operated not only to insure proper change in voltage, as more or fewer lamps were placed in the circuit, but also to prevent destructive sparking.

By this time arc lamps were installed indoors as well as out, as promoters pushed the idea of interior arc illumination. Salesmen went after the business of factories, hotels, and theaters, but they were careful not to say too much about voltage. It was a weakness of these systems that for interior installation a voltage dangerous to human safety had to be sent into customers' premises.

About this time a phrase was occasionally heard: "The subdivision of the electric light." What did it mean? Could the arc lamp be subdivided? Could anyone cut up a lamp of two thousand candlepower into twenty lamps, each of one hundred candlepower?

JIMMY WOOD'S ARC LAMP

While a score of inventors had such a small unit in their thoughts, the true apostle of incandescence had sequestered himself at Menlo Park. He was still to be heard from, still an unknown. But the hour was at hand when his genius should quicken a world to gratitude.

5

At Menlo Park

AWAY FROM THE BUSTLE OF CITIES, picturesque in its seclusion, the hamlet of Menlo Park was, until 1876, one of the byways of life. Then suddenly into it came a man who seemed little less than a magician and who raised it to fame among the cities of the nation. For a few teeming years it started into intense activity, recurring excitement, luminous nights. After that, quiet. The tide of activity, as suddenly as it flowed, was at ebb, and Menlo Park relapsed again into tranquillity, retaining only the halo which one man had given it to wear forever.

The first intimation the village had of the newcomer was when a gabled dwelling began to rise near the railroad station. Inhabitants learned that the owner's name was Edison; and after a while they began to see him—an energetic young man with searching eyes and a ready smile. Not far from his home, he erected a laboratory, two stories high and a hundred feet long, built of white clapboards, with a porch across the twenty-five-foot front. Other buildings rose about the same time—a machine shop, power house, and a library-office.

Into this small center workers began to come. The hum of

enterprise arose. Expectancy was in the air. Only shortly after his arrival the infectious enthusiasm of a young man had caught up, not alone associates, but the town where they lived. Menlo Park was a conquest of Edison's, and henceforth it was to acknowledge his residence with gratitude.

But the scientist, however great his zeal, cannot apply his ideas without practical support. Grosvenor P. Lowrey, a New York lawyer of high standing, was Edison's most loyal admirer among men of influence. Jovial and good-hearted, a typical old-school barrister with Horace Greeley whiskers under his chin, he had closely followed Edison's work with the phonograph and telephone transmitter, acting as legal adviser and acquiring a tremendous faith in the ability of the young inventor. When, around 1878, public interest began to lose itself in wonder over the arc light, Mr. Lowrey was one of several to think of electric lighting as an opportunity for Edison. Immediately he set about securing the necessary capital.

Through the interest of backers came the incorporation in October, 1878, of the Edison Electric Light Company. Edison was now committed to experimenting with electric lighting and he was provided with ample funds upon which he began to draw. He increased equipment, hired more men, and put all his characteristic intensity, his great technical imagination, into the effort of producing a small-unit electric light.

Hundreds of experiments took place for fourteen months, and more than $40,000 was expended. Gradually a serviceable lamp filament of carbonized substances along with an all-glass, hermetically-sealed bulb were developed. Lastly, the means of obtaining and keeping a vacuum in that bulb were worked out.

Toward the end of October, 1879, Edison carbonized a cotton thread. He placed it, bent in horseshoe form, inside one of his sealed glass bulbs. On the evening of October 19, this crude experimental lamp, standing upright on a table, was connected to an electric circuit. A knot of Edison workers had gathered to see what would happen. The central figure was the wizard himself. With him were Francis R. Upton, his mathematician; Charles Batchelor, his model-maker; John Kruesi, his machine-shop expert; Ludwig Boehm, his glass-blower; and Francis Jehl and Martin Force, of the laboratory staff.

Current was switched on. The lamp, responding instantly, glowed with a soft light. Quickly they measured the resistance. It was 275 ohms—ample for their purpose and overwhelmingly greater than the four or five ohms of previous incandescent lamps. Then all sat down to watch the slender horseshoe of light, half expecting it to vanish. But hour after hour it continued to glow until the night was spent.

No one had eaten, no one had thought of sleep. The grey of a second dawn found them at their vigil. Upton alone excused himself, feeling that he should not altogether desert his home, but he hurried back soon after daylight.

About one o'clock on the second afternoon, October 21, more than forty hours after it first received the current, the filament burned out.

The spell was broken. The men leaped up with cries of jubilation. Edison was quiet in the hour of his tremendous success. As the little lamp glowed, he had envisioned "great cities lighted from central stations," and his mind was alive with plans. But all he said, when the glow finally vanished, was, "That's fine—that's fine! I think we've got it! If it can burn forty hours, I can make it last a hundred."

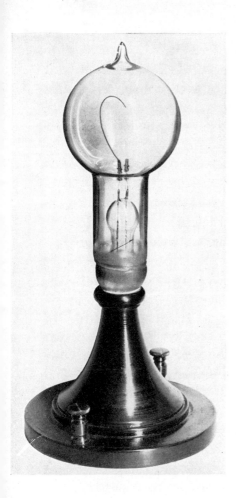

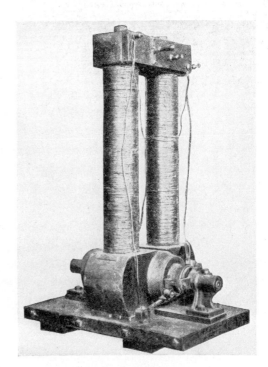

LIGHT FOR THE NEW YEAR

This lamp, with a filament of carbonized bristol board, was exhibited by Edison on New Year's Eve, 1879.

"LONG-WAISTED MARY ANN"
Edison built these dynamos in 1883.

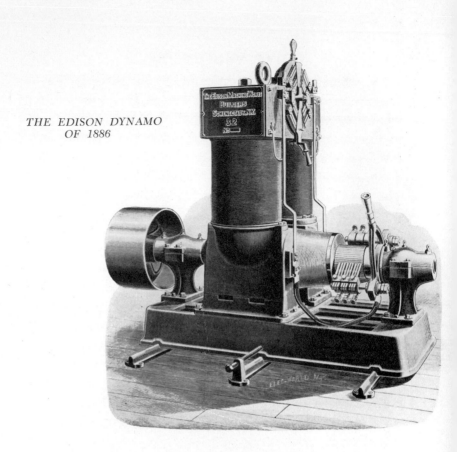

THE EDISON DYNAMO
OF 1886

BRUSH IMPROVES UPON HIS FIRST DYNAMOS

The successful demonstration of a solitary lamp left the spectators awe-struck. Little did they realize, however, that what they had seen was to expand electrical usage literally to the confines of civilization; for the incandescent lamp could go where the arc lamp could not—into office buildings and into homes. It was a lamp that could compete with gas! The London technical journal, *Engineering*, remarked that "if he (Edison) has indeed arrived at the solution claimed . . . gas has found a dangerous rival." No wonder gas stocks were disturbed!

Edison had experimented with a dynamo throughout 1879. The genius of Menlo Park had analyzed the scientific theories regarding dynamos and had studied the report of the Thomson-Houston tests at the Franklin Institute. The highest efficiency of any dynamo then examined was 38 per cent, and he determined that his machine must not lose over 60 per cent of the power put into it.

The Edison dynamo had large magnets indeed, designed to create a powerful magnetic field. They represented much experimental work. Their dimensions were odd, for the magnets rose three and a half feet into the air and were joined at the top by an iron crosspiece which completed the magnetic circuit and made the contrivance resemble an immense Roman numeral, II. Some of Edison's associates dubbed the dynamos "long-waisted Mary Anns," though officially they were termed the Edison bi-polar. The armature was modeled after the efficient drum type. But it had the advantage of being laminated; that is, it was constructed of sheets, or discs, of iron, insulated from each other although mounted on a single shaft. This innovation resulted from innumerable experiments by Edison's mathematician, Upton. When the ungainly machine was tested, the result surprised even Edison and Upton. It was ninety per cent efficient!

Notwithstanding this remarkable performance, the other inventors gave no indication of relinquishing the field to any "incandescent lighter," even though sponsored by the miracle man of Menlo Park.

[PART TWO]

The Period
of Commercial Introduction
# of Electric Lighting

6

The Arc Light Takes the Field

AN ARC LAMP, hanging from the balcony of Dr. Longworth's residence in Cincinnati, was attracting curious crowds through the early days of 1878. Current was supplied from a Brush dynamo in the basement, but to the mystified watchers the lamp was an entity in itself.

One evening when Brush was in Cincinnati to examine his invention, he walked through the crowd before Dr. Longworth's home. A man with a knowing air was explaining to his neighbors how the light was obtained.

"See that little box at the top?" he said, pointing to the metal case containing the control mechanism. "That's a can full of oil. The oil flows down through those side-pipes to the burner of the lamp and feeds the flame. That's all there is to it! . . . And what are you smiling at?" he asked the stranger who had joined his listeners.

"I didn't realize the lamp was as simple as that," answered Brush.

In Cleveland, Brush's home town, there was no such skepticism to surmount. On the streets and in Monumental Park the first large-scale installation of arc lighting, as an exhibi-

27

tion rather than a commercial development, was accomplished.

It introduced a method of early outdoor arc lighting soon to become characteristic—the elevation of lamps upon tall masts, or towers. This practice caused people to think of the arc light as a substitute for the sun and, with an immense naïvety replacing their skepticism, they thought that a few such lights, lifted high above all surroundings, would turn night into day.

This first Cleveland installation was a modest one. Twelve lamps, mounted on eighteen-foot posts, were supplied with current from a Brush dynamo in the Telegraph Supply Company's shop. They were first lighted on April 29, 1879.

The Cleveland *Plain Dealer,* describing the scene the day after the lights were first turned on, said:

"Thousands of people gathered . . . and as the light shot around and through the Park a shout was raised. Presently the Grays Band struck up in the pavilion, and soon afterward a section of artillery on the lake shore began firing a salute in honor of the occasion.

"The light varied some in intensity, when shining its brightest being so dazzling as to be painful to the eyes. In color it is of a purplish hue, not unlike moonlight, and by contrast making the gas lights in the store windows look a reddish yellow.

"The Telegraph Supply Company's establishment . . . was thrown open to as many people as could be accommodated at a time to go through the works and inspect the machinery which sends light over the wire to blaze out between the carbon points in the lamps."

Two months after Cleveland had so proudly applauded the achievement of one of her citizens, the Brush system found its way from the Middle West to the Pacific coast.

In San Francisco, on June 30, 1879, was incorporated the California Electric Light Company. George H. Roe was the organizer, and William Kerr sold the electrical equipment, holding Brush territorial license for California, Oregon, Washington, and Nevada.

This pioneer company proposed to sell electrical illumination to cash customers, something never before attempted. The few commercial installations of any inventor's apparatus then in existence had been solely for private use. Individuals, merchants, hotels, and theaters had purchased plants and arc lamps; they had had their premises wired; and the lights, supplied from their own private generating plants, were utilized for private benefit on their own property. These were designated as "isolated lighting plants."

The San Francisco Company was the first in this country, if not in the world, to enter the business of producing and selling electric service to the public. Its generating plant was in the rear of what is now the Pacific Building, and modest indeed was the equipment first installed. It consisted of two Brush dynamos, one supplying six lamps and the other sixteen. In December two dynamos of the larger size were added. Customers were not lacking, though the rate was high. A flat rate of $10 per week per lamp was charged, as metering of the current was quite unknown. As the system was improved, rates were reduced, until eight years later it was $3.00 per week for current furnished up to 9:30 o'clock in the evening (11:00 on Saturdays), $4.00 for current up to midnight, and $6.00 for all-night service. No current was furnished on Sundays and holidays. The city and county of San Francisco were eventually among the customers of the plant, setting up a street lighting system of 21 masts, 50 feet in height, each having four 4,000-candlepower lamps.

Brush saw that the early carbons had high electrical resistance and burned out rapidly, thus becoming expensive. They were made from gas-retort carbon and contained from three to five per cent of ash, which was fatal to steadiness in the light, causing a flickering.

Both Thomson and Brush worked to improve carbons as soon as they had developed their systems of arc lighting. When George S. Garrett expressed doubt concerning a satisfactory supply, Thomson accepted the challenge: "If we cannot buy carbons in the market, we can certainly make them." In 1879, with the assistance of the photographer, Thomas H. McCollin, he procured a supply of hard carbon as raw material, powdered it, mixed it to secure cohesiveness, and moulded it into sticks, which were afterward baked.

Brush attacked the problem in a totally different manner. He utilized the by-products of mineral oil distilleries to produce his "still-coke" carbon, which contained only three hundredths of one per cent of ash. After the carbon sticks were moulded and baked, he electroplated them with copper to reduce electrical resistance and to retard combustion. This was the origin of his "copper-coated" carbons, on which he obtained a patent in 1877.

Having won their way in the West, Brush lights were introduced in the East, where they were installed at Wanamaker's Philadelphia store and exhibited at the fair of the Massachusetts Charitable Association in Boston.

Niagara Falls was illuminated for the first time on July 4, 1879, by a sixteen-light Brush dynamo and arc lamps. The dynamo, driven by a waterwheel, was a pioneer hydroelectric plant. A full complement of lamps was always operated; there was no need to switch off some and leave the rest burning.

In the year 1880 the Brush fortunes were given a tremendous impetus by an actual sale of a system to a little community in northern Indiana.

The governing authorities of Wabash, Indiana, had found that electric lighting would not only cost some $800 a year less than gas lighting, but would yield a greater volume of illumination. Accordingly they contracted for a Brush installation with four lamps of 3000 candlepower each, mounted on crossarms atop the dome of the Court House 200 feet above the ground. This was the first municipally owned electric lighting plant, and Wabash the first town wholly lighted by electricity, for it was planned to illuminate the city from a single point.

Both press and public followed the progress of the experiment with intense interest. Early on the day when the circuit was to be turned on, awed and wondering folk commenced to pour into Wabash from the surrounding country. Newspaper correspondents traveled from cities as far distant as Chicago and New York. By 8:00 o'clock on the moonless evening of March 31, 1880, more than 10,000 persons were crowded about the Court House.

Let newspaper accounts tell the tale.

The Fort Wayne *Daily Sentinel:* "Promptly as the courthouse clock struck eight, the thousands of eyes that were turned toward the inky darkness over the courthouse saw a shower of sparks emitted from a point above them, small, steady spots of light, growing more brilliant until within a few seconds after the first sparks were seen, it was absolutely dazzling. A loud shout went up from the crowd, the band began to play. . . ."

A Chicago *Tribune* reporter went, he says, "up into the dome, right under the light, where (he) beheld a scene of magnificent splendor. For a mile around, the houses and yards were distinctly visible, while the far-away river flowed like a band of molten silver."

An eye-witness pictures the emotions of his fellow spectators: "People stood overwhelmed with awe, as if in the presence of the supernatural. The strange, weird light, exceeded in power only by the sun, rendered the square as light as midday. Men fell on their knees, groans were uttered at the sight and many were dumb with amazement. We contemplated the new wonder in science as lightning brought down from the heavens."

The Wabash *Plain Dealer* was pardonably exuberant: "Yesterday morning the city of Wabash woke up and found itself famous. It is today the best advertised town in the United States. From Maine to California telegrams of the Associated Press flashed the intelligence that the problem of lighting the streets of an entire city solely by electricity was solved. . . . In the street in front of the residence of Levi Linn, who is, we learn, still denouncing the electric light as a fraud, our reporter, standing three squares distant from the light, was able to read with ease the advertisement of Ebblinghouse and Austin."

Thus was Wabash given its baptism of light. For the moment Brush's competitors were out-distanced and forgotten. But one of them at least, Elihu Thomson, already had his second wind and was pressing strongly forward.

7

Transplanted Pioneering

PROFESSOR THOMSON'S PRESTIGE had already travelled into New England when New Britain, Connecticut, sent a group of men, headed by Frederick H. Churchill, to make a proposition to this promising inventor. They wanted to organize an electrical company on the strength of his patents. It was an interesting offer and Thomson was not long in giving a favorable answer.

News of his impending departure spread through the Boys' Central High School as commencement day drew near. The honor man in the class of 1880 was Edwin Wilbur Rice, Jr., who had been Professor Thomson's most brilliant pupil. A few days after graduating the young man cast his lot with the professor. Before autumn the two men, optimistic and courageous, departed for New Britain. Neither suspected that they were to spend the rest of their lives in a common enterprise, were to "team up" together through many viscissitudes, were to help shape a new industrial structure.

A company was chartered with William Parker, president; Mr. Churchill, Treasurer and General Manager; and Pro-

33

fessor Thomson, "Electrician"—a term commonly used to designate the technical man, or inventor, whose patents provided the foundation for commercial organization. Professors Thomson and Houston executed a formal contract with the new American Electric Company. Briefly, it bound the company to manufacture "with all reasonable diligence" the inventions covered by the Thomson-Houston patents. These articles, enumerated in the contract, were to be sold and put into public use "by diligent and continuous attention . . . in all reasonable and advisable ways." In case the company failed to live up to stipulations, the patents were to revert to the patentees; stock of the company, given to the two professors in exchange for the patents, was to be surrendered by them.

So Thomson, with the spirit of the scientific explorer tingling in his brain, set up his humble working quarters in the basement of an old factory; and he and his young assistant set briskly to work to improve the Thomson-Houston arc light system.

Both men personally wound the wire on the armatures of their first dynamos. When they were not helping in the shop work—factory hands were few and inexperienced at first—they were ceaselessly experimenting. They were always at work at seven in the morning; they seldom stopped before six at night. Frequently they worked in the evening, with a few assistants as devoted as themselves. On one such occasion they improvised a luncheon of raw oysters, on which somebody suggested using paraffin in lieu of butter. Thomson, however, took his without garnishing, saying that he objected to "the candlepower flavor."

His residence at that time was in New Britain's principal hotel. Rice had moved to a locally celebrated establishment, Mrs. Moore's boarding house, which became a counterpart to Mrs. Jordan's famous boarding house in Menlo Park. There Rice shared a room with a young bookkeeper and cost clerk, George E. Emmons, who had been hired by Churchill to establish a bookkeeping system for the new American Electric Company. Rice woke up once in the middle of the night and found his room-mate hard at work on the company's accounts. When he inquired what was going on, Emmons replied that he was trying to run down a shortage in his trial balance.

"How much is the shortage?" asked Rice.

"Three cents."

"Good Heavens!" cried Rice. "Come to bed and I'll give you the three cents in the morning."

Whereupon the young cost clerk laid down his pencil and gave his sleepy room-mate an academic lecture on the art of bookkeeping and the tremendous importance of a few missing cents in the trial balance.

The first machines in these days ran only about ten or twelve lights. Machines of larger capacity were demanded, and Professor Thomson set to work to design one to operate twenty arc lamps. Thomson was constantly looking ahead, and he foresaw that, as arc light systems grew in size with correspondingly higher voltages, lightning protection would become a problem. Discussing the question with Rice, he pointed out that an electrical discharge caused by lightning could be led harmlessly to earth, but that a heavy arc, produced by the current of the circuit, would attempt to follow. This arc would have to be overcome.

Thomson took a large steel magnet and walked over to several arc lamps which were shining in the test room. He placed the magnet in such a position that the arc was between the two magnetic poles. Immediately the arc vanished and the lamp went out. A magnet had blown out the arc.

As long as the magnet remained in proximity it was impossible to produce a fresh arc. From this experiment came Thomson's application of the magnetic blowout principle. He used it first in an efficient type of lightning arrester and later utilized it for electric switches.

8

Manhattan Initiated

A SINGLE MAN, IN 1880, precipitated a scientific controversy, caused dismay to gas companies, and threw the stock market into turmoil. Shares in the Edison Electric Light Company rocketed. Stock that had a par value of $100 a share was not uncommonly sold at $500. In fact, the day came when three shares sold for $2000 each, were resold in a few minutes for $3700, and later the same day for $5000 apiece. While speculative activity was at its height, stock at times rose $100 a share within an hour. Yet this was but a surface indication of a general undercurrent of excitement. People everywhere were confident that a revolution in artificial illumination was at hand. And so it was—largely through the resistless energy of Thomas Edison.

Foremost in Edison's mind was the necessity of producing incandescent lamps in quantity. Even while experimenting, he sought to begin manufacture for he knew that he had a product which could be commercially handled.

The word "filament" was Edison's contribution to the nomenclature of the future industry. His immediate purpose was to find the best possible material for this filament. Ex-

37

periment followed experiment; day-and-night activity at
Menlo Park was incessant.

"Somewhere in God Almighty's workshop," Edison said,
"there is a dense, woody growth with fibres almost geometri-
cally parallel and with practically no pith, from which excellent filaments can be cut."

For nearly eight years Edison explorers searched the
world for that "dense, woody growth" especially in the form
of some species of bamboo. Bales and boxes containing plant
specimens were shipped to Menlo Park from China, Japan,
Ceylon, Cuba, and South America. No less than six thousand
vegetable growths were tested at the laboratory, not to mention scores of non-vegetable substances.

Most of the specimens were of bamboo, the virtues of
which Edison discovered by experimenting with fibre from
a palm-leaf fan lying on one of the laboratory tables. In
those days everything that met the eye was potential filament material. Edison placed the fan under a microscope,
then had the bamboo cut into strips, carbonized, and
mounted in test lamps. They proved to make better filaments
than any he had yet developed.

In the lamps for a second public exhibition, which Edison
was planning, bamboo filaments were used exclusively. A
complete system of incandescent lighting was to be tested
on a large scale and its economy compared with that of gas.
As an underground system it was to extend along the main
streets of Menlo Park so as to provide light for most of the
dwellings.

For the exhibition Edison's men dug trenches along the
roads of Menlo Park. In them copper wire, without insulation and encased only in wooden moulding, was laid. It was
believed that a pressure of 100 volts would not require insulation, but the first attempt to transmit current in this

ONE WAY TO LIGHT A TOWN

Arc lights, mounted on high towers, were expected to illuminate whole communities from one central spot in early attempts at street lighting.

THE AMERICAN ELECTRIC COMPANY

The factory at New Britain, Connecticut, where Thomson started his commercial career.

fashion failed. Leakage of electricity blew out the whole circuit.

Experiments in insulation were immediately begun. Coal tar, a composition of powdered slate, and wrappings of muslin failed successively as non-conductors. When Wilson S. Howell of the Edison staff, after thorough study of formulas, offered to "cook" an insulating compound, he was installed with kettles and raw material in the chemical laboratory.

More stench than success attended his first efforts. Dr. Otto A. Moses, chemist, after acute discomfort, gave up trying to work. Howell not only smoked him out of his own laboratory, but earned the disgust of adjacent parts of the plant for his obnoxious "cooking." At length, however, the martyr brought forth a successful compound of refined Trinidad asphaltum, mixed with oxidized linseed oil, paraffin, and beeswax.

Boys from neighboring farms were then rounded up, the conductors were placed on saw-horses and the boys wound on strips of muslin soaked in the compound. Each boy straddled a conductor, walking along as he proceeded to wind. The tape was put on in three layers.

It was Election Day, 1880, when Edison was told that the circuit was ready. A presidential campaign was just closing. Interested in the fortunes of James A. Garfield, Edison resolved to link the first trial of his system with the result of the election.

"If Garfield is elected," he ordered, "light the circuit."

For hours a telegraph key at the plant clicked off poll returns.

Edison in his residence waited as dusk changed into darkness. Suddenly Menlo Park blazed with light as current was shot into many bamboo filaments. A political and an electrical triumph were commemorated together.

A delegation from the New York Board of Aldermen, which made the pilgrimage to Menlo Park late in December, 1880, officially appraised the new inventions. The New York *Herald*, reporting the demonstration, observed that the aldermen wanted to form an opinion of the "resident wizard's work."

"Stretching away on either side," the account went, "and intercepting the Park at intervals, ran long lines of light. There were illuminated spaces about all these gleaming points and the prospect was very beautiful as the visitors looked out upon it.

"But at a sign from the Wizard, all changed. A workman's finger pressed the key and in an instant Menlo Park was in darkness. A ripple of applause involuntarily ran through the onlookers, but before it had subsided the finger was applied again, and the landscape was illuminated in a twinkling."

The Newark *Register* recorded, on February 9, 1881, that "Menlo Park, the little hamlet where the great electro-scientist, Edison, holds communion with the hidden things of this world, was visited last evening by three hundred of Newark's best citizens."

From the country-side farming folk poured into Menlo Park after nightfall to see the lights. One old fellow who drove in twenty miles was heard to say: "It's a pretty fair sight, but danged if I see how ye git the red-hot hairpin in the bottle."

Multitudes that went to Menlo Park from New York night after night were eventually to see the "Edison lights" on their own streets. Edison and his counsellors had already planned the introduction of the incandescent lamp in Manhattan. On December 20, 1880 the Edison Electric Illuminating Company of New York was chartered to operate on lower Manhattan, in an area termed by Edison the "First

District"—roughly a square mile included between Spruce and Ferry Streets and Peck Slip on the north, Nassau and Wall Streets, and the East River.

Plans for installation were complete in essential detail, from a standardized lamp socket to the indispensable current-meter. It was one of few instances in electrical history of the invention by one man of an article for public use together with a perfected system for bringing it into acceptance. It was a Herculean task to plant this acorn of the electric light and power industry—a far greater undertaking than the impatient public realized.

Thus it was that there came first to Manhattan lights of the older type. In December, 1880, Brush lamps were installed along Broadway for three-quarters of a mile, the first electrical illumination of the famous street. The operating organization was the Brush Electric Light and Power Company of New York. This company also contracted to illuminate Union and Madison Squares by means of masts 160 feet high.

The system was a spectacular success, and the New York *Evening Post* of December 17, 1880, tells of prospective customers other than the city of New York: the Steinway Ware Rooms, the Park Theater, the Brunswick and Sturtevant Hotels, and Koster and Bial's music hall.

While sophisticated New York showed less excitement upon first seeing Brush lamps than did Wabash, Indiana, they were nevertheless well received. Nearly two years were to pass before the wizard of Menlo Park, with his bamboo filament and his ninety per cent efficient dynamo, would make good his promise to supplant the gas jet.

During the winter of 1880–81, hundreds of persons wrote to ask the Edison Electric Light Company how soon incandescent lamps would be available. Hundreds of others so-

licited agencies for the purchase of territorial rights. Had
the company sold territory that winter, it could have en-
riched its treasury fabulously. But no one knew what problems would be encountered in putting the proposition on a
commercial footing, and Edison himself had not obtained
sufficient experience in the practical operation of his system;
so the company refrained from engaging agents, who could
not possibly have given satisfactory service to customers.

A single agreement was made that winter with the Edison
Electric Illuminating Company of New York regarding the
famous "First District" where the Edison Electric Light
Company was to make the installation. Edison would personally direct the work, conduct the necessary tests, start
the central station machinery, and satisfy himself that the
system was functioning properly.

When Edison "personally directed the work," he was on
the spot every day. He neglected sleep, and spent hours after
the workmen had gone home going over the ground or
solving minor problems.

Meanwhile activities of a different character were developing downtown, where Edison had acquired a factory on
Goerck Street for the establishment of the Edison Machine
Works to manufacture the Edison dynamo. Miles of piping,
or "tubing" were required to contain the underground conductors; likewise shafting and pulleys, for connecting dynamos to the steam engines that drove them, lamp sockets,
switches, meters, fuses, cutouts, brackets, junction-boxes, instruments, and electroliers. Most of these were Edison's inventions, created in perfecting the system. As no existing
manufacturers produced them, he set up plants of his own.
"There was nothing that we could buy," he said, "or that
anybody else could make for us."

So, simultaneously with the Edison Machine Works, the

Laying the Electrical Tubes

ELECTRICITY UNDER MANHATTAN

An artist for Harper's Weekly pictures the laying of the Edison "tubes" or cables in the City's streets.

EXTERIOR OF THE PEARL STREET STATION
Edison's first generating plant.

Edison Tube Company was started on Washington Street, and the Edison Shafting Company on Goerck Street. Auxiliary appliances were produced by Bergmann and Company on Wooster Street, where Sigmund Bergmann, a former Edison employee, was proprietor. The manufacture of lamps by a force of forty-five men had been going on for six months at Harrison, New Jersey, at the rate of 700 a day. In the summer of 1882, among other new "hands," it gave employment to a youth named George F. Morrison, whose job was to unwrap and smooth tissue paper from lamp bulbs as they came from the glass works at Corning, New York, so they could be used again in packing finished lamps. His pay, if he worked sixty hours, was a dollar a week. This boy, undismayed by hard work, diligent and intelligent, was one of the future managers of the plant.

As a "man of business" Edison showed himself courageous as well as sagacious. He did not hesitate to manufacture a lamp himself when the Edison Electric Light Company was reluctant to do so. He recognized that the company's policy was to hold patents, issue licenses, and promote commercial efforts, but not to manufacture. Accordingly on March 8, 1881, he executed a contract to sell the company all the lamps it needed for forty cents apiece, delivered in quantity, ready for commercial use, and with a manufacturer's guarantee as to quality, the contract to run through the life of his patent. Each lamp cost Edison $1.10 to manufacture.

In the first year not quite 30,000 lamps were sold to the Edison Electric Light Company. Each year thereafter sales increased, and manufacturing costs lessened. In 1881 Edison produced lamps at seventy cents apiece; in 1882 at fifty cents; in 1883 at thirty-seven cents, realizing then a profit of three cents per lamp. The volume of sales that year wiped out deficits of the previous three years. In 1884, the cost dropped to twenty-two cents, and lamps were sold by the hundred thousand. The Edison Lamp Company was at last a profitable enterprise.

All this while, there was going on at the Edison Machine Works a relentless search for a monster generating machine. The idea came to Edison as he studied the ten eight-horsepower dynamos which supplied current at the Menlo Park exhibition of 1880. A slow-speed engine drove all dynamos through a complicated system of belting and shafting. The power loss indicated considerable inefficiency. Hence Edison conceived the plan of substituting for the ten dynamos a single large-capacity unit with a direct-coupled, high-speed steam engine.

No outsider saw the test, in the engine room at Menlo Park, of the experimental unit which preceded the first practical Jumbo.

The steam engine used in that test was planned for a high speed of 600 rpm, and was to operate at a steam pressure of 120 pounds per square inch. Heretofore the average speed of stationary engines was rarely more than 60 rpm and the average steam pressure ranged from 60 to 80 pounds.

It was a winter's night when the test took place. Charles T. Porter, who had designed and built the engine, opened the throttle a little at a time, his eye constantly on the governor. It did not rise until the engine was making a racket that sounded "like an immense drop-forge foundry with ten thousand hammers in operation." The link motion was so rapid that it "looked like a triangular-shaped bit of haze or fog."

Edison related this experience with appreciative gusto:

"We set the machine up in the old shop that stood on top of one of these New Jersey shale hills. We opened her up, and when she got to about 300 revolutions, the whole hill shook under her . . .

"After a good deal of trouble we ran her up to 700 revolutions. Every time the connecting-rod went up, she tried to lift the whole hill up with her."

After this experience the engines finally built for driving the Jumbo dynamos were not run above 350 rpm.

The first practical Jumbo dynamo was built at the Edison Machine Works in New York in 1881. Its size alone made visitors pause and stare. But they were chiefly puzzled by the seemingly endless operation of winding. They saw workmen carry insulated copper wire around and around the long cylindrical cores, from one end to the other, with patient repetition; then start on a second layer and a third and a fourth, until six had been completed. The wire was wound around the core almost two thousand times, and there were six magnet cores.

One further innovation was devised by Edison to meet the difficulty of a drop in voltage in the multiple circuit. While lamps nearest the dynamo received a full current of 110 volts, the next lamps beyond received only 109 volts, the next 108, and so on. In the simplified system at Menlo Park such a defect was not serious, but when Edison began his layout for Manhattan, he perceived that, to correct a voltage drop, conductors would have to be thick at the generator end, and taper off gradually to a small diameter at the other end. To supply a large area by this means would have meant a prohibitive copper bill. Edison's tireless critics remarked that there was "not enough copper in the world" to permit of such a plan.

Defeat seemed close at hand. But its very proximity pro-vided the spur which led to the invention of the feeder system of current distribution.

Instead of starting the parallel circuit direct from the dynamo, Edison interposed feeders, which ran between dy-namo and central points in the parallel circuit, solely to sup-ply current to the latter. This system was employed with complete success in the First District.

A group of Jumbos was built for the District, which in the late summer of 1882 became a scene of activity prepara-tory to actual operation. Edison was a tireless director, ex-amining the work in the trenches where his tubing for the conductors was being laid, with insulating compound poured into every tube and junction-box.

"I used to sleep on piles of pipes in the station," he said, "and I saw every box poured and every connection made on the whole job." A total of eighteen miles of street mains was put in.

By August, 900 buildings had been wired and more than 14,000 incandescent lamps placed in their sockets. No one knew, except Edison, when the station was to start gen-erating. He told only his associates that it was to be Monday afternoon, September 4, 1882, at three o'clock. He wanted no publicity or excitement, for he was apprehensive of the outcome.

He gave no appearance of this when he entered the dy-namo room at Pearl Street about nine o'clock on Monday morning, attired in frock coat and tall derby—neither of which went through the day unscathed.

The day's work started prosaically. Through the forenoon Edison and his chief engineer gave the equipment a final inspection. Early in the afternoon their seclusion was interrupted by a tread of many feet, and a murmur of voices; newspaper reporters had learned, in the manner peculiar to their craft, that on this day the Edison light was at last to shine. They met no welcome, however. Edison, famous for his friendly smile, leaped upon them, and pushed the foremost bodily back to the door, exclaiming, "Get out! Get out!" He posted a man at the street door with orders to admit no one except the personal associates invited.

Edison's motives were natural enough, for the gas companies, in his own words, "were our bitter enemies in those days, keenly watching every move and ready to pounce upon us at the slightest failure. Big issues were at stake. Success meant a world-wide adoption of our central-station plan and its principles. Failure meant loss of money and prestige, and the setting back of our enterprise. . . .

"All our apparatus, devices, and parts were home-devised and home-made. Our men were comparatively new, and of course without the slightest central station experience. What might happen when a big current was turned into the conductors under the streets of New York, no one could say."

A few weeks before, the system had been tested with curious results. A young man burst into the dynamo-room, crying excitedly, "Your electricity has got into the pavement up in Fulton Street and all the horses are dancing."

When an Edison crew dashed to Fulton Street, they found the report was not exaggerated. The leak carried enough voltage to give horses setting hoofs upon a certain spot in the street a galvanic electric shock. Several days were required to locate and repair the faulty conductors. Small wonder that Edison was so inhospitable to newspaper representatives on the morning of September 4!

There were scarcely twenty persons at the Pearl Street

station when the great moment arrived. When Edison gave the signal, the connection was established and current flowed. The Edison system was working at last!

Fifty-nine customers were served with current on that memorable day. Among them were the banking house of Drexel, Morgan and Company; the *Herald* and the *Times* offices; J. T. Pratt and Company; the Park Bank; and Sweet's Restaurant on Fulton Street. This was an eating place of great fame, frequented by Booth and Jefferson, and a stage-coach terminal for uptown and Harlem. On the night of September 4, 1882 it was alive with excitement—as were the other places where the wizard's lamps shone.

"The giant dynamos," said the *Times* in recording the event "were started up at three in the afternoon, and according to Mr. Edison they will go on forever, unless stopped by an earthquake."

The system worked perfectly, except for a setback when a second engine and dynamo were started. The two engines seesawed, or "hunted," with a terrific racket. As Edison put it: "Of all the circuses since Adam was born, we had the worst!" He and Clarke spent two nights and a day in continuous session, trying to devise a remedy. They did not surrender until Edison had contrived a temporary solution, which permitted him to employ more than one generating unit at the same time.

DESPITE THE SUCCESS of the incandescents, inventors and exploitors of the arc lamp systems were not to be downed. The Boston *Journal of Commerce* said in January 1882: "They (the incandescent lamp companies) claim to furnish light as cheaply as gas. But this is a subject that will require to be proved, as they also admit that they only furnish seven lights to a horsepower . . . It costs less than a horsepower

to furnish a single Brush light of 2000 candlepower . . .
On this basis, neither the Brush Company nor the gas companies have anything to fear from Edison."

The American Electric people of New Britain also believed they could meet the incandescent lamp in eye-to-eye competition, with their more efficient arc lamp and their self-regulating dynamo. In fact, the Thomson-Houston system participated in such a tilt—and came off the victor!

In 1882 the P. and F. Corbin Company of New Britain went into the matter of electric lighting. They were approached by representatives of the Weston Electric Company, the Edison Company for Isolated Lighting, and the American Electric Company. The Corbin Company finally determined to give each system a week's trial.

First to be tested was that of the Weston Company, introducing an arc lamp developed by Edward Weston. One of the Corbin firm inquired:

"Now that you have the lights going, can you turn any of them off?"

"Not one at a time," was the reply. "They all turn off together."

The following week an Edison system was installed, with a bi-polar dynamo and a circuit of sixty incandescent lamps. Edison's system depended upon a voltage which had to be regulated constantly. In isolated plants, there was a pilot lamp on the headboard of the dynamo which allowed the dynamo tender to watch voltage variations. When necessary, voltage was adjusted, through a resistance box, which caused the voltage to increase or decrease at the will of the operator.

"Does a man have to be there all the time?" inquired one of the Corbin firm.

"Yes," was the reply, "he has to regulate the voltage and

adjust the commutator brushes as the load varies." The firm discovered also how fragile early Edison lamps were.

When the Thomson-Houston system was tried Thomson and Rice personally installed a twelve-light arc dynamo, with its lamps. After starting the dynamo and assuring themselves that everything worked properly, they left the system to run itself. The Corbin Company found another advantage in the fact that it was possible to shut off some of the lights and leave others shining.

At the end of the week the firm sent word to the American Electric Company: "Your check will be ready for you any time you call." The Edison system was not yet able to outdo its rivals.

Meanwhile Thomson's laboratory continued to be the scene of incessant activity. In those days smooth, well-joined copper wire for winding armatures and field magnets was unknown. Lengths of wire were hard-soldered together with brass. Then the joints were roughly filed and cotton insulation wrapped around the wire. Frequently slivers stuck through the insulation, or the joints were so irregular as to puncture the insulation and to leak current.

Thomson demanded better joints of the wire manufacturer. "Don't solder them," he said. "Weld them and then draw the wire, instead of filing it."

"But copper cannot be welded," exclaimed the wire manufacturer.

"Yes it can," said Thomson, "if you'll use my method."

Thomson explained the method of electric resistance welding which he had come upon unexpectedly during one of his lectures at the Franklin Institute four years before.

While Thomson continued to tap new veins of knowledge, he realized that he was not receiving from the company the cooperation he had a right to expect. He was convinced that

THE DYNAMO ROOM OF THE PEARL STREET STATION

GENIUS RIDICULED

This cartoon, which was published in a popular magazine of the time, illustrates the ridicule which was directed at Edison while he was working on his incandescent lamp.

"JUMBO"—THE EDISON STEAM DYNAMO

SUPERPOWER IN THE 80'S
The interior of a Thomson-Houston power plant in Boston, 1884.

it was not marketing his inventions with "diligent and continuous attention," and "in all reasonable and advisable ways" as his contract demanded. He therefore tendered his stock in the American Electric Company, and that of Professor Houston, demanding the return of their patents on the ground that the company had not lived up to its agreement. It had no sales office outside of New Britain and lacked adequate facilities for manufacture or experiment. Thomson's future was, for the moment, uncertain.

9

The General Electric Succession

A<small>BOUT</small> 1873 A FIRM under the name of C. A. Coffin and Company appeared in Lynn, Massachusetts, famous for its boots and shoes. Partners were Charles A. Coffin, a young man of twenty-nine, and Micajah P. Clough. They prospered, for Coffin, though young, had a reputation for selling goods and designing styles.

One morning he announced to Clough that he had joined a financial syndicate to buy up an electrical manufacturing company.

"I'm putting some money into it, Clough," he said. "We can go in together or not, as you like."

Though Clough did not join the syndicate, this step was the turning point of his partner's career.

Until 1882 electric lighting had been little heard of in the shoe city. Yet a rumor was sufficiently enticing to interest the Lynn Grand Army Post, which was considering the illumination of its new building. Silas A. Barton of the Post was chosen to investigate the possibilities of electric light.

Having learned of an arc light exhibition by the American Electric Illuminating Company, Barton went to Boston, taking with him a prominent leather manufacturer, Henry A. Pevear. Their questions regarding a dynamo system and its manufacturers met with evasive replies, probably because the Boston company was more interested in selling stock than in installing equipment.

The visitors made their way surreptitiously to the basement of the exhibition building. There they found a six-light dynamo. The nameplate, which the exhibiting company had forgotten to remove, read: "Manufactured by American Electric Company, New Britain, Conn."

A day or so later Barton and Pevear got off a train at New Britain, engaged a station hackman to take them to the plant of the American Electric Company, and there met a young man by the name of Rice. The "electrician" he said, was out of town. Thomson was visiting several cities in an effort to interest capital in the electrical manufacturing business. While he searched for a rescuer, the rescuer came to him.

As Barton and Pevear went through the New Britain factory they were impressed with the practical success of the arc light. They were impressed also by Rice's personality and technical knowledge. Their Yankee business minds sensed a beckoning opportunity.

The Lynn men made tentative arrangements to secure a dynamo and lamps. Then they went home, called together some business friends and organized, on April 26, 1882, an arc-light central station company which they called the Lynn Electric Lighting Company. Electrical generating equipment was soon installed. When Thomson visited the plant, Barton was able to verify his understanding that the American Electric Company was in the market.

Barton interviewed half a dozen shoe manufacturers in Lynn, and a syndicate was organized to buy control of the American Electric Company. Pevear joined the group on

condition that Charles A. Coffin should also join and should
agree to help actively in managing the unfamiliar enterprise.
The syndicate made sure of the cooperation of Professors
Thomson and Houston, holders of the patents.

This time there was no quibbling over the contract with

THE THOMSON-HOUSTON FACTORY—1884
*The first building occupied by this pioneer company in Lynn,
Massachusetts.*

the two professors. Mutual faith and cooperation persisted
unbroken throughout succeeding years. The new company
decided to reorganize at a meeting at New Britain on February 12, 1883, under the name of Thomson-Houston Electric Company.

Removal from New Britain to Lynn was not accomplished
before the latter part of 1883, when a building was erected
on Western Avenue consisting of three stories and a basement—ample, it was supposed, to accommodate the plant
for a considerable period. Pevear thought of using some of
the extra space for drying skins for his leather factory. But

orders flowed in too rapidly for anything more to be heard about drying skins on the premises.

Largely through Coffin's leadership, the young Thomson-Houston Electric Company began to obtain business in increasing bulk. Dynamos and arc lamps rolled away to the freight yards in a constant stream. Shop hands increased from seventy-five to a hundred and fifty. On January 1, 1883, there were five central station plants whose Thomson-Houston equipment supplied current to 365 arc lamps. One year later thirty-one stations supplied 2400 arc lamps.

At this time the company sold equipment to private individuals and concerns. It was not until 1884, under a policy suggested by Coffin, that the company began to establish central generating plants. Like Edison, Coffin foresaw that in this field lay the future of his company.

Electrical science had its great inventors and technicians, but none of them were leaders of commerce. They were neither trained nor fitted to raise capital, or to finance the marketing of their inventions, particularly on a scale essential in a country of tremendous size. Both Brush and Edison for example worked out in detail their central station systems. Yet each of these men was glad to relinquish the commercial development of his ideas to others.

And of the latter Coffin was the greatest. He it was who looked decades into the future and guided his policies toward ultimate ends. His influence was undeniably the principal factor in shaping a great development which began with the Thomson-Houston Company. Unsuspected by anyone, a line of succession was being set up which consisted of two branches; and the roots of the second branch were just beginning to appear in the first of the Edison companies.

Because of what it led to and because it was an unbroken chain of development, we have called it the General Electric Succession. The term might have been applied when the Brush Electric Company or the Edison Electric Light Company were conceived. Both of these in due time were drawn into the succession. But the Thomson-Houston Company was the first in the succession in which policies and methods that were later to be perpetuated took form.

And the Thomson-Houston Company meant Charles A. Coffin. For the former "shoemaker" had become a master mind in guiding America's progress in the age of electricity.

10

Lighting Up with Incandescents

In the summer of 1883 the Brush Electric Company became interested in the American rights of an incandescent lamp invented by Joseph W. Swan, an Englishman. With the Swan lamp, Brush visualized an illumination system which would include both arc and incandescent lighting. He had completed a storage battery of cast-lead plates, which were pasted over with lead oxides and treated in an electrolytic bath. Experimenting with the battery, he found that one horsepower, applied to a dynamo, would charge the battery sufficiently for it to operate ten Swan lamps for an hour.

A number of these batteries Brush connected to an arc-light system, operated by a dynamo of large capacity. During the daytime he charged the batteries and at night operated incandescent lamps from them. The lamps did not interfere with the arc-light system, as the batteries were equipped with an automatic "manipulator" which cut them into the circuit when they were to be recharged or cut them out as charging was completed.

This worked so well, notwithstanding occasional trouble with the automatic manipulator, as to increase substantially the business of the Brush Electric Company for several years.

Scarcely more than a year passed before another incandescent lamp, backed by the Thomson-Houston Company, entered the incandescent field, as Thomson resolved to promote both arc and incandescent lamps and let the public decide the issue. Where Brush used a storage battery to operate his arc and incandescent lamp circuit, Thomson used a "distributor box." This he designed for hooking up (anywhere in the arc-light circuit) a group of eight incandescent lamps, each requiring the same voltage but only one-eighth the current of an arc lamp. The entire group absorbed the same current as the arc lamps, 9.6 amperes, thus preserving the constant-current characteristic of the system.

Independent control of each lamp was secured through the distributor box, which contained eight resistance coils, one for each lamp. The coils, which were loops of wire of the same resistance as the lamp filaments, were disconnected while the incandescent lamps were in use; when one of the lamps went off, a resistance coil was switched into the circuit by a magnet to pass current in place of the lamp.

For a lamp to operate in this system, the company secured a license from the Sawyer-Man Electric Company to manufacture and sell their incandescent lamp. A year or two later Thomson-Houston came out with its own dynamo and began to install complete incandescent systems, with both series and multiple distribution of the current.

In adopting the Sawyer-Man lamp, the Thomson-Houston interests accepted the Sawyer-Man contention that they had invented a workable incandescent lamp before Edison had done so. Their lamp had a distinctive type of base, although it utilized a filament of carbonized bamboo

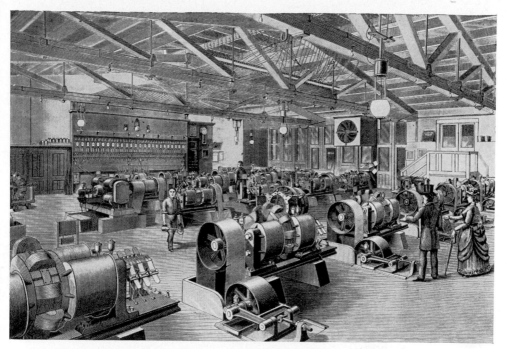

STYLES IN DRESSES AND DYNAMOS

*A woman visitor inspects the Brush central station in Philadelphia,
1883.*

ONE OF EDISON'S EARLY POWER STATIONS

and embodied the three features which Edison had patented
—filament, vacuum, and glass container.

When the Edison company refrained from bringing action, various explanations were advanced to account for
their passive attitude toward competitors. It is likely, however, that both Edison and his backers were too absorbed in
the project of establishing their system to undertake patent
litigation. They preferred to win against competition by
commerical rather than by legal success.

The first District was in full operation with five thousand
lamps burning by May 1, 1883. Licenses for Edison companies in other places had been issued. Edison had worked
out a plan for installing his system in thinly-settled communities by means of overhead wires strung on poles, call-
ing this idea the "village plant system." And he had conceived brilliant improvement upon the parallel circuit.

One morning he came to the Machine Works on Goerck
Street with a rough diagram. "I want you to lay out an experimental line in the laboratory and connect some lamps
to it like this, and put two dynamos in series on the circuit.
Then test it out and give me a report of what happens." The
sketch presented the rudiments of the three-wire system,
one of the greatest single factors in the success of illumination. It was to place electrical service within the limit of
every purse. Edison had developed it in an effort to save
copper in the conductors of his system. The saving that it
finally effected amounted to as much as 62 per cent. Electrical systems of today could hardly operate without it.

Four months after Edison found that the three-wire plan
would work, William S. Andrews and Frank J. Sprague, who
had come from London to join the Edison staff, left New
York for Sunbury, Pennsylvania. A license for a local central-

station had been issued to the town of Sunbury by the Edison Electric Light Company. Andrews and Sprague were to install the lighting system for operation throughout the entire town by the evening of July 4.

They arrived at Sunbury with forty-eight hours to work in and proceeded to hook up two "L" type bi-polar dynamos in the local generating station, then to wire the town for five hundred 16-candlepower lamps. From the station to the main circuits, feeders which embodied the three-wire plan were carried on poles instead of underground. Andrews and Sprague might have slept the second night had not Sprague in his enthusiasm given the dynamos a trial run. He burned out the engine bearings and with his partner spent most of the night scraping babbitt metal.

Edison arrived at noon on the Fourth to inspect the plant. Half an hour before sunset he ordered the dynamos started. As the glass bulbs glowed, excited shouts arose in the town. At the City Hotel a noisy crowd gathered. There was an incessant fusillade of firecrackers, and as evening drew on fireworks such as the little town could rarely afford were set ablaze.

Townsfolk asked Edison and his men all manner of questions, "What makes the hairpin red hot?" "How do you light it from a distance?" "Can you blow it out?" Almost distracted, Andrews complained that they were asking questions he couldn't answer. "This is a new business," Edison told him, "we must invent answers to go with our appliances."

Andrews recalled the advice on a day later in the summer, when a severe thunderstorm broke. In the midst of it, a boy ran into the central station, yelling that the City Hotel was afire. Andrews hurried downtown, found a crowd standing about the hotel in the rain, but he could see no smoke. Inside a dozen people told him excitedly that they had seen sparks and flashes leaping from the electric light wires to the metal gas fixtures around which the wires were twisted.

The wires were insulated only by a cotton wrapping painted with white lead. Static electricity, built up by the storm, had leaked through the insulation and shot along the metal fixtures.

Although Andrews calmed the excited crowd the hotel proprietor sent for him next day and demanded the removal of the wires.

"You may not realize it," said Andrews, "but your hotel was struck by lightning yesterday. If it hadn't been for us you'd be proprietor this morning of nothing but a heap of ashes. Those sparks were the lightning being shunted into the ground on our wires."

"Well!" exclaimed the astonished proprietor, "if that's the case, we'll let the wires stay, of course."

Andrews left Sunbury, not long after, to install another Edison three-wire system in Shamokin. And in the fall of 1883 Sprague became identified with a much more pretentious installation. This was the Edison central station at Brockton, Massachusetts, where the three-wire system was for the first time put in by means of underground conductors.

The system, supplying about 150 lamps, was installed despite considerable apprehension on the part of the public. Officials of the local gas company were particularly dubious. One of them remarked that if the lodge rooms were ever lighted by electricity he would stop going to the sessions. Timid citizens wrote to the newspapers, expressing the fear that life and property would no longer be safe.

Within a year the number of lamps in circuit exceeded two thousand. In 1885 it was reported to Edison that only two customers had gone back to gas—one other had gone so far back as to resume the burning of kerosene!

Sprague was the electrician of this station, and served as Edison's representative. He was also acting as Edison's mathematician at that time, calculating the size and cost of conductors for projected central stations. Blueprints of proposed systems were regularly sent to him at Brockton.

This was one of Edison's concessions to the mathematicians. His own methods were not mathematical. But he realized that Upton and Sprague could substitute precise, time-saving calculations for cumbersome, protracted experiments. The method in the matter of conductors had been first to construct in miniature an electric-light system for individual towns. By experimenting with the miniature system, dimensions of the conductors were fixed upon. This method took time and money, and Edison was willing to allow mathematics to simplify it.

Sprague's calculations showed that Edison's original plan for main conductors and feeders could be improved. The mains were intended to be tapering in diameter; Sprague made them of uniform thickness throughout. The resistance in the feeders was intended to be alike in all cases; Sprague made the resistance low for heavy loads of current and high for normal loads. This proved to be efficient, and the covering patent was presented by Sprague to the Edison Electric Light Company. Sprague had joined Upton and Thomson in being among the first to show what the college-trained man could do in electrical engineering.

Sprague now seized the opportunity to experiment with an electrical device he had long dreamed of. Ruthlessly he converted the little office of the Brockton station into a temporary electrical workshop. The office had a luxurious tapestry carpet and lounge. Sprague soon had them littered with armature cores, magnet wire, jack knives, asphaltum varnish cans, japan and shellac bottles, paper insulation, and magnetic testing bells. Most of this bric-a-brac was stored under the lounge during the hours of mental activity devoted to the central station blueprints—at which times the blueprints were spread on the tapestry carpet.

, Not the most favorable conditions, one would say, for contriving anything so intricate as an electric motor. Yet the motor this young enthusiast finally put together was to lead the way for electricity across the boundaries of illumination and into the vast field on the other side of the fence—the field of electric power.

It has seemed a long time from Edison's promises in 1878 regarding incandescent lighting to their fulfillment in 1882. But four years was a brief period in which to devise and introduce on a commercial basis so far-reaching a system. It was his original purpose to introduce his light solely by means of the central-station method. Only after tremendous pressure had he acquiesced in the formation of the Edison Company for Isolated Lighting. Pursuing its purpose aggressively, this company engaged lighting salesmen and sent them at an early date into conservative New England. Isolated Edison plants came to be numerous in that region within a year. And the business activity which resulted furnished training and experience to one of the later apostles of electric power, Sidney B. Paine.

As a youth of nineteen Paine entered a textile mill at Fall River, Massachusetts. After four years of learning this business he became in 1881 a sales agent of the Edison Electric Light Company, and later was established in Boston as assistant manager of the New England department of the Edison Company for Isolated Lighting.

During the next few years Paine went up and down New

England, interesting textile mills in Edison lighting. He could meet the mill men on their own ground; he knew their business and how electric lights could best serve them. Among his first installations was the Hampden Mill of Holyoke, where 120 lights were put in circuit. Mill after mill became a customer. So energetic were Paine's efforts and so universal his success that in ten years not a textile factory of any size in New England lacked its isolated Edison plant.

A great stir was always caused by the lights. The Lowell *Morning Times* proudly announced as its "big news" on February 21, 1882, that the prominent Merrimack Mills were being equipped with 262 Edison lamps, one for each loom in the plant.

Paine was constantly meeting incredulity and bedrock conservatism. One mill owner would not hear of lighting his mill by any such "new-fangled method."

"All right," said Paine, "I won't say any more about it. But I have an hour till train time and I'd like to tell you how the electric light works."

"Go ahead," said the mill man, "provided you don't try to tell me why I should light my mill with it."

As Paine talked, the skeptic listened more and more intently. At last he said in an apologetic tone, "How much would it cost to light my mill by this system?"

And Paine walked out of the mill with another signed contract in his pocket.

But men were developing Edison central stations, just as Paine was cultivating the isolated lighting business. Arthur R. Bush, trained both in engineering and commercial practices, aided many generating stations to take the first step in supplying current for the "red-hot hairpins" in their air-tight bottles.

Bush had begun his electrical career on the vessels of the

Old Colony Steamship Company, which operated the two sound steamers, *Pilgrim* and *Providence,* between New York and Fall River. He helped to wire the *Providence,* for which 2000 lamps were required. Every stateroom had incandescent lights, so that at night the vessels were a blaze of glory and soon were famed up and down the coast.

At Rutland, Massachusetts, Bush helped to establish a small generating station. Realizing that the station attendant had little knowledge of things electrical, Bush stayed in the neighborhood for several days after the installation. Early one evening the attendant asked him to fill in a supper relief. The attendant had scarcely gone when Bush discovered that the clutch mechanism connecting the jack-shaft to the dynamo driving pulley was out of order and the clutch was slipping. If the dynamo stopped, all the electric lights in town would go out.

Bush knew that it would take two men to repair the mechanism without stopping the engine—and he was alone. It was a case of leaping into the gap as best he could. He grasped the clutch lever with both hands and held on. He was able to keep the clutch in place by main force. The minutes passed; the strain increased. His muscles ached sorely, but nobody came. Desperately he stuck to the job. The tardy attendant finally arrived. And Bush, faint with exhaustion, discovered that he had held the clutch for an hour and a half.

Until the late 'eighties there were more Edison isolated plants than Edison central-station plants. In 1883 there were 154 isolated Edison plants in the country, employing nearly 30,000 lamps.

The Detroit *Post* in January 1883 published the following summary of the lighting situation in New York:

"A year ago there were a dozen companies ready to promise any city incandescent lights—that is, ready to light interiors with small shining bulbs like gas jets—but at this moment Edison's company is the only one actively in the field. It not only occupies the field, it comes near to filling it.

"The *Times* is lighted on the circuit of the first district. I went into the counting room and editorial room last night to inquire about it. They spoke warmly in its praise. 'The best artificial light I ever wrote by,' said the manager."

The tide was running strong—and there was little doubt as to its direction.

Frank J. Sprague

Charles J. Van Depoele

E. M. Bentley

W. K. Knight

THE FOUR WHO PIONEERED IN ELECTRIC STREETCARS

11

Lighting Up with Arcs

Paying scant attention to the prophet of incandescence, the pioneer sales agent of the arc light—resourceful, rough-and-ready, versatile as a Jack-of-all-trades—was going everywhere and accomplishing a great deal. He flourished from 1882 until the early nineties. And he was more than a salesman; he was a missionary and a promoter.

He went into communities where electric light was known only by hearsay and where even intelligent folk had their superstitions about it. He won over men of means; interested them in financing an electric light company; helped them find property sites; persuaded the town government to grant an operating franchise, which he frequently drew up himself; assisted in the organization of the company; sold it the necessary equipment, personally drawing up the contract in proper legal form; and considered his task completed only upon the arrival of the construction man who took charge of the actual installation.

The training that electrical manufacturers gave their field representatives was of the utmost importance in the conduct of their business. Young men educated at college in electricity were hard to find. Technical schools had not yet begun to offer special electrical courses. In physics courses then offered, emphasis was on the principle of static electricity.

So electrical companies themselves had to teach the men to sell and install their equipment. The Thomson-Houston company lost no time in establishing a regular course of instruction. Men who completed this course were known as "experts" and were sent out either as salesmen or construction men.

They took their work with profound earnestness, but they got plenty of fun out of it as well. They called themselves "expects" because they expected to do bigger things and receive bigger pay. The first "experts" were a rather nondescript lot. They were recruits from the "highways and hedges," and comprised machinists, steam fitters, carpenters, school teachers, and anybody else with a turn for the mechanical who was willing to pitch in. "We took agents and peddlers, prize fighters and preachers," as Coffin put it.

Their first duties were menial. They took turns keeping the floor of the testing room clean. They fired the ovens where dynamo windings were dried, and carried coal the length of the shop. They operated machine tools, or labored at the workbenches. Eventually they wound up in the testing room, where they had to measure and adjust arc-lengths in the lamps, paint dynamo rods, fit belts to the dynamos, and sweep up shop at the end of day.

A good deal of fun came when they were taught to climb poles. As construction men, they did all the work of linemen today. Sometimes they became nervous when they reached the top of the pole and wrapped their arms around it desperately. This brought their bodies perpendicular, loosening the grip of their spurs. Down they would slide with hands and arms full of splinters. But there was no respite; it was "up and at 'em" again.

Sometimes arc-lamp salesmen penetrated into frontier regions. The veteran expert of the Brush Company, Thomas E. Adams, later the joint inventor of the Brush-Adams lamp, spent months on the upper Mississippi, installing and adjusting arc headlights on lake and river steamers engaged in logging operations day and night. The Brush arc headlight, with suitable reflector, was so popular that more than half the steamers were thus equipped, and a sales agent was kept busy throughout the logging season.

On one of these trips Adams put up for the night at Lansing, Iowa, where the lodging house was by no means luxurious. In the dead of night there came a thundering rap on his door. The voice of the landlord bellowed, "Say, mister, are you an electrician?"

Adams emerged in his night clothes to meet a couple of men from a river steamer whose lighting outfit had gone wrong. In response to their entreaties he got into his clothes, walked with them half a mile along a railroad track, and rowed in their skiff six miles down the river.

He found that a novice who installed the headlight had adjusted it in such a manner that the carbons would not separate when current was applied. It took Adams about two minutes to set things right.

The following season Adams went into Canada to install a Brush arc headlight for Gilmore and Company, a large concern that was cutting timber in the wilderness. He took the apparatus into the woods by boat and pack. It was installed on a company steamer, and successfully tested.

When Adams prepared to return, the Gilmore people objected. "If you go back," they said, "we'll have trouble with the light right away." Adams assured them that everything would be all right—he couldn't take up a permanent residence in their midst.

He roughed it for several weeks, getting back to the border and finally reaching Buffalo. There he made for the first barber shop he could find. It was filled with men who turned and stared at him. He looked like a wild man, with tangled hair and a thick beard, and his face, neck, and wrists were swollen from bites of the Canadian black fly.

Months later the Brush offices received a letter from the Gilmore Company which said curtly, "Your man came up here, put your light on our boat and then abandoned it. We must confess, however, that it has given no trouble."

Colorful legends have also been handed down of the breezy methods of R. T. McDonald, general manager of the Fort Wayne Electric Light Company. The chance which created this electrical plant in Fort Wayne has been recounted by John Kise, one of its earliest employees.

Kise, who in 1881 was employed in the warehouse of Evans, McDonald & Company, overall manufacturers, made a week-end excursion to Cleveland in July. There he saw the dazzling light of Brush arc lamps, and was so attracted by them that he visited the works of the Brush Electric Company to learn more about electric lighting.

When, some time later, Kise met two strangers in the dining room of the old Aveline Hotel, in Fort Wayne, he could talk of nothing but electricity. He was astonished to learn that his table companions were themselves electrical inventors.

"We are in Fort Wayne," they said, "trying to arrange a demonstration for an arc lamp we've designed, but no one seems interested. You can't sell patent rights without a demonstration."

"Have you tried my employer, R. T. McDonald?" asked

A CLEVELAND TROLLEY POSES FOR ITS PICTURE

This Bentley-Knight car got its power by contact with an electric conduit between the tracks.

A SPRAGUE STREETCAR IN BOSTON

THE CAR THAT FRIGHTENED JAY GOULD
*Frank J. Sprague and his demonstration electric car. It was here that
Jay Gould tried to jump off when a safety fuse blew out.*

Kise. "He'll help you exhibit the lamp. We've a small steam engine that could run your dynamo. You come out to the factory tomorrow and I'll introduce you to Mr. McDonald."

So James Jenney and his son Charles, who had invented an arc lamp in their home town of Ann Arbor, Michigan, were introduced to Ronald T. McDonald. The moment McDonald understood the nature of Jenney's invention, he saw its future possibilities. Not only did he offer the warehouse for an exhibition of the light, but with characteristic vigor he also rounded up his townsmen, invited them to the demonstration, and then stood by to give Jenney the opportunity of proving his invention.

McDonald soon interested other Fort Wayne men in the new lamp. After a brief interval of negotiations and conferences, a new concern came into existence, on November 1, 1881. It was known as the Fort Wayne "Jenney" Electric Light Company—though legally Jenney's name was not included in the title. McDonald went after business with unbounded energy, and was usually successful despite his erratic methods.

McDonald is said to have traveled sometimes in a private railroad coach. He would roll into town with a flourish, hire a local band, and start a parade to draw the crowd to a public hall. There McDonald addressed them on the wonders of electric light and the importance of a local company for the community. Before he left he usually had a company started, and tucked away in his pocket was an order for electrical equipment.

Frequently his salesmanship outran his company's ability to meet contracts. But he had a remarkable construction man, W. H. Driftmeyer, and from all accounts Driftmeyer saved McDonald's bacon more than once.

During some jobs Driftmeyer slept on the premises, working every minute of his waking hours. On one occasion a pulley burst and struck him on the head. He couldn't afford to quit work, so a private hospital was rigged up for him in the power plant and he directed the installation from a cot, his head wound in bandages.

While he was completing an installation in New London, he received a hurry order to go out to Paris, Illinois, where McDonald was in difficulties. Two dynamos had been installed with the understanding that they were to be self-regulating. When the company had found that they were not, payment amounting to $28,000 was held up. Could Driftmeyer build a regulator and get it on in time? He rushed home on a Friday night, worked until the following Tuesday, hardly stopping to sleep, and made a regulator to fit the dynamos. It worked. McDonald received the delayed payment and entertained the whole construction crew at a celebration dinner.

In New York and the nearby territory, during this period, the Fuller-Wood Company and the compact, low-weighted dynamo of "Jimmy" Wood continued to find numerous customers. Wood himself did not hesitate to canvass for prospects.

By the middle eighties each of these companies was marketing a dynamo of respectable capacity. The Brush dynamo operated forty arc lamps; the Thomson-Houston, twenty-eight; the Wood, twenty-five; the Jenny, thirty. The Edison bipolar incandescent dynamos at that time were made in four sizes: the "E" lighting fifteen lamps of sixteen-candlepower; the "Z" 60 lamps; the "L" 150; the "K" 250.

Now as arc-light stations multiplied and incandescent stations began to appear, there came upon the scene a new type of experiment—the electric streetcar.

PART THREE

Electric Transportation, Motors, the Transmission of Power

12

Broomstick Cars

Oliver wendell holmes, at the age of eighty, wrote a set of rollicking verses called, *The Broomstick Train; or The Return of the Witches.* He fancied that the curious pole on the roof of every electric streetcar, reaching up to the slender "cobweb" of wire above, was a witch's broomstick put to prosaic use.

Thus in 1889 did a poet herald the innovation in methods of transportation. He discerned, as many did not, the spirit of conquest which it typified.

"Look here!" he exclaimed in *Over the Teacups,* "There are crowds of people whirled through our streets on these new-fashioned cars, with their witch-broomsticks overhead —if they don't come from Salem they ought to!—and not more than one in a dozen of these fish-eyed bipeds thinks or cares a nickel's worth about the miracle which is wrought for their convenience . . .

"We ought to go down on our knees when one of these mighty caravans, car after car, spins by us, under the mystic impulse which seems to know not whether its train is loaded or empty."

75

To be introduced to the reading public by Oliver Wendell Holmes was a bit of fortune. Such lines in the poem as "On the rattling rail, by the broomstick train," must have made many persons feel more kindly toward the strange electric car. But for years after an indubitable triumph over technical difficulties the electric car struggled against popular prejudice. People who felt at home with the "red-hot hairpin" could not get accustomed to a vehicle moving through the streets with nothing to pull it.

Men had been attempting to move locomotives or single cars by electricity for two generations. Thomas Davenport of Brandon, Vermont, in 1835 "ventured his little all" in striving to construct an electric motor, operating a miniature railway with it; Robert Davison of Aberdeen, Scotland, drove a five-ton electric locomotive in 1839 between Edinburgh and Glasgow. Dr. Werner Siemens in 1879 operated a sizeable electric railway in Berlin, the first to be driven by current from a dynamo instead of storage batteries.

And Thomas A. Edison built and operated two experimental electric railways at Menlo Park in 1880 and in 1882. He employed reversed dynamos for his driving motors, as Siemens had done, conducting current from dynamos to motors and back again through the rails and wheels of the locomotives.

The first of these railways was a crude and ludicrous affair. The locomotive was a four-wheel species of flatcar with board seats and a medley of apparatus, from which two long brake-handles protruded. Motive power came from a "long-waisted Mary Ann" utilized as a motor and laid upon her side.

With this queer locomotive Edison "rode to glory," or at least to newspaper fame, at a speed of twenty miles an hour.

He hauled a train of two cars, one of which had a canvas awning and was fondly dubbed "Pullman."

The second experimental railroad had two locomotives and was far more sophisticated. The track was two and a

THE PLEASURES OF ELECTRIC TRANSPORTATION
Edison's electric railway at Menlo Park, in 1880.

half miles long and the locomotives were capable of forty miles an hour.

Nothing tangible came of Edison's adventure into the realm of electric railroading, nor of the joint three-ton locomotive which he produced with Stephen D. Field in 1883 to appear under the name of "Judge" at the Chicago Exposition for Railway Appliances. The locomotive was supplied with current from a third rail and had a Weston dynamo for a motor. In two weeks the "Judge" had run 446 miles. But though it led to nothing practical, Edison's experimental electric railway set people thinking for the first time about electric traction upon the elevated roads of Manhattan. The New York *Herald* took up the idea and used the Edison railway to create considerable agitation. But it was twenty years before any action was taken.

The electric locomotive was never thought of as adaptable for street railways. And the "broomstick car" was finally evolved through long and arduous effort by a memorable group of American pioneers, among them Frank J. Sprague, Leo Daft, Charles J. Van Depoele, Edward M. Bentley, Walter H. Knight, and J. C. Henry.

Sprague had worked out a motor in his luxurious office in Brockton. His development of the trolley pole was later to bring him into a dispute with Van Depoele. To follow the contribution of Bentley and Knight, however, carries us back to Cleveland and the Brush Electric Company, which furnished shop facilities for these two men who set out to master one of the most obdurate problems in the electrical field.

"If you want to pull a car, you must put something in front to pull it," said a serious street-railway official in 1884. That was the way people talked when electrical men announced their plan of moving a car by means of a motor installed inside.

Frank J. Sprague put the problem of the electric street-car a little differently. He summed it up as follows:

"On the car must be mounted one or more motors, weighing anywhere from 1000 to 3000 pounds, whose speed must be reduced ten or twelve times, while perfect freedom of axle movement and resilience of car springs must be preserved, as, with this additional weight and system of gearing the car is driven over irregular tracks, around sharp curves and up heavy grades. It must, moreover, be handled by men ignorant of electrical technique; must be reliable, not apt to get out of order; and must have a reasonable depreciation, although exposed to the worst abuses of any class of machinery."

The word "abuse" sums up the contrast between the streetcar motor and its brother, the stationary motor. The latter is started in the morning and runs all day at the same speed. But the streetcar motor is started and stopped hundreds of times a day and is made to run at all speeds up to its capacity. It is constantly in the hands of strangers.

It was a nerve-straining enterprise upon which Bentley and Knight embarked when they ran their first electric car on Garden Street, Cleveland, July 26, 1884. The Associated Press announced it as the "first electric railroad for public use in America."

Unquestionably electrical apparatus was ready at that moment to venture into the domain of transportation. For several years the dynamo had been earning its salt, though its construction had become increasingly intricate.

Electrical men had known for ten years what would happen if a dynamo, supplied with power by a steam engine, was connected to another dynamo in the same curcuit so that current generated in the first machine would flow to the second. They knew that the mysterious interaction between magnets and armature would cause the armature in the second dynamo to rotate with enough force to drive a machine shaft or car axle. Thus the mechanical power which originated in the steam engine would reappear in the second of the two dynamos—called now a motor. This is the idea of dynamo reversibility, revealed as far back as the days of Pacinotti and Gramme.

Means had been found, long before this, to magnetize field magnets in a direct-current dynamo by a connection of the armature coils with the field-windings. Variations in this practice resulted in the series-wound, shunt-wound, and compound-wound dynamos.

Bentley and Knight understood the principle of the motor, but to apply it to propelling cars was not easy. The problem was three-sided. There was the design of the motor, the manner in which it was to be installed in the car, and the method of transmitting power from the motor armature to car axles.

Bentley and Knight used as their source of power a thirty-horsepower, 500-volt constant-current dynamo of the Brush Electric Company, located at the car barns on Euclid Avenue, Cleveland. Another Brush dynamo, series-wound and of smaller capacity, was used as a motor. It was suspended underneath the car body and connected to front and rear axles by belts of coiled wire.

The attitude of the railway company toward the new-fangled mode of locomotion seems to have been one of chilly tolerance. The electric car was assigned to the worst piece of track on the system and left to bob along as well as it could.

Prejudice against overhead wires was so widespread that the inventors enclosed them in an underground wooden conduit which ran in the middle of the track. It had a continuous slot through which a contact device called a "plow" reached down and carried current for transmission from the wires to the motor.

The backers of the East Cleveland Railway were not exempt from the general feeling of awe which the strange, horseless vehicle aroused.

Said the Cleveland *Herald* when cars commenced to make regular runs: "It was amusing to watch the passengers who boarded the car. Some took the invention as a matter of course, while others, especially the ladies, evinced great curiosity . . . An unexpected drawback is the fact that half the horses that pass the car are frightened by it. There is nothing unusual in the appearance of the car; it makes no noises besides the whirr of the motor . . . But even old plugs were frightened; and one passenger opined that the horses, jealous of a loss of business, had combined to express their disapproval of the invention."

This was all very fine. But within three days the electric car encountered difficulties. The motor was supported at one end by a spring connection, and the springs started to break, with loud reports, at the rate of one an hour. When the wire belts began to give way, the car had to go to the repair shop.

A new method of connection between motor and axles was tried. Friction wheels made of strawboard with a system of link belts were employed. But the first time the car endeavored to move a heavy load the friction wheels slipped and developed flat spots. Finally the inventors adopted spur gearing, built up of paper to lessen the noise. This worked fairly well. But when two and then three cars were run in parallel operation electrically, with a fixed or constant current, the dynamo balked. It was being overloaded to almost double its capacity.

Despite these problems Bentley and Knight struggled to keep one or two cars running. They did so through the rest of the year and well into 1885, changing their methods to use constant voltage and varying current. The service proved sufficiently reliable during winter storms to give a hint of the superiority latent in electric traction. It was certain, however, that the conduit method of supplying current was impractical, for it involved heavy expense.

Bentley and Knight did not make a practical success of

the electric street car. But they with Van Depoele and others started a ripple of expectation which lasted until the electric car seriously took up its task.

Charles J. Van Depoele was early apprenticed to a cabinet-maker in his native town of Lichtervelde, Belgium. Artistic in his tastes and skillful with his hands, he became a wood-carver of considerable reputation, until the mechanical and scientific side of his nature began to gain the upper hand. He hob-nobbed in the railway shops of East Flanders, where his father was a master mechanic. There he found an atmosphere to his liking, and there, despite his father's disapproval, he served another apprenticeship, this time to study elementary electricity.

In 1869, at the age of twenty-three, Van Depoele came to the United States and established in Chicago a prosperous wood-carving business. Unexcelled at this trade, he was soon making more money than he needed—and the surplus went promptly into a series of experiments with electric arc lights.

In less than ten years he had an arc-light system of his own; had installed lamps in Chicago; and had lighted the front of an opera house in Detroit, where the strange glow of the first lights caused a nervous citizen to send in a fire alarm.

Van Depoele was also experimenting in a modest way with motors, operating them on his series arc circuit. On one of these motors he placed a current-collecting brush made from a block of carbon, which served the purpose as well as the old copper brush. Without knowing it, he had made one of the most valuable discoveries of his life which was one day to play a dramatic role on streetcar development.

By 1880 this erstwhile wood carver had made friends in financial circles, and his own manufacturing concern, the Van Depoele Electric Manufacturing Company of Chicago, was in the forefront of those trying to move the streetcar by electricity. Most notable of his early demonstrations was the mile-long railway which he operated in 1884 from the street-car terminal in Toronto to the Toronto Annual Exhibition. The cars were made up in a train and drawn by a motorcar.

The method conceived by Van Depoele for supplying current to the motor was an innovation. On the roof of the motorcar he mounted a pivoted beam with a contact wheel on its upper end. This wheel was placed against the under side of an overhead wire. At the opposite end of the beam was a powerful spring which pressed the beam, and hence the contact wheel, continuously against the wire. Connected to the wheel was a flexible cable which provided a path for the current from wire to motor. This was nothing more than the simple trolley pole, now universal. It was the most practical and workable method that had been tried.

Upon applying for a patent a year or so later, Van Depoele found himself in conflict in the United States Patent Office with Frank J. Sprague, who laid claim to the invention of the under-running trolley as far back as 1882. He was at that time an officer in the United States Navy, on a year's leave of absence. While riding on the Metropolitan District Railway in London, Sprague had pondered the notion of running the road by electricity, with a conductor supported on insulators between the tracks, and automatically kept in tension. But at the Kensington Station he saw such a formidable complication of switches connecting the four tracks that the idea came to him of substituting an overhead conductor and an upward-pressing contact mounted upon the roof of the car.

The patent office refused to recognize Sprague's inventive work previous to his return to the United States in 1883, despite the fact that part of the time he was on board an

American vessel and hence on American territory. The ruling gave priority to Van Depoele, to whom the patent was issued.

In November 1884 the Sprague Electric Railway and Motor Company was incorporated under an agreement which committed Sprague to experiment with motors both for traction and stationary work. It represented his major ambition and had caused his resignation from Edison's organization the previous April.

Under the agreement, Edward H. Johnson, later president of the Edison Electric Light Company, assumed the financing of whatever work was undertaken. This was probably one of the most unusual concerns, as regards its finances, in the whole range of electrical activity. For months it existed mostly on paper.

The company did little to attract public notice until the winter of 1885–86, when Sprague gave a demonstration before officials of the Manhattan Elevated Railway on a short stretch of track in New York. Beneath an ordinary flatcar mounted on an elevated-railway track, he placed two of his motors. The experiment was not without results despite the fact that, in working the controller too abruptly, the safety-fuse blew out with a startling flash. Jay Gould was one of those who tried to jump from the car, and never afterward could he be persuaded to take the slightest interest in electric traction.

The results came when Sprague was approached a few days later by C. E. Chinnock, superintendent of the Pearl Street Edison Station, with an offer to purchase for $30,000 one-sixth of Sprague's interest in the company. At the moment Sprague did not have enough ready cash to pay his boarding-house bill, yet he declined the offer.

Sprague was away on a vacation when he received a telegram from Johnson announcing that he had promised to show Cyrus W. Field, chief owner of the Manhattan Elevated Railway, an electric car in operation on his road the following Tuesday—only four days distant.

Sprague rushed to New York and set feverishly to work. Monday night found him with one assistant completing the electrical connections of the motors by candlelight. He had no opportunity to make tests and had no idea whatever whether the motor would work.

The situation was tense. But the motors responded without a fault. For two hours every possible feat was performed with the car, including regenerative braking, which seems to have been tried that day for the first time in America. Geared motors were mounted by the "wheelbarrow" method, later universal; interpole winding was used, as well as rheostatic control and other innovations.

At the end of the day Sprague received another call from Chinnock, who offered $25,000 for one-twelfth of Sprague's interest, nearly double his first offer. And this time Sprague accepted.

He was rather mystified about the proposition, however, for Chinnock was not a man of means. Later he learned that the Superintendent was acting as agent for an officer of the Edison Electric Light Company, who had been advised to buy into the Sprague Company by a spiritualistic medium!

In less than three weeks another twelfth interest was sold for $26,500 to other parties, who doubtless bought on more materialistic advice. When officials suddenly lost all interest in the project, the Sprague Company had to abandon its attempts to electrify the elevated railway. It turned consequently to the street-railway field, where half a dozen electrical inventors had small installations operating with just enough success to encourage the sanguine, just enough failure to arouse scoffers.

With people beginning to talk of electricity as the emancipator of the horse, it was high time for an emancipator to appear. Horses frequently collapsed in the traces from the heat. They could be worked only two or three hours a day. The streetcar stables were immense, and property surrounding them invariably depreciated in value.

As William Wharton, Jr., put it: "Electric cars never get sick with epizooty or other diseases, and during strikes or other periods of enforced idleness do not require to be fed."

But opposition to electric transit, continuing up to 1888 and even later, revealed human motives at their worst. The backers of cable roads did everything they could to impede the entrance of electric cars. Superstitions of the people were played upon; the danger of electric wires was exaggerated; readers were gravely informed that the heavy currents passing over the wires would kill the shade trees; or that the presence of so much electricity in the air would cause sickness.

Meanwhile electric light companies were coming more and more to be an important factor in the transit situation. The day was near when the Edison Electric Light Company and the Thomson-Houston Electric Company were to place themselves solidly behind electric traction.

THOMSON-HOUSTON DYNAMO, ABOUT 1890

A TYPICAL SWITCHBOARD OF THE EARLY PERIOD

ELECTRICITY COMES TO NARRAGANSETT PIER

Construction gang of the Thomson-Houston Company engaged in erecting poles and stringing wires.

ASSEMBLY ROOM OF THOMSON-HOUSTON PLANT, 1885

13

From Shoes to Dynamos

THERE WAS NO SPOT IN Lynn, Massachusetts, more industrious than the factory of the Thomson-Houston Electric
Company in 1885. But it was a mysterious business. Passers-
by loitered as their ears caught the unfamiliar drone of dynamos. Through basement windows they beheld with startled eyes the weird green flashes of commutator brushes and
the steady blue gleam of arc lamps.

By 1885 a broad, smoothly functioning organization was
shaping. Executive minds were developing above the common level and gravitating into their proper spheres. Rice
was made general superintendent, his career diverging at
this point from his former close association with Professor
Thomson. He held a combined engineering and plant-
production office. Under him was an able assistant engineer,
Albert L. Rohrer, and under them both was a fast-growing
and efficient departmental organization. George E. Emmons,
meanwhile, had become factory auditor from which he advanced by logical steps into the realm of factory management.

The company was expanding from insignificance to first

importance. Routine was in flux; minor departments were taking shape. There was one draftsman, W. O. Wakefield, and the small supply of blueprint paper he required was home-made.

Everywhere there was teamwork. Rohrer was in the shop at seven in the morning, laying out work with the foreman and starting the production of new products as they were worked out in Thomson's laboratory, a definite procedure for manufacture having been decided upon in consultation with Rice. Thomson's was the true analytical mind. He perceived difficulties before they were reached, and altered his plans accordingly. It was the antithesis of the "cut-and-try" practice, which demanded innumerable experiments, and was a conserver of time and effort.

Sometimes he and Rice received helpful suggestions unexpectedly from Charles A. Coffin, the man of finance and commerce. They would look at each other in surprise and confess that he had brought up a technical idea which demanded consideration.

From intensive activity and the rising hum of industry the nucleus of a great corporation was emerging. Already the company contained rich human talent. It had a great scientist-inventor in Thomson, a keen engineer in Rice, a capable factory manager in Emmons, and a genius of finance and salesmanship in Coffin.

One thing alone clouded its horizon—the restriction of competitive patents. This was a problem in which the whole future of electrical development was inextricably bound up.

Finance rather than patents absorbed Charles A. Coffin in the first two years of Thomson-Houston activity. It was a double-headed problem with a manufacturing side, and a public-service or operating side. The company did not sell direct to the public but to local electric lighting companies whose welfare meant the success or failure of the Thomson-Houston Company.

Local companies must receive financial stimulus. Much depended on them; yet they were small and inexperienced, and their problems were considerable. The investment required for launching local companies often was prohibitive to the small capitalist. As an associate of Coffin's said in later years:

"The business was new and presented problems which were substantially without precedent . . . People generally did not at all appreciate the need or the value of electricity . . . There were few who had the courage and the necessary capital to buy and install apparatus. Customers did not exist; they had to be created."

These matters filled Coffin's days with anxiety and his evenings with study. But the policy which he finally inaugurated was simple.

He offered to sell electrical equipment for part payment in cash and the balance in securities of the local company. That was all, but it was enough to assist many local companies in getting a start. It was a policy which resulted in many new Thomson-Houston customers.

Twenty-eight local companies were equipped with Thomson-Houston apparatus during 1884, and forty-seven during 1885. Three thousand arc lamps were sold in 1884, and seven thousand in 1885.

Meanwhile Coffin was working out a commercial organization. The young company needed salesmen—men with youth, initiative, and brains. He found such men now and then among young leather salesmen who came into his office at C. A. Coffin and Company. Whenever one of these men made a favorable impression, Coffin talked electricity to him and offered a chance with Thomson-Houston. Between 1883 and 1885 he drew an appreciable group of salesmen from shoes to dynamos, and the Thomson-Houston yearly class of "experts" swelled in proportion.

Coffin realized about this time that he must give up either the manufacture of shoes or the manufacture of electrical equipment. He could not do justice to both. Should he stake everything upon the innovation of electrical development?

In the midst of his doubts there came an unexpected proposition. The American Electric and Illuminating Company of Boston made overtures to Coffin for the purchase of the Thomson-Houston Company for $300,000.

Coffin's decision was quickly made. He informed them that he could not consider the offer and told his shoe partner that he was giving up shoe manufacturing to devote himself to electricity. From that decision he never turned back.

About the beginning of 1885 Coffin asked one of his former shoe customers, J. R. McKee, if he would take over the managership of one of the Thomson-Houston commercial departments.

"But I don't even know what electricity is!" answered McKee.

"That's just our trouble," Coffin replied with a laugh. "We've too many men who know what electricity is, or think they do. What we want now is somebody to care for the commercial side. Perhaps the less you know about what electricity is, the better!"

Coffin felt that Thomson-Houston needed in the commercial field men with reliable merchandising instinct, who were free from the conservatism which technical electricians would be apt to display in the selling field. Coffin was exercising his talent for picking out individuals of ability. He had known McKee for years, since the time when as a young man McKee had gone farther west than any other salesman

STANLEY AND HIS ORIGINAL TRANSFORMER

FOURTH OF JULY—1890

The Thomson-Houston float in the Lynn parade.

PROFESSOR THOMSON AND HIS WELDING TRANSFORMER

on the road. He believed that McKee had the energy and enthusiasm to take the electrical message wherever he could get a hearing.

So McKee took charge of some of the supplemental activities carried on under Thomson-Houston auspices. He became president of the Thomson-Van Depoele Electric Mining Company, a subsidiary organized to sell an electric drill invented by Van Depoele, and an electric coal-cutting machine. He also headed the Thomson-Houston Motor Company, which began to compete with other electrical manufacturers in offering stationary motors in sizes ranging from 1½ to 110 horsepower.

The Thomson-Van Depoele Company also embarked upon a campaign for equipping mines. A line of electrically driven hoists and pumps and a type of electric mine locomotive made their appearance. In 1889 the first installation of a mine railway was made at a colliery near Scranton. A forty-horsepower electric locomotive operated on a track having a gauge of thirty-six inches.

Thousands of dollars were spent in endeavoring to develop mining mechanisms, particularly electric drills and coal cutters. Young men just out of college, some from aristocratic Boston families, were hired to operate coal-cutting machines in the mines. But eventually the line of electric coal-cutting apparatus had to be abandoned. The machines were not commercially feasible.

The Thomson-Houston International Company was organized in 1884. Men had been sent abroad from the first and had found opportunities for trade as good as at home. The South American business became extensive. An arc-light station at Hammerfest, Norway, was long the most northerly electrical installation in the world. Products went to Egypt, Hawaii, Peru, Russia, Spain, and elsewhere.

Thomson brought out his transformer for electric resistance welding in 1885, thereby creating a new division of the electrical art. It was introduced commercially by the Thomson Welding Company, organized in 1888 for that purpose.

In 1885 Thomson designed a direct-current dynamo for incandescent lamps. Thus the Thomson-Houston Company was prepared to compete with the Edison Electric Light Company in the field of incandescent lighting. Desperate rivalry and astounding expansion were close at hand in the commercial development of this little unit of light, which Edison could not keep in his own hands without a struggle.

When the first glow-spots of incandescence shone out around the First District in lower Manhattan, the lamp was transformed from an experiment to a standard utility. Its welfare and its future became the concern of the factory as well as of the laboratory, and the saga of its commercial development had begun.

Skeptics flourished, nonetheless, on through the middle eighties. Conservative Henry Morton, President of Stevens Institute of Technology, was not yet won over. In December 1884 he dourly remarked: "Ten thousand mechanical engineers are wanted to every ten electricians; and it would be a mistake for a very great number of young men to determine to devote themselves to electrical enterprises." In that very year 125,000 incandescent lamps had been sold, an increase of 55,000 over the previous year!

It was impossible to make lamps more than just so fast, however great the demand. Manufacturing processes at Edison's factory at Harrison, New Jersey, were mostly handwork. A hundred workmen produced only three hundred lamps a day. Expert glassblowers were necessary to blow the bulbs and other glass parts. The bamboo filament went through eight operations, all performed by hand, before it was ready for carbonizing. And it took five hours to exhaust the air from each bulb to produce the vacuum.

Men sat for weary hours at workbenches handling bamboo. The cane, received in long strips, was slit with a knife over and over until the smallest possible diameter was obtained. One piece of cane yielded five filament-strips, each of which was planed on one side before it was baked. Next it was finished in straight form, then bent into horseshoe shape.

The same laborious operations were in vogue at the Thomson-Houston Electric Company, where the Sawyer-Man lamps were manufactured. But here the filament went through an extra process of treating, or "flashing," the invention of William E. Sawyer. The filament was placed in a bulb containing rarefied hydrocarbon gas, such as gasoline vapor, and was heated by passing a current of electricity through it. Heat decomposed the vapor and deposited a coating of graphite upon the filament.

The filament produced by flashing was a better conductor of electricity, and was practically uniform throughout its length. It could be treated to the correct resistance to obtain proper voltage and efficiency, and treating increased its life. The incandescent lamps of the Thomson-Houston company were now better than Edison's, which gave them an advantage on the market. There were doubts among their own men, however, whether in using a bamboo filament instead of the original thread they might infringe on Edison patents. But, as Thomson put it, "We started out to make the best incandescent lamp we knew how."

The Thomson-Houston Company was planning an output of 2000 lamps a week. Already the Edison Lamp Works was producing almost this many, and Edison was seeking to simplify his manufacturing processes so as to get costs below the forty cents per lamp for which he had contracted to sell them to the Edison Electric Light Company. He had in his employ an engineer, John W. Howell, whose ingenuity contributed one of the most valuable manufacturing advances of the period. Howell reduced the time of exhausting air in the lamp bulbs from five hours to a bare thirty minutes.

Toward the end of 1883 Edison, while watching pumps working on his lamps, noticed a bluish glow inside the glass globes. This glow kept up until a high vacuum was obtained, then disappeared.

The glow had no effect upon the lamp, which gave its incandescent light as brightly as ever, but seemed merely incidental to the process of exhausting the air. Edison suspected that it came from a current inside the loop of the filament, because the glow appeared only when electricity was sent through the filament, heating it so that the gases would be driven out.

To see if he was correct, he inserted a wire inside the loop between the two "legs," connected it to one of the contacts outside the bulb through which current flowed to the filament, and placed a galvanometer between the terminal and the wire. The needle of the galvanometer showed a small current flowing between the legs of the filament. But it flowed only when the wire was connected to the positive side of the circuit.

Edison had answered the first question about the bluish glow when he took out a patent based upon the "Edison Effect" in October 1884; however, he did not suspect how much more lay back of it. Electrical science was not sufficiently advanced to explain the glow. Not until thirty years later did other minds make the "Edison Effect" the basis of radio.

Edison's inventive ingenuity, spurred on by a forty-cent contract, made several cost-reducing changes in his lamp. The lead-in wires were of platinum, because that metal could be sealed into the glass neck of the bulb in an airtight joint. But the cost of platinum was too high for Edison to reduce his costs below the forty-cent limit.

He overcame the difficulty by placing the platinum-copper weld in the glass seal, benefiting the lead-in wires, which thus could be made appreciably shorter. Changes in the structure of the base aided still further the reduction in platinum, until finally each lamp contained only one-eighth of the amount used in 1881.

Electric light companies were now springing up on every hand, scattering through communities, as lavishly as citizens would allow, the "bottled sunlight" of incandescent or the "blue moons" of the arc. But a generating station able to operate day and night was then unknown and apparently unthought-of. Central stations started their dynamos shortly before sunset, ran on a reduced scale after midnight, and shut down entirely at dawn. For the most part they were places of night work only, their function being to supply illumination.

Edison wrote to W. S. Andrews, under date of January 2, 1884, on the general subject of central station operation:

"I think the wages for men at the station should be as follows: Engineer, $65 per month, daylight to daylight running, starting, of course one-half hour before required in the evening. The meter man should be called manager, salary, $50 a month. Duties, taking meters, collecting, keeping books and running electrical part from one-half hour before dusk until seventy-five per cent of the load goes off. . . .

"You should have these men on probation and subject to

passing an examination by me. That will wake them up. Also I think it very essential that for several days steam should be raised in the morning, and if there is a spare engine at the station they should be practiced. We have found that the Brockton men were not sufficiently practical, hence if anything went wrong they lost their heads."

This last referred to an incident the previous autumn at Brockton, where the engine was run by a locomotive engineer who was supposed to be fearless with machinery. The electric wiring in the station was somewhat crude, as was often the case in those days. The large conductors from the dynamos to the switchboard were laid in grooves cut in the wooden flooring and carried to a wooden partition, where they were connected to outgoing feeders. One quiet evening the insulation on these conductors gave way. There was a sudden flash and flames shot along the floor. The "fearless" engineer jumped out of the window, while the fireman hid behind the boiler.

About this time there came a change in the policy of the Edison Machine Works as to the finished appearance of its dynamos. Seeking to keep down cost, little effort was made toward ornamentation. The castings were rough and indifferently painted. One day there came a complaint from Baltimore—something the matter with the Edison dynamos.

An inspector went down. He found that the Baltimore dynamos were all right except for an accumulation of dirt due to pure neglect. And the neglect was due to the fact that the station owned several dynamos of another manufacturer, handsomely painted, neat and trim. They were the pride of the station attendant, who lavished all his time upon them at the expense of the Edison dynamos. The inspector's report caused the officials back home to sit up and take notice.

As central stations multiplied, so did inexperienced operators. And instruments by which voltage and amperage could be measured were not yet to be had. At Pearl Street the voltage of the lamps was regulated by a homely, though ingenious, device, which was an arrangement of magnets by which a red lamp was lighted if the voltage was too high and a blue one if it was too low. New stations at first did not have even this crude voltmeter; yet upon the regulation of electrical pressure the life of the lamps depended.

It was small wonder that some stations boasted of good records for their lamps, while others had such poor records that the managers thought there was something wrong with the lamps. Complaints of this sort were heard at meetings of the Association of Edison Illuminating Companies, organized in 1884.

A central station manager got up and declared the lamp was "rotten," that it could not last two hundred hours. Whereupon Wilson S. Howell, manager of the unusually successful station at New Brunswick, N. J., reported that very careful records had been kept of the life of their lamps, and the average had been 3000 hours. Whereupon the original speaker exclaimed:

"Gentlemen, it is easy to account for this difference—the poor quality of my lamps and the excellence of his. The man who runs the New Brunswick station has a brother in the lamp works!"

Not long after this Edison selected the New Brunswick station for the first commercial test of a high grade lamp having a hydrocarbon bamboo filament. It was one of the first steps in increasing incandescent efficiency.

To the public, however, efficiency seemed to appeal less than convenience. An old German shopkeeper who had arc lamps in his place tried to explain their failings to an electrician of the arc-lamp company. The lamps had behaved strangely a few evenings before, and he threw up both hands and brought them down slowly, pantomiming their action.

"I don't like dot ding," he solemnly remarked. "Why not you have dose schmall condensed lights what comes in bottles?"

The spectacular was not overlooked in exploiting "dose schmall condensed lights." Blasé Manhattan was startled on the evening of October 13, 1884, to see a singular procession coming down aristocratic Fifth Avenue.

Several hundred marching men moved in the form of a hollow square, each wearing a helmet surmounted by one of the little glow-bulbs. Inside the hollow square moved a portable steam engine and Edison dynamo; and the marchers carried a long rope containing a conductor from which current was drawn through flexible wires passing inside their sleeves to the lamps on their hats. A marshal led the column on a war charger, bearing a baton tipped with a light.

This was also the year of the "Edison darky," a negro attendant at Edison exposition booths, whose clothing was wired to connect with an incandescent lamp on top of his helmet. The heels of his shoes were equipped with copper plates that had sharp points which pierced the carpet and made contact with hidden conductors. Many a timid lady was startled upon seeing a sudden glow of light appear on top of the darky's head just as he handed her an Edison leaflet.

EDISON MACHINE WORKS IN SCHENECTADY, N. Y.—1886

The two buildings of the McQueen Locomotive Company, on the Mohawk flats near Schenectady, to which Edison moved his machine works.

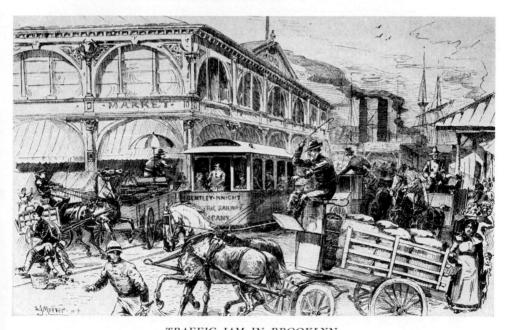

TRAFFIC JAM IN BROOKLYN

The first Bentley-Knight "tram cars" upset the peace of Brooklyn's streets.

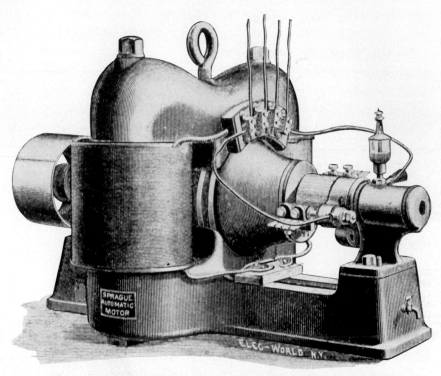

THE ELECTRIC MOTOR DEVELOPED BY FRANK J. SPRAGUE

14

Onward with Volts

Ten years had now passed since Charles F. Brush built his first dynamo and Elihu Thomson started to design a one-light arc machine with which to astonish his audiences at the Franklin Institute.

It had been a brilliant decade. At its beginning electric lighting was largely in the realm of the magical. Hard-headed business men smiled at the notion that it was practical, or that it could serve a utilitarian purpose. American industry, in the column marked "electrical," was an absolute blank.

But within a single decade—what a transformation! The hum of dynamos was in the air. Factories, generating stations, lights, and horseless cars were proving what the blue spark could do.

The growing array of essential minor apparatus was keeping pace with the development of the basic processes and machines. Meters and switches had appeared. Edison's chemical meter in 1882 took its share of the day's work, measuring the current that each customer used.

This meter was remarkable for its simplicity and operated

entirely by electrolytic action. A fraction of the electric current which entered the customer's premises was shunted
through a pair of cells, each containing two zinc plates immersed in a solution of zinc sulphate. The cells, connected
in series, served as checks upon each other. Through the
effect of the electric current zinc in proportion to the volume
of the current was removed from the positive plate and
deposited on the negative plate. From weighing the plates
before and after use, the amount of current consumed could
be calculated.

The weighing was done with the utmost precision. Central stations had a regular meter crew, which made the
rounds with a horse and wagon. New meter plates were put
in to replace old ones, which were tagged with the customer's
name and carried back to the station for weighing.

Experience proved this meter perfectly reliable. Mistakes,
when they did occur, were usually caused by human fallibil-
ity, as was the case at Sunbury, where the meter in a large
clothing store indicated at one time that $200-worth of cur-
rent had been consumed in a month. The meter-man was
aghast. He lost sleep for two nights. Then suddenly the explanation came to him. In order to fit the plates into the
meter-box he had been obliged to clip off an inch or two of
copper wire, forgetting that he had previously weighed the
plates, wire and all. The loss in weight represented by two
inches of wire had registered about $150 to the customer's
debit.

Another humble device was the switch. Yet of what practical value was it to know how to produce electric current,
efficiently and in volume, if the current could not be controlled? How could an electric circuit operate daily unless it
could be closed and opened at will?

Before the end of the decade 1876–86, the switches, while

still serving each its own dynamo, were grouped together on a single frame. In large stations these switchboards were formidable affairs, the multiplicity of plugs suggesting a gigantic game board. The early switchboards worked on the plug principle and were constructed of wood. If a poor

THOMSON'S DYNAMO WITH THE AUTOMATIC CONTROL

contact occurred between plug and terminal, the frame was liable to take fire.

With the incandescent lamp, the switch entered a new phase. Edison's system reversed the relation between amperage and voltage. Arc-lamp systems had a current which remained fixed or constant; but they had a changing voltage, increasing according to the number of lamps in circuit and going as high as 2000 volts. Edison employed a constant voltage, no higher than 110; but the operating circuits handled over 700 amperes of current. The switch now controlled an electric current beyond all previous experience.

Edison developed perhaps the first type of knife-blade switch, certainly the first of large capacity. He was the first to grapple with the erratic arc in an electric switch. The voltaic arc in the arc lamp is useful, desirable and encouraged by the construction of the lamp; but the voltaic arc at almost any other point in an electrical system is harmful. Seven hundred amperes of current, suddenly interrupted by a switch, was likely to cause such an arc, resulting in damage to the apparatus. Edison prevented this by arranging the knife-blade contacts of his switch so that the current passed through them in series, one contact after another.

IN THE FIRST TEN YEARS of electrical growth, the forging of policies was hard put to catch up with the brilliancy of invention. In various executive offices, at desk or council table, America's economic future was taking form. In the plain office of Edwin W. Rice, Jr., general superintendent of the Thomson-Houston Electric Company, were originated some historic policies, determined by him through sheer necessity. There were few industrial executives of that period who were so young in years, so discerning, or so prolific as Rice.

It was a time of crowding emergencies and unremitting labor. Upon the young superintendent fell the task of analyzing a multitude of perplexing situations. He watched the extraordinary growth of the plant and studied the question of factory efficiency. And he developed methods so strategic and fundamental that they became steppingstones toward a day of huge production, methods that worked a revolution in industrial supervision.

He divided plant operation along functional lines. A new staff of supervisory officials was created—all of them familiar in present industry, but each one then of a fairly unknown type.

There was a production manager, responsible for getting the manufactured product out on time; a mechanical superintendent in charge of mechanical work, new building construction and factory discipline; a cost manager, with jurisdiction over cost accounting, bookkeeping, and pay-roll; a purchasing agent, directing the purchase of all raw materials, supplies, and equipment; and a technical superintendent, supervising engineering, research, and drafting. All reported directly to the factory manager.

Then the young general superintendent introduced a second innovation in factory management, a new method of determining manufacturing costs in which scientific principles superseded guesswork. The company set about accurately calculating its overhead—taxes, insurance, fuel, maintenance, depreciation—and the variation of overhead as applied to different products of manufacture. To the actual cost of direct labor and materials were added the computed percentages of overhead.

The first ten years made large and flourishing enterprises out of the Thomson-Houston and Edison companies and they also brought prosperity to the Brush Electric Company. Out of Cleveland had come in the latter part of the decade news of the first experiments with an electric industrial furnace.

The promoters of this endeavor were Alfred and Eugene Cowles, two brothers interested in the production of aluminum by electric smelting. They contracted with Charles F. Brush for a dynamo to be used in their experiments, specifying a constant-potential, direct-current unit, capable of producing 300 amperes at 60 volts.

Current was conducted to carbons mounted in a horizontal

position in the interior of the furnace, which was a clay retort, and the experiments, begun on October 2, 1884, resulted in the production on October 9 of the first alloy of aluminum obtained in the United States by this method. It is also recorded that on October 11 synthetic rubies and sapphires were produced in this furnace.

The Cowle brothers now ordered a larger unit, which was built for them in 1886. This dynamo was one of the early "monsters." It was of the characteristic Brush open-coil type, and had a capacity of 3200 amperes at 80 volts, or 256 kilowatts. It was larger than Edison's Jumbo and next to the largest dynamo in the world.

The Brush Company toward the end of 1887 embarked upon a new field to keep abreast of the times. Following the lead of Thomson-Houston, it entered the alternating-current field. A visitor to Cleveland would have been impressed by the Brush factory, one of the most pretentious of its day. It was a beehive of activity, for there were local Brush companies in numerous cities, all of them licensees of the parent company.

"Six years ago," wrote Charles Lever in 1885, "a few Brush arc lamps strung up along Broadway comprised nearly all the electric lighting New York could boast of . . . Now there are nearly 3000 arc lamps in operation every night in New York and Brooklyn . . . These lights are supplied on the rental system . . . The usual charge is forty to forty-five cents per lamp per night . . . Cleveland, the home of Brush, is the largest manufacturing city for electric light apparatus in the world."

The Fort Wayne Electric Light Company had branched into the field of incandescents in 1885. R. T. McDonald, head of the concern, had induced a new electrical man, M. M. Slattery, to join his company and work up a system of incandescence, using the alternating current. Within a short time Slattery's system—an alternating-current dynamo, a transformer, and auxiliary apparatus—was on the market. Customers were expected to purchase their lamps of other manufacturers—thus did the Fort Wayne company avoid the danger of patent infringement.

Wood, in the meantime, had pioneered in arc lighting by installing an outfit, despite competition, for lighting the Statue of Liberty on Bedloe's Island. Representatives of several arc-light systems interviewed General Stone prior to Wood's call. Wood found the General nourishing a notion to throw electric light upon the clouds so that reflected rays would illuminate the statue.

"General," said Wood, "such a scheme as that would make you the laughing stock of the country. What you need for the job is direct lighting."

The General sprang up with an outburst of emphatic language. "By gad, sir," he cried, "you're the first one who has told me the truth. Those other rascals simply agreed with me, with all sorts of flatttery about the fine results I would get with my plan."

Wood got the order. And there was no reason for laughter when the current was turned on and electric rays cast their brilliance upon the symbolic figure of Miss Liberty.

THE SECOND DECADE of electrical development was inaugurated by an event in the Berkshires which influenced the years that followed. This was the establishment on March 6, 1886 of a local lighting system in Great Barrington, Massachusetts, which was totally different from any preceding it.

First it made use of alternating current and was the first such system to be commercially installed. Second, it used transformers which were of a particularly efficient type. The system was the work of a young man of twenty-eight, an accomplished electrical technician, William Stanley.

Stanley was the first to develop commercially a practical transformer, although not the first to conceive it. He utilized the only efficient principle of design and the only efficient system of circuit connection.

As far back as 1879, Thomson's dynamo fulfilled the elementary requirements of an alternating-current generator, and he had devised two induction coils in a working circuit that were perfect counterparts of the modern transformer. But he did not utilize alternating current, because of the greater simplicity of direct current. In 1885 he foresaw that the day of alternating current was near; and he set up an experimental system at the Thomson-Houston plant, sending current from Factory A to Factory B, and making use of transformers for so doing. This of course was not a commercial installation.

Stanley, meanwhile, was working in the same direction independently of Thomson, and what he did had in the beginning no relation to the General Electric Succession. It was an outgrowth of his association with George Westinghouse. The latter had founded, in 1884, the Westinghouse Electric and Manufacturing Company, which has become one of the large electrical manufacturing units of the present day.

Westinghouse saw the possibilities of alternating current, and the need of such a device as the transformer to give the current utmost utility. He bought the American rights to the patents of a Frenchman, Gaulard, and an Englishman, Gibbs, who had worked out transformers. Then he commissioned Stanley to experiment with the transformers, whose principal drawback was in their series connection so

ALL HANDS TO THE RESCUE

*Derailed cars were frequent enough occurrences on the Richmond road
to inspire this picture by a magazine artist.*

that they were dependent upon each other in operation and could not work independently.

Stanley's notable contributions were two. First, he connected the transformers in parallel, giving independent operation, such as Edison obtained by connecting incandescent lamps in parallel; and second, he made each transformer automatically regulate itself, thus permitting independent control of the devices supplied by the transformer.

Thomson in 1879 had already accomplished the same things. He, too, had connected induction coils in parallel and had designed those coils to be self-regulating.

Stanley obtained a patent covering the method of designing his transformer, rather than the method of connection in circuit. Thomson made application for a patent in November 1885, but it was stubbornly contested by several opponents, one of whom was the Gaulard-Gibbs combination. It was nearly twenty years before Thomson's patent was granted, only to be declared invalid in its first court test.

Thomson, Stanley, and Westinghouse all perceived that the transformer was the key to a new door in electrical progress. Up to this time men generated electric current with great success. They distributed current after it was generated and utilized it in ways that were expanding every year. But they could not transmit the low-voltage current employed for incandescent lighting farther than three miles. To send it over greater distances required heavy currents, hence large conductors and the incurring of a prohibitive expense for copper wire.

The arc-light systems had an advantage due to the higher voltages used. Brush had used his forty-light dynamo to operate thirty lights at full brilliance ten miles away. This restriction of transmission was the serious limiting factor of

Edison's system. An Edison generating station could not economically supply a territory greater than sixteen square miles. Transmission became feasible only when the transformer was made practical.

In Stanley's historic installation at Great Barrington, current was sent from his laboratory in an old rubber mill on the outskirts of town into the town proper, a distance of four thousand feet, the current being transformed from 500 volts to 3000 volts for transmission, and then reduced back to 500 volts for use.

Thomson did not place an alternating-current dynamo upon the market until the spring of 1887. His policy in one regard was distinct from that of Westinghouse and Stanley. He believed that high-voltage systems, which would obviously grow up as alternating current came into extensive use, required protective devices to safeguard customers. In 1885 he devised such protective equipment and incorporated it into his first commercial transformers. Until he had done this, he would not allow the Thomson-Houston Company to exploit the alternating current commercially. His feeling on this point was inflexible and won the endorsement of both Coffin and Rice. Thomson told his colleagues that he would not permit an alternating-current system to enter his own house without protection and therefore he would not sanction its use in the houses of others.

Westinghouse and Stanley disagreed with Thomson. They recognized the latent danger in a high-voltage line, but they held that it was exaggerated. So they went ahead, while the Thomson-Houston Company refrained from entering the field—though at no time did it condemn or criticize its competitors.

Not so the Edison Electric Light Company, which assailed alternating current and kept up the attack against competitors that ventured to advocate it. At first the Company trained its guns upon the Westinghouse people. When the Thomson-Houston Company put a transformer in the field with a Thomson protective device it was also included in the attacks. Sales agents had no trouble convincing customers that its transformer was now perfectly safe. But the Edison Company remained adamant toward the alternating current, regardless of whether protective devices were in use or not.

In a printed pronouncement, "A Warning from the Edison Electric Light Company," it sought to show that the alternating current was a menace to life and limb. And this attitude persisted despite the obvious electrical advantages of utilizing that kind of current.

The clash of opinions was intensified by the decision of the New York State prison authorities to adopt electrocution for capital punishment and to employ alternating current for the purpose. That was ammunition for the direct-current artilleries! What could be more convincing, they demanded, than the official selection of this current as the most efficacious means of executing men?

So there grew up this curious conflict known as the "War of the Currents." The Westinghouse group frequently struck back at the Edison camp, and these two became the principal antagonists. Coffin never permitted Thomson-Houston to participate in the skirmishing. He insisted that his men keep quiet.

As a matter of fact there was never quite the protective advantage in the direct current that its protagonists supposed. At equal voltages, alternating current, as Thomson said, is less deadly than direct. The danger in alternating current is that the primary coil in the step-down transformers, from which circuits enter houses and offices, may accidentally come in contact with the secondary coil, allowing the high voltage of the former to enter the secondary circuit. Should that occur, any person touching the secondary was likely to receive a serious shock. Under prevalent methods of manufacture and installation Thomson believed that the two coils might readily short circuit.

To take care of such a contingency, he invented three methods of protection, each of them effective. The one finally adopted, because of maximum reliability and simplicity, was to ground the secondary wires of the transformer with a metallic conductor. Once adopted, the Thomson-Houston Company did not hesitate to exploit the alternating current. A complete commercial system was planned at once, using Thomson alternators and transformers. The latter raised the current pressure for transmission to a thousand volts, which was for some years the standard Thomson-Houston transmission voltage.

15

Destiny Comes to Town

IN THE BRIEF STRETCH of her existence America has grown with unbelievable swiftness. It has been such a lusty growth that the present has almost lost sight of the past from which it developed. The "good old days" have disappeared with the inrush of machinery, inventions, innovations—in a word, with the touch of progress. Transformations in individual communities have come about almost within a generation. And electricity has taken a prominent part in working these social changes.

In the eastern reaches of the Mohawk Valley of New York State, along the course of that low-banked, quiet-moving stream, stands the city of Schenectady. In bygone times it was a peaceful, prosperous town of Dutch settlement and Dutch atmosphere. Washington Irving might have said of it, as he did of Tarrytown: "It is in such little retired Dutch valleys, found here and there embosomed in the great state of New York, that population, manners and customs remain fixed . . . They are like those little nooks of still water which border a rapid stream, where we may see the straw and bubble riding quietly at anchor, or slowly revolv-

111

ing in their mimic harbor, undisturbed by the rush of the passing torrent."

Schenectady was much like that in 1886. It had no large pretensions, no particular desire to alter its simple mode of life. The worthy citizens who traversed the grass-fringed cobblestones of elm-shaded State Street were content with their Dutch traditions and their unassuming place in the affairs of the nineteenth century.

Small local industries supported the fourteen thousand inhabitants. Broomcorn in spreading abundance waved in the breezes up and down the river banks, for the town manufactured most of America's brooms and brushes. The one large-scale factory was the plant of the Schenectady Locomotive Works, colloquially known as the "big shop."

No citizen of Schenectady in 1886 supposed that the community would be noted industrially other than as a place where locomotives were built. No more did the president of the Schenectady Locomotive Works, Charles G. Ellis, or his plant superintendent, Walter McQueen. These men had been associated for years. They had guided the growth of the works; they were fast friends. But they had a falling-out, and their quarrel, by an odd chance, swayed the whole future of their community. McQueen, with the assistance of local capital, organized the McQueen Locomotive Works and began the erection of two factory buildings.

He secured as a site a broad expanse of level ground west of the town and along the river. Once it was called the "big flat," a famous Indian hunting ground. Now it offered many advantages for the industrious white man with his machines, his mechanical skill, his manufacturing genius.

McQueen began to build his factory on this spot in 1885. He had two structures completed, except for the roofs, when his principal financial backers died, and the project was

halted. The unfinished buildings stood in plain sight from
the railroad as the spring of 1886 came in.

In New York, meanwhile, another event occurred which
bore upon Schenectady's future. Edison dispatched agents
in various directions to scout for suitable sites for a new

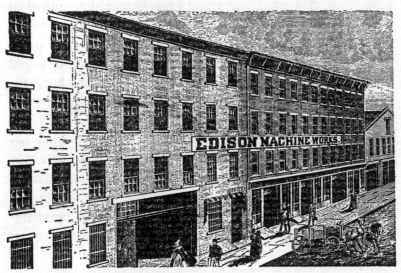

EDISON MACHINE WORKS IN NEW YORK CITY—1885
The factory on Goerck Street, New York, shortly before it was
moved to Schenectady.

factory. One went to New Jersey, one to Pennsylvania, and
a third to up-state New York.

So it was that Destiny called to the Mohawk Valley one
day in the spring of 1886 a man who felt an immediate interest in such a spectacle as met his eye from the car-window of
a train puffing across the "big flat," past the two lonely factory
buildings on the outskirts of Schenectady. He was Harry M.
Livor, who reported promptly to Edison. Edison went up to
inspect the site in person and the location made a favorable
impression. An appraisal of the property had placed its value
at $45,000. Edison felt it was too high, and offered $37,500,

declaring he would not pay a cent more. The owners were equally adamant.

It would have been an impasse had not civic pride burned in the breasts of some of the townsfolk. These men wanted to see Edison's plant located in their community. They held a meeting, discussed ways and means, and determined at length to appeal to the merchants of the town to make up the difference between Edison's offer and the owners' price. The merchants of Schenectady were canvassed, and urged to consider what it would mean for the town to have the plant of the famous Edison. The necessary amount was raised, so that the owners, as well as Edison, were satisfied.

The stage was set for Schenectady to emerge from her seclusion into industrial prominence among American cities.

The shops immediately took up the task of turning out the dynamos needed by the numerous Edison generating stations. Within a few months, other buildings sprang up alongside the original shops which McQueen had reared.

RONALD T. McDONALD

The organizer of the Fort Wayne Electric Company, and the Company's factory in 1883.

16

The Motor Marches On

Edison, with his incomparable system of incandescent lighting, utilizing only the direct current, Brush, Thomson, and Wood, the great arc-light pioneers, ready to exploit the alternating current as well as the direct—these four constituted the great pioneers in the nation's electrical illuminating field. All of them had given some thought to electric power. But none of them, even as late as the middle eighties, had expressly designed an electric motor as such, nor made a business of developing electric motors for stationary work.

Edison, when questioned by a journalist in 1884 as to the "transmission of electrical force," said: "That problem has been pretty well worked out. A young man named Sprague . . . has worked the matter up in a very remarkable way. His is the only true motor."

Sprague had vigorously pursued a well-defined theory of electric power since his days as a member of Edison's company, when, in his office at Brockton, he had found time to work out his motor. After forming the Sprague Electric Railway and Motor Company he perfected the design of a constant-speed, non-sparking motor to be used on direct-current circuits, as well as a motor adapted particularly for street-railway work.

Specimens of these types were displayed at the Philadelphia Electric Exposition in September, 1884. The largest was of six-horsepower capacity; the smallest, rated at one and a half horsepower, drove a weaving loom. These motors were so designed that they would run at a constant, uniform speed despite variations in load, with a fixed, non-sparking position for the commutator brushes.

In the spring of 1885 endorsement of Sprague motors came from the Edison Electric Light Company, which sent out a circular to its local companies advising them that "A practical motor has been a want seriously felt in our system . . . The Sprague motor is believed to meet . . . all the exigencies of the case, and the Edison Electric Light Company feels it can safely recommend it to its licensees as the only practical and economic motor existing today. Our own company has no interest whatever in the Sprague company, and does not derive any benefit . . . through this agreement."

The Sprague Company soon had sales agents in Philadelphia, New England, and elsewhere. A dozen motors were installed in textile factories at Lawrence, Massachusetts. The man who was perhaps most active in the field was George F. Steele, who served for several years as superintendent of the New England Electric Company, eventually becoming president. Steele was an able salesman with a good product to sell. He made a reputation for the Sprague motors and for himself by introducing it into the Boston garment trade.

Scores of small clothing factories and tailor shops in Boston used batteries of sewing machines operated laboriously by hand. Larger establishments were equipped with machine-tables, which had a shaft connecting all the sewing machines, so that they could be run by power. This device gave Steele his opportunity, for the Boston Edison Company had just opened up, making central-station power available.

It needed only one or two Sprague motors, belted to the shafts of these machine-tables, to sell the idea to the trade.

A SPRAGUE MOTOR OPERATING A HOIST

They eliminated the necessity of a steam engine on the premises and lessened the expense for power. Steele came into all the business he could handle; and as he visited the motors regularly, making any adjustments needed in their operation, he made staunch friends of his customers. The clothing men would take no motors except the Sprague.

In December, 1886, the first 220-volt Sprague motor was installed in a building at Purchase and Pearl Streets, Boston, for the purpose of running a freight elevator. The motor was a fifteen-horsepower unit, connected by about three thousand feet of copper wire to the three-wire system of the Boston Edison Company.

The length of the line was a new factor at the time, and the size of copper wire had been incorrectly calculated for maintaining the voltage under load. Steele realized this the moment he looked at the wires, but it was too late to make changes, as the elevator was needed to move a new wheel concern to the sixth floor. A load of big wheels was immediately rolled into the elevator. When the attempt was made to start it, the voltage of the motor dropped to 170 and the elevator could not be stirred. All the time fresh consignments of wheels kept arriving until the sidewalk was blocked with them.

Steele, in desperation, changed the connections on the motor so that it would operate with the reduced voltage. But in doing so he had to subject the motor fields to such intense heat that the winding insulation began to boil and flow out through the motor frame. Continuous operation with over-heated windings was impossible. Steele stood duty ten hours a day, in an unheated building, to start and stop the motor for every trip made by the elevator. Between trips he had to jump up and down to keep from freezing.

But the wheels were moved in without further difficulty. Everyone was delighted. Steele accepted the compliments of the building owners with a frostbitten smile and was wise enough to keep his comments to himself. Within a few days he had another circuit run into the building so that the motor, supplied with proper voltage, could operate contin-uously under normal conditions.

At the end of 1886 the Sprague Company had 190 stationary motors installed and in use, and 80 more under construction. In many cities in the East and Middle West, they served more than a hundred trades and industries. They drove boot and shoe machinery in Detroit and Boston; coffee mills in Elgin, Illinois, and Lancaster, Pennsylvania; emery wheels in Des Moines and Chicago; lathes in Chicago, Boston, and New York; and printing presses, ventilators, ice cream freezers, and various other mechanisms. The Chicago fire department; the Gold and Stock Telegraph Company of New York, where Edison started his career as mechanical repair man; Drexel, Morgan and Company; and the New York Stock Exchange installed Sprague motors.

No meters had yet been installed on motor circuits, so that in most cases a flat-rate charge was made. In Boston, for example, a five-horsepower motor cost about $33 a month.

The metering of motors began toward the end of 1886. Steele installed a metered motor for Bigelow and Kennard, jewelers, in October of that year, to operate a buffing lathe for polishing silverware; and this motor was destined to continue in operation for thirty years, staunchly exemplifying by is own performance the tireless, muscle-saving power of the electrical handyman.

But the difficulties the stationary motor had encountered were small compared with those at that moment besetting the traction motor.

17

Tribulation on Wheels

BENTLEY AND KNIGHT IN 1887 had abandoned Cleveland as a scene of operations and now had a contract with the street railway company at Woonsocket, Rhode Island. By agreement, the Thomson-Houston company furnished the generators and motors. After consultation, a rugged fifteen-horsepower machine was adapted. It was planned for 400 volts, and its speed was twice reduced, by gears and pinions, before the power passed into the car-axles; that is, it was a "double-reduction" motor.

Rohrer, one of their engineers, was apprehensive lest a complicated rig would be required to shift the brushes of the motor when the direction of operation was reversed. During the tests, Knight acted as motorman on the front platform, while Rohrer stretched himself at full length on the floor of the car, trap door open, to observe the behavior of the motor. For some hours they ran the car back and forth, Rohrer shifting the brushes on the motor each time by hand. Finally he discovered a fixed position for the brushes where the electrical neutral point was identical for either direction, and he realized with considerable relief that a brush-shifting rig would not be needed. A laminated copper brush and a fixed yoke were accordingly manufactured and attached to the motor.

In October, 1887, the Woonsocket road went into commercial operation with one car. On the first day this car ran steadily for thirteen hours, carrying eleven hundred persons, "curiosity loads," as they were termed. The road had an elevated conductor.

The Bentley-Knight Electric Railway Company now obtained a contract for equipping the road of the Observatory Hill Passenger Railway Company of Allegheny City, Pennsylvania. This was one of the most difficult propositions they could have accepted. The total ascent on Observatory Hill was a rise of 295 feet in a stretch of 4900 feet, an average grade of six per cent, with a maximum grade of twelve per cent located on a sharp curve. On the entire road there was scarcely a fifty-foot stretch where a car could stand without the aid of brakes and there were thirty-four curves. This was a tremendous undertaking for a car still in the experimental stage!

The line was four miles in length. It was decided that one-quarter of the distance should be of conduit construction and the remainder of the overhead system. The cost per mile of the conduit was $23,000; of the overhead wire, $4000. These figures indicate the reason why the overhead wire, except in densely populated centers, survived the conduit.

So severe was the grade on Observatory Hill that the cars were given additional mechanical assistance in making the ascent. This consisted of a steel rack laid parallel to one rail, the teeth of which engaged a gear wheel mounted on the car axle.

The Thomson-Houston men again went into conference over the type of motor to serve the road. They determined upon a voltage of 500, and placed two motors instead of one on each car. Generating current were four dynamos, built for 250 volts each and operated as two units, two machines in series constituting a unit.

The road opened in January 1888, and service was maintained for nineteen hours a day. The records show that on one occasion a single car carried forty passengers up the long grade at eight miles an hour.

That seemed to indicate success. Yet a few months later the Thomson-Houston company received an urgent call for help. There was trouble with the commutators on the motors, and six cars were laid up for repairs. A few days later Rohrer, who had been sent out to adjust the difficulty, had his first contact with what proved the most vexatious difficulty in the history of the streetcar motor.

"I well remember my sensations," he said, "when I stood at the end of the road looking up the street on which the underground conduit was laid, and saw two streaks of copper dust on the paving. . . . I donned my overalls, got busy with file and sandpaper, and after working the rest of that day, all night, and all the next day, I had four of the cars in service. After getting some sleep, I soon had the other two ready. Fortunately, I had carried with me a supply of new copper brushes, which I put on the motors. The old brushes had become cutting tools, the edges having melted from the severe sparking, and the commutators were a sight."

The severity of streetcar service, repeated starts and stops, reversal of direction, all going on for nineteen hours a day, had been accompanied by flashing and sparking whenever these variations occurred. Every flash melted copper from the brushes until their edges were so sharp that they ground copper off the commutators.

It was said that there was a small fortune in copper de-

NUMBER TWO MACHINE SHOP AT SCHENECTADY, ABOUT 1888

BUSTLES AND TAIL-COATS IN INDUSTRY
A view in the wire-insulating department at Schenectady, about 1888.

posited along the tracks of the Allegheny City street railway, and for a while express shipments of brushes left Lynn almost nightly.

The day of triumph for the electric street railway seemed far in the future. Yet with all its present uncertainty, an enterprise far more audacious than this venture at Allegheny City was being planned. And the man to undertake it was Frank J. Sprague.

Out of a clear sky his company was offered the contract to build an electric road at Richmond, Virginia. Sprague himself remarked years later, "We had little to show, but faith was strong and the contract was taken under terms, price, and guarantee easily placing it in the 'knave or fool' class, especially in view of the unprepared state of the Company to undertake work of such magnitude." Probably no one familiar with the circumstances would have dreamed that the enterprise, foolhardy though it seemed, meant the turn of street-railway fortune.

Certain it is that no particular attention was drawn to Sprague's departure for the Virginian capital with his carefully designed motor, his boundless faith—and little else.

The astonishment of the darkies in Richmond gave Sprague his first taste of renown. His car eliminated animal power on the city lines. He was the "emancipator of the mule." An old negro, watching with bulging eyes the mule-less vehicle steadily climbing a long hill, cried out:

"Fo' Gawd, what am de white folks a-gwine do nex'? Fust dey freed de darkey, an' now dey freed de mule!"

Certain it is that nothing so "impossible," so beset by difficulty, discouragement, and tribulation was ever turned into a virtual success. Yet it is universally conceded that the birth of electric traction dates from the solution of the technical problems presented by Sprague's road at Richmond.

It was Sprague's first attempt to set up a street railway system of any size. It was to be an entirely new road—new construction throughout. It was to be city-wide, twelve miles in length, and the contract specified that forty cars were to be equipped and thirty were to be operated simultaneously. No electrical railway in America had yet operated more than a dozen cars at once.

Electrification, under the contract, was to be completed in ninety days from the time work started, and the price to be paid was $110,000. The contract did not state that Richmond has several hills, making the steep grades many and the curves sharp. Yet Sprague signed that contract without either sight or knowledge of Richmond or the route of the road, and knowing that not a foot of track had yet been laid.

The construction syndicate did a poor job of roadbed construction. The track was laid with light-weight rails of inferior quality; the curves were built on a radius of thirty-three feet, some only twenty-four feet, and were not bound in any way; the track was not ballasted from one end to the other. All this added heavily to Sprague's task. And already he had enough to weigh him down. He needed advice, assistants, time, and experiments.

Sprague knew that he must have trained, reliable men at the scene of operations; as he put it, he needed "a man who has nerve and grit and coolness, one who, if he gets on the front of a car going seventy-five miles an hour and there is danger ahead, will stay there." So Oscar T. Crosby was persuaded to resign his commission in the Army engineer corps and join the new enterprise. Not long afterward Ensign S. Dana Greene offered his services. It was soon arranged that Greene should handle affairs at Richmond, while Crosby took charge of manufacturing details in New York.

Experiments were begun with the utmost perseverance.

Trolley poles were tried out, including an under-running wheel; motor-control received unending attention; motor-suspension beneath the car, brush construction, current supply, powerhouse equipment, absorbed everyone's thoughts. Cars were run up and down an experimental track in the yard of the Sprague company works in New York. During one of the first attempts, before a reliable motor controller had been devised, the car got out of control and smashed through the side of the office. The only thing that stopped its wild career was the office safe, in which by an odd chance there lay the one asset of value possessed by the company—the Richmond contract.

Within a few weeks the motor was under control and the system began to take tangible shape. Sprague had heard that Van Depoele sent out his cars with a man riding on the roof to keep the trolley wheel from jumping the wires, and he was determined to avoid a similar arrangement.

But overwork and loss of sleep lowered his physical vitality, and without warning he came down with typhoid fever. It was the very moment when the organization needed to drive ahead at full speed. Yet for nine weeks during that crucial period the helmsman's hand was absent, while the complication of problems grew and difficulties multiplied with every day that passed. The entire burden of piloting the Sprague ship of fortune during those nine weeks rested upon the shoulders of the two young assistants, one trained in the Army and one in the Navy.

When Sprague, convalescent from his sickness, went to Richmond late in 1887, the tracks had been laid and the overhead wire system was in place. He was now able to go over the route, and he watched with dire apprehension as the car approached a ten per cent grade. As he himself recalls that moment:

"My heart fell within me, and I said, 'It is utterly impossible for any car to climb that hill.' I felt that there were two things that would probably happen. First, the car would not ascend the grade, no matter how powerful the machines, for lack of track adhesion; and second, the machines were not powerful enough, even if the wheels would cling to the track.

"We had built very light machines (motors) with one reduction of gearing, to which the street-railway practice is now gravitating, and the torsional effort of these machines, while great, was not sufficient for the duty now demanded of them. An eight per cent grade would strain them, a ten per cent grade would be fatal. . . .

"Should we operate the particularly heavy grades with a cable, to be run by electric motors, in sunken pits underneath the track, and depend upon motors for the regular duty on the rest of the road? This seemed feasible if the cars could not by their own adhesion mount a ten per cent grade. On the other hand, if a car did have sufficient adhesion to mount this grade, it was plain that there must be a change in the machines. We must double the reduction of gearing, and this was a serious problem to face. . . .

"We had on board a number of our employees and General Manager George Burt, who was in Richmond representing the syndicate's interests. . . . A short distance from the end of the line we stopped in the middle of a sharp curve. Burt thought we could not get out of it. I said we would if I wrecked the machine, and out of it the car came. No more enthusiastic man, I think, was on the car that night than Burt himself, after seeing that exhibition of what a motor could do when pushed to an abnormal strain. . . .

"Arriving at the foot of the hill we stopped and I said, 'Burt, we won't make it!' He said, 'You will; if you can get

out of a curve like that, you can go up the side of a wall.'
I offered to bet him five dollars, but needless to say I was
in hopes I would lose. If we succeeded in climbing the
hill, I knew what would happen to the machines. But it was
vital to know whether a self-propelled car could be made to
go up that grade."

It did go up the grade. Reaching the top, the highest point
on the line, it came to a stop amid the cheers of an enthusiastic throng. But the motors were hotter than the outside of
a furnace.

Sprague was in no hurry to proceed. He hoped the motors
would cool down after a brief delay. But the crowd was
impatient, and he again applied the current. As the car
stirred, Sprague felt a peculiar bucking movement and realized that it was seriously disabled. One of the armatures
was crossed, and the odor of burning insulation filled the air.

Sprague called out loudly enough for all to hear, "Greene,
there is some trouble with the circuits. You'd better go back
to the carbarn and get some instruments so that we can
locate it."

Greene realized the situation at once. IIe took his time
about getting the instruments. Sprague turned the lights off
in the car, and the crowd, tired of watching a dark, motion-
less car, gradually dispersed. Greene finally arrived—with
four powerful mules, which corrected the trouble by hauling
the car back to the shed.

The long hill had been surmounted. But the problems left
in the wake of this achievement seemed as insurmountable
as the hill itself. A change in the gearing between motors
and car axle was imperative. But time was practically up
and the construction syndicate was clamoring for operation
to start.

Sprague went to Brown & Sharpe of Providence, and told

the foreman, "We have forty cars and are under contract to run. If we fail, we're likely to go under. I have everything at stake. The electric railway is largely at stake. The road has to succeed. Would you put some of your men and material at my disposal until I recover the position we have lost?"

The foreman said he would. In a few weeks the only practical mechanism for converting the single-gear reduction equipment into double reduction equipment was completed. Sprague had conceived the method himself.

There were countless other problems to be solved. Between forty and fifty schemes of trolley construction were attempted before one of Sprague's draftsmen, Eugene Pommer, thought out the plan of the swivel trunnion mounted on a tripod. This supported a trolley pole with a retrieving line attached to it. It proved to be the happy solution and was installed on all the cars.

The brushes on the motor commutators were as aggravating to Sprague as they had been to Bentley and Knight at Allegheny City. Every shape and design of metal brush was tried. Flat brushes wore through, doubled over, and stuck to the commutators; solid and laminated brushes caught in the commutator bars or split and straddled half a dozen bars, causing crossed armatures and burnt-out fields. Tilting brushes would not work. Brushes of copper, bronze, or brass in various shapes, set on end and pressed down by springs, served for a while but finally gave out. At last a number of bars of brass about three-eighths of an inch square were installed and lasted tolerably well. But as the cars moved through the streets, a shower of brass particles fell —at the rate of nine dollars worth a day!

In October, 1887, experimental operation had been attempted, and on February 2, 1888, in a drizzling rain, the road was opened for public service. People swarmed upon the cars. Service was satisfactory until cars began to stop and could not be budged. The new gears had developed a trick of locking. One of Sprague's workmen thought the trouble was lack of lubrication. And so it proved.

During a sleet storm workmen had to get up on the roofs of the cars and knock the ice off the overhead wire by clugging it with a broom.

Then the metal brushes began to ruin the commutators, and in turn the armatures. Interruptions became continuous. Motor fields had to be rewound and rewound. It was a ceaseless nightmare. But the road kept running, regardless of mental anguish and financial drain. Dismay stalked through the offices of the Sprague company in New York as reports of these troubles came in every mail.

Somehow the cars continued to run. Mechanics sweated and electricians swore, and Sprague himself spent his time commuting between Richmond and New York. The public, unaware of the strain upon tempers behind the scenes, exclaimed over the electric cars whose fame became widespread.

Sprague gradually increased the number of cars in service from ten to twenty, then thirty, and finally forty. "We felt that we owned the whole street, and the city as well," he said the first time thirty cars were run—May 4.

By the end of April nearly 6000 passengers were riding on the cars every day. There were delays and interruptions, but the public was tolerant and patient. The motormen were referred to as "motoneers." Sometimes a car ran off the poorly-laid rails and passengers and pedestrians alike would hoist it back on the track.

Sprague's practice in motor installation on these cars in general adhered to the plans adopted for his Elevated Railway experiment of the preceding year. He was the first man

to sleeve the motor on the car axle at two separate points,
and to support the free end of the motor from the car-body.
This arrangement maintained parallelism of the gears under
all conditions of car movement.

In distributing current Sprague won success on the principle of the parallel circuit. There was a working conductor,
a main conductor, and a feeder. The first was suspended over
the center of the car track; the two latter ran above the
center of the street curb, parallel to the road. Current from
the dynamos travelled at 450 volts over the feeder, which
supplied the main conductor at four widely separated points.
The main conductor in turn supplied the working conductor
by connecting wires placed at intervals of five hundred feet.
Each car was driven by two motors, originally of seven and
a half horsepower each.

Trouble with the metal brushes continued. A man was on
duty all day in front of the carbarn to meet each car as
it came in. The motors would be cut out of circuit in turn,
and while the car was run backward and forward, the workman would smooth off the mutilated commutators with a
file. This trouble with the brushes was far more serious than
people realized. Not to solve it was to endanger the prospect
of ultimate success.

Relief for the Richmond road, and for many others as
well, finally appeared in the fall of 1888. The nightmare was
laid forever when Charles J. Van Depoele, then in the service of the Thomson-Houston Electric Company, made one of
the most brilliant suggestions in the history of electric streetcars.

Early in January, 1888, Charles A. Coffin told Professor
Thomson that he believed the Thomson-Houston company
should undertake electric-railway development. Coffin's decision to enter this new field came before the success of

FACTORY STYLES OF 1902
Coil winder and helper in the Schenectady plant.

THE LUNCH BRIGADE
Taking father's lunch to the Schenectady Works each noon used to be a small boy's chore.

ELECTRICITY ON MOUNT WASHINGTON
The searchlight tower erected on the summit in 1892.

the Richmond road was consummated. He foresaw at an early period the great possibilities of electric traction in urban development. People could live in residential suburbs if quick transportation was at their disposal. Every city and town the country over could use electric streetcars.

Coffin's faith was rising at the moment when that of others was declining. One magnate who had grown faint-hearted was Aaron K. Stiles, manager and chief financier of the Van Depoele Electric Manufacturing Company. The company had been doing an excellent business. Van Depoele himself was as optimistic and persevering as ever. But Stiles found the financing of the company far more difficult than he had expected.

The previous autumn Van Depoele had told the American Street Railway Association that the electric railway was "ready for the market." He had enumerated eight electric railways installed by his company, all of them running at that time, and averaging seven or eight cars in operation. The most notable railway was at Montgomery, Alabama, a road thirteen miles long, with twelve cars running simultaneously.

But Stiles had not sufficient resources upon which to draw, and he knew he would have to look elsewhere for financial backing. He had already approached Sprague in the matter at the very time when Sprague was swamped with activities at Richmond. But Sprague, too absorbed in his own problems to undertake new ones, rejected the offer.

So it happened that Coffin purchased the Van Depoele Company and brought it into the Thomson-Houston company, which acquired the rights to Van Depoele's patents, and added Van Depoele himself to its staff of engineers.

Terms of sale were largely on a royalty basis. Stiles was to receive a royalty of $50 for every streetcar equipped under Van Depoele's company patents; and Van Depoele received a royalty of $5 per car in addition to his salary. Before a year had passed Stiles was satisfied that electric streetcars would never amount to much, and asked for a cash settlement of his interests in lieu of further royalties. Years after his interest was bought, enough cars had been equipped to make him a wealthy man had he retained the old royalty basis.

In the month of March, 1888, the month of the great blizzard, two men were added to the Thomson-Houston organization. One was William J. Clark; the other was Eugene Griffin. Griffin had made an extensive trip through the United States, gathering data on the electric-light business, and incidentally on the electric street railway.

Now began a new and busy era in Thomson-Houston affairs. The company was committed to the great enterprise of electric traction. Yet the disquieting situation centering around the metal brush was unsolved. Until that spectre was laid, the development of electric traction could not proceed.

Van Depoele had his own ideas. He had been placing the motor on the front platform of the car. This arrangement required a sprocket chain to convey the driving power from the motor to the car axle—which Thomson and Rice at once pronounced a clumsy method. Van Depoele's reason for so placing the motor was that the motorman could shift the brushes by hand whenever serious sparking occurred, and especially when the direction of rotation was reversed.

But the plan was abandoned in the system which the company now sought to design. Hoping to dispose of the metal brush dilemma in some other way, Thomson and Rice put the motor back under the car and equipped it with the best type of metal brushes they could make.

Then they set about electrifying their first streetcar line, a modest road a mile and a half long, at Crescent Beach, a coast pleasure resort between Boston and Lynn.

On the evening of July 3, 1888, a party of five men registered at Young's Hotel in Boston. Three of them were directors of the newly organized electric railway company of Des Moines, Iowa. The other two were Thomson-Houston sales agents, Theodore P. Bailey and William J. Clark.

The clerk on duty handed Clark a note which he and Bailey read with dismay. They managed to conceal their feelings from their three prospective customers through dinner, and made an appointment with them for the next morning.

Alone together, Bailey and Clark exchanged looks of consternation. Their guests had come east expressly to see the first Thomson-Houston road at Crescent Beach, where they expected to be taken the next day. But the note announced briefly that the motors on both cars at Crescent Beach had burned out and the cars were not yet back in service.

No need to ask the cause of the trouble. The copper brushes were again working havoc, and the cars might not be running for two or three days. What should they do with their prospects?

The next day was a holiday and Clark and Bailey suggested a sight-seeing trip for their guests before starting for Crescent Beach. First they visited Nantasket Beach, which proved so delightful that they missed their return boat and had to wait two hours for the next one.

At lunch the service was painfully slow, although the westerners were fortunately unaware of the covert signals passing between Clark and the waiter. After lunch the visitors were persuaded to go out to Bunker Hill, which they might not have another opportunity of seeing. On their return the carriage broke down, and the driver devoted himself endlessly to searching for a lost bolt in the road, while the close of day drew on.

When they finally got back to Boston, it was too late to visit Crescent Beach, and the unsuspecting Des Moines directors agreed to postpone the trip until morning. Returning to their hotel, Clark and Bailey were greeted by another note. It said, simply:

"Motors replaced. Crescent Beach road running beautifully." It had been delivered early that morning!

They lost no time in getting to Crescent Beach the following day. The cars behaved perfectly on every trip. The Des Moines men were greatly impressed, and signed a contract with Thomson-Houston in due course.

It may be surmised that the success obtained at Crescent Beach was hardly more than superficial. But it was no time for giving up, and before long the company signed a contract for equipping the Eckington and Soldiers' Home Railway at Washington, D. C.

No sooner were preparations under way on this work than the United States Senate reported a resolution revoking the permit previously granted to the railway company to erect overhead wires in the city of Washington. The railway company, however, was granted a public hearing before the resolution was reported.

Documentary evidence, amassed in considerable bulk, was laid before the committee. Several street-railway officials sent letters asserting in positive terms that overhead wires were not dangerous and that 500 volts, such as these systems employed, and not yet caused a fatal accident.

The argument of the Thomson-Houston counsel concluded with the following excellent logic:

"No doubt there is danger in electric wires, but the danger

CHARLES P. STEINMETZ

A portrait taken shortly after his arrival in America.

to people generally in the city is extremely small. The danger in crossing the streets is thousands of times as great. The danger on the railroad train, on the steamer, in eating your lunch or drinking soda-water, is far greater; you do these things without a care for the consequences. The other day I read of two or three fatalities caused by falling bricks blown from a chimney, but the paper said nothing about a proclamation by the mayor ordering all chimneys taken in."

The committee of the Senate was not proof against such a strong defense, and the resolution was not passed.

On October 17 the road was opened and created favorable comment because of its neat and ornamental appearance. At the same time the hearing before the Senate committee and particularly the endorsement of the overhead wire system had given electric street railways excellent publicity.

By the fall of 1888 the Thomson-Houston company had equipped several electric railways. The work was done with the utmost care, and under Coffin's policy the company gave service along with the sale of the products. Hence there were continual reports on the behavior of the motors, continual supervision by the experts over the commutator brushes.

An alarming situation was created both by unexpectedly heavy operating loads placed upon the street-railway motors and by the neglect which the motors had to undergo. Sparking at the commutators became so troublesome and the efficient operation of roads so difficult that something had to be done before the company was financially ruined.

Thomson immediately called a conference. Everyone agreed there was desperate need for a remedy. But no one appeared to know what could be done. Finally Van Depoele spoke in his quick way:

"Why don't you try carbon for a brush?"

Rice exclaimed, "Carbon has a resistance a thousand times

greater than that of copper. It would be impossible to carry the current from the commutator."

Van Depoele was unperturbed. "I tried carbon brushes on a motor in Chicago once, and they worked pretty well."

"What did you try them on?" persisted Rice.

"On a small motor operating on a series arc circuit."

"Well, they might work for a current of ten amperes and a small motor for one-quarter or one-half horsepower, but they wouldn't be likely to work on the fifty or sixty amperes current which our railway motors use. But we can try them."

The trial was made. Van Depoele and Rohrer fitted the extemporized carbon brushes to one of the standard F-30 motors and gave it a test. Rohrer was delegated to inspect the motor every half hour. Before long he reported with considerable excitement that the commutator showed not the slightest sign of sparking and was taking on a smooth, glazed surface!

A severer test was immediately conducted, with a fairly heavy load. Still no sparking, not even when the direction of rotation was reversed.

The good news was soon all over the plant. One of the most disturbing problems ever encountered had been banished. The spectre of the metallic brush was laid!

Rice communicated with the carbon manufacturers and before many days passed, carbon brushes had been placed on a Thomson-Houston railway motor in Woonsocket. In due time a report was made that the motor had run 4000 miles without the renewal of either brush or commutator, an incredible distance in those days. The report added that the brush showed hardly any wear and that the commutator had taken on a splendid polish.

Those were days of rejoicing in the Thomson-Houston organization. Congratulations were bestowed upon the amiable, quick-spoken young Belgian, who had remembered at the crucial moment about his block of carbon.

Only a few weeks slipped by before the news of the carbon brush went among other electric railway inventors. Sprague heard of it almost at once and seized upon it for his widely heralded, but sadly harassed, road at Richmond. The carbon brush saved the day for that famous undertaking.

Thomson said of the brush, "It is the most important invention ever made in the electric-railway field." It seems almost incredible that on this unobtrusive little block of carbon the whole future of the streetcar rested. But the only alternative, had no satisfactory brush been discovered, would have been some form of alternating-current streetcar far more complicated and far less efficient than the direct-current apparatus.

It was probably fortunate that the serious nature of the brush problem had not been obvious to the laity. For there came to Richmond in the early summer of 1888 a man who was to set the streetcar humming at a faster pace. This was Henry M. Whitney, president of the West End Street Railway of Boston who was considering either electric or cable propulsion for his road.

Sprague arranged a special demonstration for him in Richmond. There had been some criticism as to the ability of electric power to handle traffic when the cars were closely bunched. To prove that it could be done, Sprague gathered twenty-two cars at one end of the line, far removed from the powerhouse. Operations had concluded for the night, and Whitney was aroused from sleep to witness the demonstration.

At the wave of a lantern, twenty-one motormen all started their cars at once. The line pressure, which had been raised to 500 volts, immediately dropped to 200 volts, dimming all the car lights. Then it gradually rose again, and the cars, which had started slowly, went rapidly forward. There was no more talk of cable power in Boston. Sprague, however, did not get the contract, but that story will be taken up later.

Meanwhile, a new contribution to the electric street-railway had been made, an invention of Professor Thomson's. It embodied the magnetic blowout principle of his pioneer lightning arrester, used also for correcting other disturbances than lightning. In the design of an efficient control device for streetcar motors the idea proved of the utmost value. The controller is simply a form of switch, and as with all switches, it is necessary to prevent the current from forming a destructive arc when it is interrupted. Thomson's arrangement was easily adapted to Thomson-Houston railway work, and was embodied therein from the outset. It consisted of two metallic horns surrounded by a magnet, the latter "blowing out" the arc by forcing it toward the tips of the horns where it broke harmlessly.

It was one more step toward reliable streetcar apparatus which would hasten the final departure of the plodding horse from the car tracks of American cities.

[PART FOUR]

The Period of Expansion
and Consolidation

18

The Dilemma of Patents

As THE YEAR 1889 came in, the Thomson-Houston Company had little reason to feel dissatisfied with its progress. The volume of business per year had grown from $300,000 in 1883 to $3,500,000 in 1888.

The only fly in the ointment was the question of patents. During the hours that mean to most men leisure and relaxation, Coffin pondered over this problem. Suppose some of his customers should desire an underground conduit instead of an overhead trolley? He could not install a conduit system without the risk of infringing the Bentley-Knight patents.

Regarding the best type of motor and the best method of motor installation he was again on uncertain ground. The practice of the Bentley-Knight company had been followed in a general way in the Thomson-Houston product. There were many who felt that this motor summarized the best qualities of its predecessors. It was a fifteen-horsepower unit weighing almost a ton and having a speed of a thousand revolutions a minute. It delivered its power by double-reduction spur gearing, the armature revolving about nine times as rapidly as the car axle. The magnetic strength of the fields was particularly good in proportion to the total weight. Two motors were used per car, one to drive each axle.

Successful as it was, no one supposed that this represented the ultimate in streetcar motors; and rumors that there were others which embodied radically new ideas hardly lessened Coffin's perplexity over the prospect of patent difficulties.

The principal advocate of the single reduction motor at this time was no longer Sprague, who had had to abandon the type at Richmond, but Professor Sidney Howe Short, whose inventions formed the nucleus of the new Short Electric Railway Company of Cleveland. His experiments with single-reduction motors were awakening excitement in the offices of other electrical manufacturers. Before his retirement, he was to produce the first motor that operated without gears of any sort, having its armature direct-connected to the car axle.

All of Short's experimental work was performed at the plant of the Brush Electric Company, which also manufactured his motors for the market. In effect, Short was the successor of Bentley and Knight. He made use of Brush dynamos for his generators and motors as they did. In so doing he took full advantage of the easy regulation afforded by a series-wound motor. This regulation could be accomplished simply by properly shifting the commutator brushes whenever a change in speed was desired. In the Sprague motor the regulation was obtained by means of a commutator field, and in the Thomson-Houston, a resistance rheostat was employed.

The Brush company itself never entered the street-railway field. Its specialty continued to be arc lighting, and as such it was a powerful rival of Thomson-Houston. Brush had patent control over the double-carbon arc lamp, and it was believed that his storage-battery patent was so broad as to exclude any competitor in that field.

Another competitor was the Fort Wayne Electric Light Company, which was active in the middle west and south, installing Jenney and Schaffer direct-current arc dynamos and Slattery alternating-current incandescent dynamos. McDonald was a personal friend of Coffin's, and toward the middle of 1888, perceiving the need of additional working capital, he entered into negotiations with Coffin. As a result the Thomson-Houston company purchased a majority of the stock of the Fort Wayne company, obtaining a controlling interest. Coffin did not seek to acquire any patents by the transaction, as he felt that his company could hold its own in the open markets without infringing upon the Fort Wayne patents. What he had in mind was the desirability of conciliation and confidence among competing concerns. Coffin appreciated McDonald's unusual executive ability, and knew him for a bluff individual, erratic and daring, but just and shrewd. McDonald's methods were not Coffin's, but the two men were probably the most successful merchandisers in the electrical industry in that period.

Almost simultaneously, the Schuyler Electric Company entered the market. This concern had started a competing arc-light campaign in New Britain, in the days when Thomson and Rice were working there, under the guidance of a commercial promoter named Spencer D. Schuyler. Its principal inventors were D. A. Schuyler and A. G. Waterhouse, who had put out a sixteen-light arc dynamo and a lamp. In 1887 they moved to Middletown, Connecticut, and carried on a fairly prosperous business. In 1888 they were installing a 45-light machine in New England under the nose of the Thomson-Houston people.

But the company lacked Coffin's genius for securing new capital and could not expand as its operations required. In a financial quandary, the Schuyler officials were apprised that the Thomson-Houston company needed additional plant facilities. When Coffin made an acceptable offer, the chief construction man, J. A. Dalzell, as well as Schuyler and Waterhouse, joined the Thomson-Houston forces.

THROUGH THE 'EIGHTIES, the Thomson-Houston experts continued to meet with adventure at home and abroad. Their day's work was seasoned with more than the average spice of excitement.

One of them, William B. Potter, who had technical training to his credit, and who went through the instruction school with unwavering zest, was sent out to adjust complaints from the central stations of local companies.

He was delayed in a small town in North Carolina one night when there was no train out until the following morning. While chatting with an attendant at the generating station, the door suddenly opened and a determined-looking gentleman stalked in. He was the president of the local gas company with a few threatening remarks to address to the arc-light people.

"I've heard how your plant is going to put our gas company out of business," he said, "and I've come around to see that you don't do it. I'm going to shoot the daylights out of your machine."

He whipped out a revolver and advanced upon the dynamo. Potter acted quickly.

"Here, have a care!" he cried. "You put a bullet in that dynamo and you'll cause a flash of electricity that will kill us all. Don't go near with metal in your hands."

As he spoke, the dynamo emitted a bright, blue flash. The gun was drawn back in panic. The dynamo flashed again, and the gas president waited no longer. He dashed for the door and disappeared into the night. The two electrical men wiped a cold perspiration from their brows. And the dynamo placidly continued its intermittent sparking.

Shortly after this Potter was despatched to San Antonio, Texas, to install the Alamo Electric Railway, with instructions that it must be in operation in forty days, generating station and all. The road was about five miles in length, and there was one street within the city where right-of-way permits had not been granted. Potter decided he would have to lay track on that street between Saturday and Monday and get the permits afterward.

About two A.M. on Sunday, while operations were at their height, he was arrested. The chief of police was particularly hostile because he had been awakened from sleep. But Potter was able to put his arguments so convincingly that the chief sent him back to work. The right of way was legally secured a day later. Operation was begun on the thirty-eighth day. Potter himself broke in the green motormen, stressing the importance of deft work with the hand brakes in making emergency stops.

Meanwhile, at Lynn, Professor Thomson was doing significant work with alternating current. His experiments had been suggested back in 1884, when he built an electro-magnet, large for those days, having a core six inches in diameter and twenty inches in length. He had noticed that after it was magnetized, if he dropped a disc of sheet copper about one-sixteenth of an inch thick upon one of the magnetic poles, the disc would not fall with a quick contact but would settle gently, at variance with the laws of gravity. It was evidently slowed up as it encountered the magnetic field.

Before long he found that when alternating current, instead of direct current, was passed through the coils of the magnet, the copper disc was alternately attracted and repelled—but repulsion was stronger than attraction. He explained the cause as "electro-inductive repulsion."

It was not until 1887 that he worked out a practical device based upon this discovery. Then he built a motor having a laminated field; that is, a field constructed of many discs of metal pressed together, and a laminated iron armature, with three coils, three commutator segments, and brushes. He short-circuited the armature coils and passed an alternating current through the field coils. The armature of the little machine thereupon set up a revolution and he obtained considerable power. It was one of the first induction motors ever built, and certainly the first repulsion motor.

But motors, both traction and stationary, had not yet come into their own. There were scores of Sprague motors already spinning in countless New England industries. But Thomson's repulsion motor was to become the father of a long line of machines which were to outstrip them in efficiency and number.

Thomson described his experiments with the repulsion motor in a paper before the American Institute of Electrical Engineers in May, 1887. It aroused scientific excitement, and started the keenest among contemporary inventors working with alternating current. As a result, refinements of practice in alternating-current design were accelerated throughout the whole electrical world.

Every effort was made to introduce the safeguarded alternating-current system. Old customers were encouraged to substitute it for the direct-current system. By the end of 1887, the shipping department at Lynn had seen twenty-one alternators go out to central station customers, and more than four hundred transformers. These represented a capacity of more than 10,000 incandescent lamps of sixteen candlepower. In 1889, over 300 alternators and more than 9000 transformers left the works.

In one period of twenty-four months, no less than 300 local companies were established by Thomson-Houston efforts; and year after year the number of new companies regularly averaged between 100 and 150. On January 1, 1887, there were 171 companies in existence, operating 21,-000 arc lamps; two years later there were 419 companies and 51,000 lamps.

Coffin kept himself posted on everything. It is hardly conceivable that one man could follow so intimately and so unfailingly the intricacies of a many-sided business, growing by such tremendous bounds. At the same time he was interviewing some of the biggest men in Boston to offer them stock in the company. He believed whole-heartedly in the electrical business. It was a subject which he presented with all his innate friendliness of spirit, and with the utmost earnestness of purpose.

He encountered far more than the usual hesitancy in such matters. He heard all the customary inquiries as to the earnings and volume of business of his company, plus expressions of skepticism as to the future of electricity. But he was able to win over prospective stockholders nine times out of ten. He secured the participation of such influential men as F. L. Ames, former Governor of Massachusetts; Henry L. Higginson, of Lee, Higginson and Company; T. Jefferson Coolidge; S. Endicott Peabody; and George P. Gardner. These were among the most conspicuous men in Boston and they became a phalanx of strength to Thomson-Houston.

No man more completely held the trust and admiration of his co-workers than did Coffin. No man exercised his leadership with greater simplicity, greater humility, greater

regard for others. He dominated, it is true; but he never
domineered. His dominance sprang directly from the confidence which others placed in him; those outside the company, who watched his masterly direction, and those within
the company, who served under him and found that service
a memorable experience.

19

Beside the Mohawk

EDISON WAS PROSPERING ALSO. So satisfactory had the placid Schenectady river site proved that the two original Mc-Queen buildings became the nucleus around which a thriving plant took form.

The Edison Tube Company and the Edison Shafting Company had followed the Machine Works to its new quarters on the Mohawk. A species of amalgamation was accomplished on July 30, 1886, when both companies were formally merged, with the consent of their stockholders, into the Edison Machine Works. All auxiliary equipment required for a lighting system, from dynamo to lamp, was manufactured in these three plants.

Two men of pronounced mechanical talents had followed Edison from Menlo Park. One was Charles Batchelor, former Shop Superintendent at Goerck Street, and the other John Kruesi, the skillful Swiss who built the first model of Edison's phonograph and heard it "talk back" to its inventor. He had been in charge of the tube works and now began to oversee several departments, with the title of Assistant General Manager.

Under Kruesi was that well-remembered figure, William B. Turner, familiar to the working force as "Pop." He was a rough and ready individual, a type which predominated in the Edison personnel. His manner was genial and he addressed his men as "lad"; he was seldom seen with his coat on, and never was known to appear at the plant in a white collar.

Turner was an expert millwright, and his services were invaluable in setting up the machinery that was brought up from New York. Kruesi, although rough after his own fashion, came to be known as the most gentlemanly among the immediate bosses. He, like "Pop," was a hard worker and drove his men. He gave his directions in a bluff bass roar, but kept his language free from profanity, which was something unusual. His heart was kindly—the interests of the men became a personal concern, and he revealed a fatherly manner when dealing with a subordinate who he thought was not making the most of himself.

The Edison bosses soon became personages of standing in the town. Indeed, the entire plant rapidly took on the status of a local institution. There was always smoke coming out of its chimneys. The ring of the hammer and whir of the saw were heard as new shops rose. The community discovered that it had acquired an energetic, progressive enterprise where the old McQueen buildings once stood in forlorn desolation, and felt in it considerable civic pride.

With the spring of 1887 the plant began to spread, and this enlargement continued with recurrent pauses for nearly forty years. The original of Building 11 (destroyed by fire in 1892) was reared as a new home for the underground tube works and for the manufacture of wire and cable, under the general foremanship of Christian Rach. This building stood

CHARLES A. COFFIN

A portrait of the first president of the General Electric Company, taken at about the time he took office.

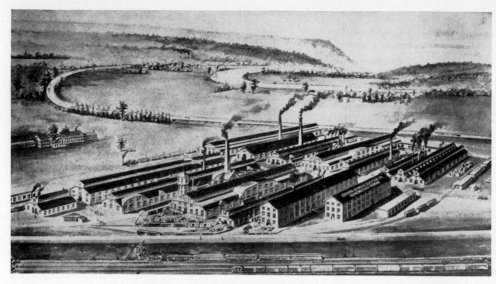

THE EDISON GENERAL ELECTRIC COMPANY—1891

The Schenectady plant the year before Edison and Thomson-Houston joined forces to form the General Electric Company. In the background can be seen the Mohawk River and the Erie Canal.

THE THOMSON-HOUSTON PLANT, IN LYNN—1892

In eight years the Thomson-Houston company had expanded to this size from the single building on Western Avenue, seen at the extreme left.

on the other side of what was later to become the mile-long main street of the works.

Two years later Thomas Cromerford Martin, writing for the *Electrical World* of August 25, 1888, sketched graphically his experiences during "A Day with Edison at Schenectady." Had he known that the handful of shops he then described would one day become a huge industrial center, he could hardly have written with more enthusiasm.

"We are looking," he said, "at one of the greatest exemplifications of the power of American inventive genius, and at an establishment where, from beginning to end, a new art is illustrated by new processes."

The works by that time embraced twenty-six separate buildings and employed from 750 to 800 hands. "The departments," wrote Martin, "include the building of Edison dynamos, the construction of Sprague electric motors . . . every branch of the insulated wire business . . . Sims-Edison torpedo work, the Edison processes for dealing with refractory ores, and a general business in shafting, pulleys, and hangers, and in millwright and foundry work."

Martin was greatly moved by the "noble machine shop." "In such a place as this," he says, "the prosaic and the marvellous jostle each other. Here are six thousand feet of shafting and some fifty thousand feet of belting, driving nearly four hundred separate mechanisms in the production of apparatus whose birth was yesterday."

Even in those days the schedule of work-hours in the electric generating stations was beginning to undergo a revolution. The days of night-duty only were beginning to pass. Says Martin: "The telegraph office, requiring current for its circuits; the telephone exchange, with its magnetos to be run; the medical establishments, with patients to be cured by electricity; the printing offices; the ice-cream saloons; the buildings with elevators; the wood-working factories; the chemical works with bad ventilation . . . each of these and hundreds of other places need current all day long for direct use or to drive motors, and they are all becoming customers of the central stations."

Nor had the day of the isolated plant come to an end. Mills, iron works, machine shops, publishing offices, and asylums, as well as theaters, clubs, banks, office buildings, steamships, and ferry-boats, in considerable numbers had installed Edison isolating lighting plants.

In 1886 the Edison Electric Light Company took over all the business which had been previously handled by the Edison Company for Isolated Lighting. After four years it was merged back into the parent company. The Edison Electric Light Company still had its headquarters at 65 Fifth Avenue in New York City. It issued licenses, under Edison's electric-light patents, to the teeming family of Edison local companies.

Two other Edison organizations did not move to Schenectady. These were the lamp works at Harrison, New Jersey, and Bergmann and Company. The latter was operated by Sigmund Bergmann, of the Menlo Park group, who combined to a high degree both mechanical and executive talents. The plant, at Seventeenth Street and Avenue B, New York, manufactured practically everything Edison needed in the line of auxiliary equipment, such as meters, switches, lamp-sockets, cut-outs, fuses, and electroliers.

20

The Edison Consolidation

PROSPERITY IN THE FORM of new business had also poured her bounties upon the Sprague Electric Railway and Motor Company during the years of 1888 and 1889. The long nightmare at Richmond was past, and the prestige of the final triumph there brought other street-railway contracts flooding in. Moreover, the company's business in stationary motors was far more important than its competitors realized.

The company had for an emergency man Dave Mason, known as the "wet nurse" because he had hurried out at short notice to save many an infant electric road from the fatalities of babyhood. He had installed and watched over the first long-distance circuit on which Sprague motors worked, one of the earliest instances of transmission over any appreciable stretch of territory.

It would seem like child's play to the present electrical engineer, for this line was but eighteen miles in length. But for 1887 it was a considerable undertaking. It was located in a mountainous California wilderness on the Feather River where it encircles Big Bend Mountain. A hydroelectric generating station supplied the circuit, in which were connected fourteen Sprague motors scattered along the course of the stream. Their work was to drive pumps and hoists and run dinky cars in the operations of placer mining, for the Big Bend had gold within its rugged bosom.

Officials of the Sprague Company had formed no conception of the amazing welcome which would be accorded the electric motor. It was instantly recognized as a worker whose driving arm would never tire and whose disposition fitted well with that of the human operative.

William L. R. Emmet, who like Sprague was trained in the navy, and Horace F. Parshall, a young man skilled in engineering mathematics, were valuable additions to the Sprague personnel. Parshall took charge of the establishing in Cleveland of the Euclid Avenue electric street railway. Sprague was astonished one morning to find a letter from Parshall condemning the No. 5 motor in such language as only a much-irritated man would employ.

"That motor," he wrote, "is so extremely rotten that unless a No. 6 type is immediately developed, I'll quit the job."

Sprague knew its weaknesses well; and shortly thereafter the No. 6 motor appeared. It was larger in capacity—fifteen horsepower—and embodied the double-reduction principle. Its greater physical size was accommodated by the practice, begun by car builders, of producing independent car trucks.

Emmet, while promptly recognizing the good qualities in Sprague's apparatus, did not consider that it was always well built, either in the Sprague or the Edison shops. "In most cases," wrote Emmet at a later period, "the motors gave very expensive trouble and had to be settled for on terms more or less disadvantageous to the manufacturer. In spite of these troubles, there was a great demand for equipment which would run."

Because of poor workmanship in the shops, Sprague found

DR. STEINMETZ AT WORK AT HIS DESK

W. B. POTTER AND THE STREETCAR CONTROLLER

it imperative to have Emmet rewind many of the No. 6 motors after they had been shipped. He was equipping sixty cars for a new road at Allegheny City. Under instructions from New York, Emmet rebuilt the trolleys and the controllers, altered the system of lubrication, and enclosed the gears in gear cases. The road ran under Emmet's direction for nearly a year with little trouble. Maintenance costs and electrical efficiency on the road were good.

This experience brought out Emmet's faculty for finding the weaknesses in apparatus and correcting them. It was a faculty which was one day to solve one of the great engineering problems in the realm of apparatus design.

Yet with all its success, the internal condition of the Sprague company during 1888 was far from stable. Possessed of a splendid future, it lacked proper financing. Its president, Edward H. Johnson, was burdened with two presidencies—that of the Edison Electric Light Company being the second. Sprague spoke his mind freely upon the question of Johnson's relation to both companies.

"Unless this company were to sacrifice everything for which it has worked so long, and which after such hard work it has won," he said, "I see no alternative, certainly for the present, save that you should give up one position or the other. The two are antagonistic, and held as they now are will, I fear, end not only disastrously to this company but to your career as business manager." The crisis was not resolved until early in the spring of 1889, when the status of the Edison company itself was changed.

Edison, as a man of inventive genius, is perhaps unique in entering successfully the field of electrical manufacture and the field of public-utility operation. But it was as inventor that he was greatest, and from the other activities he withdrew little by little.

Edison dropped out of active relationship with the Edison Electric Illuminating Company. The separation was consummated suddenly in the spring of 1889 by a merger of individual Edison manufacturing enterprises into a corporate organization, the Edison General Electric Company.

Four companies were consolidated by this move—the Edison Electric Light Company, the Edison Machine Works, the Edison Lamp Company, and Bergmann & Company. In addition, the new concern bought out the Canadian Edison Manufacturing Company, and the Edison United Manufacturing Company, which was the selling outlet for the three American manufacturing units.

The Edison Electric Light Company had throughout its life been comparatively inactive in exploiting electric power. Few company officials, from Edison down, could give much consideration to motors while the lighting business continued to be so brisk. In issuing licenses to local Edison companies, the Edison Electric Light Company found business at flood tide. It had its own sales agents, of the promoter type, supervised by W. Preston Hicks and similar to those of the Thomson-Houston Company. And it had a policy similar to Coffin's of accepting stock from local companies in payment of royalties due the parent company under Edison patents. By the autumn of 1889 the parent company had an interest in more than seventy Edison licensee companies over the United States. The company's month-to-month revenue was composed of dividends and interest on stocks, and a royalty for every incandescent lamp. In the fiscal year ending in 1889 the total receipts from these two sources were $160,500.

Nearly all the large Edison central-station companies had been established by 1889—Boston, Chicago, Detroit, Brooklyn, Philadelphia. It had been sufficiently absorbing to maintain relations with these ventures, to meet expanding needs for equipment, to supply lamps, and to cope with the progress of sales agents in securing new contracts. But an attempt to consider electric motors while electric lighting was so rapidly expanding would have precipitated serious problems. The addition of a new department could only come about through a general enlargement of facilities—and this the new merger accomplished.

The Sprague company needed healthier financing; and the Edison company was now in a position to enter the field of electric power. What resulted was the bodily absorption of the Sprague company into the Edison General Electric.

Joseph P. Ord, a capable executive and a master of financial procedure became comptroller of the new organization. Young Whitestone, the bookkeeper of the Sprague concern, was hard at work over his books when the red whiskers and strapping figure of Ord appeared in the doorway, totally unannounced. No official announcement had been made to the Sprague personnel concerning the change in officers. Ord strode over to the counter and demanded to see Whitestone's general ledger. The lad gave one look at the towering apparition and shoved the ledger onto his stool and sat upon it. The bookkeeper's fears were soon put at rest. Indeed, Whitestone and Ord became fast friends, despite that first encounter.

Thus came into corporate life the Edison General Electric Company. From the shoulders of Edison it lifted the multitudinous details essential to the manufacture of his inventions. Edison, in alliance with the new corporation, gravitated with it away from the utility operating field. Since the manufacture of his inventions was now to be handled by an organization fortified by large financial resources, he began to turn from the manufacturing field as well, back to that mysterious realm which no true inventor can forsake.

As for Sprague, his affiliation with the new company was

brief. While the change of control was maturing, he continued as vice president of the Sprague company, but in July he resigned his office and started out again by himself.

When President Whitney and his directors decided to proceed with the electrification of the West End Road of Boston, they turned to the man who had accomplished the Richmond miracle, and in the autumn of 1888 awarded to Sprague's company a contract for a trial installation on the Brookline division of thirteen miles of track to be equipped for the operation of twenty cars. The Sprague overhead wire was built from the Brookline terminus to the Boston city line, making use of tapering steel poles. Within the city limits overhead construction was not allowed, so the Bentley-Knight underground conduit was laid between the two tracks instead of in the center of each track. The beginning of actual operation on the line was delayed by the construction of the conduit, regarded by Sprague as a necessary evil.

The first official run occurred on January 2, 1889, amid snowstorms which caused trouble with the conduit. Sprague equipped a snow-sweeper with one of the motors used in his demonstrations of 1886 upon the elevated railway in New York, and with this the way was cleared for an impressive demonstration. The press registered enthusiasm; and the people through official bodies and organizations hastened to taste the thrills of riding on this grown-up brother of the "broomstick cars."

But Whitney was not so easily satisfied. As a business man he relished competitive trial, and it was to the Thomson-Houston company that he assigned the Cambridge division of the West End system. The road was equipped with overhead wires, utilizing a cross-arm method of suspension from iron poles. Its cars were supplied with fifteen-horsepower motors, larger in capacity than Sprague's No. 5, more rugged, more powerful, and giving a better electrical performance.

Operation of this division began on February 16, 1889, from which day Coffin and his associates argued the merits of their system before Whitney with all the vigor and diplomacy at their command. They knew the prestige it would mean for their company should they win the final contract.

Three months slipped by. Whitney was a keen trader. He wanted reliable electrical equipment and required guarantees that would protect him from unforeseen reverses. The Sprague company would not make a proposition which would guarantee to assume the risks.

It was Charles A. Coffin who produced what Whitney required. It consisted of supporting the work of his electrical engineers with financial guarantees. As a result on June 27, 1889 Whitney placed the contract for the West End Road in the hands of Thomson-Houston.

A new shop—Factory C—had to be built to fill the huge order. Manufacturing schedules were adjusted and the working force increased. Rice recommended a program of expansion, which Coffin immediately endorsed.

Already intensive redesigning of the dynamo for the severe conditions of electric railway service had set in. The slotted armature, as finally designed, was freely ventilated by air ducts and was of the four-pole arrangement, finally rated at 270 horsepower. Rohrer followed the shop work and conducted the tests. It required two days to assemble the first machine for trial, using wooden blocks and hydraulic jacks in lieu of cranes, which had not yet come into extensive use.

The big dynamos created considerable stir among the entire force. Yet still larger ones, rated at 360 horsepower and having six magnetic poles, were brought out for use on the West End Road. By 1892 the powerhouse of this road was the talk of street-railway men far and wide. There were over a hundred generators weighing some thirty-five tons apiece. They were driven by belting which aggregated a length of 1800 feet—over a third of a mile—and was fifty-four inches in width.

By 1891 the line was running 130 electric cars at an average speed of eight miles per hour—two miles an hour better than the best horse-cars could do. Traffic on the road had increased enormously. During snowstorms, more than the normal number of cars could be run, as well as electric plows and sweepers. After the first snowstorm, when the system was stalled for an hour, the elements were unable to derange its operation.

Nor was this the only success that electric traction won on the fateful West End Road. A clause in the original contract stipulated that the Thomson-Houston Company should maintain in good working condition and keep in proper repair the entire overhead wire system on the West End Road, as well as the motor equipment on the cars, for a period of five years. Compensation for this service was to be paid by the West End Company according to a graduated scale based on the revenue per car mile. Back of this provision can be discerned the doubts which Whitney still entertained regarding the practical value of electrical equipment. Opposed to this was the complete confidence of the Thomson-Houston Company.

In less than two years of operation Whitney was completely convinced. Cost of maintaining the overhead lines and car equipment was so much less than what he paid Thomson-Houston for such maintenance that the latter were realizing a substantial profit. Whitney thereupon exercised an option allowing him to take over the work, which saved his company several thousands of dollars yearly.

The skeptical years were definitely at an end. Electricity, as a practical agent of power, had come to stay. From then on there were few to doubt that the pigmy which in 1876 had whispered such unintelligible secrets of the future would become in time a giant. Not a master, to rule the peoples of the earth, but a giant slave, to serve with unlimited strength and unending efficiency those who would command him.

21

"Experts" on the Job

IN THE MIDST OF SUCCESS Charles A. Coffin was troubled by visions of the future. He would never be satisfied until the day he offered his customers complete electric service. Only thus, as he saw it, could the electrical era dawn in America. The alternative was a feverish, interminable period of conflict between patent holders, during which the major competitors in the field exhausted their energies trying to avoid each other's patents or fighting alleged infringements.

That was the depressing picture of the future which troubled his mind, even while the tap of the mason's trowel proclaimed the rearing of new factory buildings.

Coffin already had a glimpse of what the future would be like. The Thomson-Houston Company was trying to discover a double-carbon arc lamp that would avoid the Brush patent. After hours of conference by engineers and attorneys, the lamp was declared legally sound. But the Brush Company promptly served notice of an infringement. A legal combat loomed, and its menace caused Coffin to think again of amalgamation.

To his colleagues it seemed a daring proposal. The Brush

162

POWER PLANT OF THE G-E EXHIBIT AT THE CHICAGO FAIR
OF 1893

GENERAL ELECTRIC AT THE COLUMBIAN EXPOSITION
Exhibits and installations by the Company at Chicago in 1893.

Company was as strongly entrenched as Thomson-Houston, possessed the prestige of a firstcomer in the field, and boasted of successful installations throughout the land. Coffin nevertheless dispatched a personal representative to Cleveland with an offer to purchase Brush's stock, which constituted a controlling interest in the company.

The emissary arrived in Cleveland in October, 1889, empowered to offer $40 per share. Brush had no interest in this figure and held out for $75 per share. When he remarked that he did not suppose the Thomson-Houston Company would pay his price, the agent wagered a new overcoat that the offer would be accepted. The wager was promptly taken.

Next day Brush received a telegram stating that he owed Coffin's representative a new overcoat. The price of $75 per share for forty-thousand-odd shares of stock had been accepted and control of the Brush Electric Company passed into Thomson-Houston hands for a sum in excess of $3,000,000.

So rapid and so quiet had been the negotiations that the electrical world was taken by surprise. The first reports of the transaction were scarcely credited.

No change in the conduct of the Brush Company's operations resulted from the transfer of control for many years thereafter.

By purchasing control of the Brush concern, Thomson-Houston strengthened its position as proprietor of one of the soundest electrical manufacturing organizations in the United States. It was doing business on a scale equal to that of the Edison General Electric Company.

A year later there came a new alignment among the Thomson-Houston subsidiaries. The Fort Wayne Company believed that the Jenney arc-light apparatus could be improved. To do this job, they selected a young man named Wood. At that time Wood was affiliated with the Thomson-Houston Company, conducting a modest manufacturing enterprise in Brooklyn which turned out three or four dynamos a week. McDonald effected a transaction by which the Fort Wayne Company purchased from Thomson-Houston a part interest in Wood's arc-light system with the understanding that the designer become a member of the Fort Wayne organization.

Wood, accompanied by a hundred employees, arrived in Fort Wayne on December 3, 1890. It was the beginning of the most productive period in his career. McDonald encouraged Wood with characteristic ardor in every inventive idea which offered practical possibilities. Before long McDonald's tactics had established Fort Wayne as the home of the Wood system of arc lighting.

Hopeful young men kept arriving at the now celebrated plant of the Thomson-Houston Company, seeking to become "experts." By the beginning of the 'nineties, college graduates were noticeable among them. But they were novices when it came to practical electrical work, and there was nothing "greener" around the shops than a new expert.

Most of the young men needed all the ambition and grit they could muster to carry them through weeks of soul-trying work at menial tasks. But these weeks separated the wheat from the chaff. The men who survived the testing were ready to advance in the company.

The expert course had developed into a separate department. In early years the General Manager of the company, Silas A. Barton, hired the beginners. Later J. B. Cahoon was chief of experts.

How green the new arrivals were is revealed in the

reminiscences of A. K. Baylor, who has described his feelings when he first entered Factory C.

"On either hand crackled and hummed various mighty dynamos. Belts! I had never seen so many—horizontal, vertical, and slanting. Those driving the generators were wide and heavy, flapping as they ran, and shooting little spurts, here and there, to an occasional guard rail . . .

"By the time we had gone half-way down the line— becoming accustomed to the racket and observing that no one was being struck dead—I gained courage and became quite elated . . . Then I came to earth, almost literally, with the proverbial dull thud, as I was put to work wiping up grease on the floor under the frame of a railway motor. The task was uninspiring, to say the least; and it seemed so useless. What mattered a little grease, more or less, on an area already covered and impregnated with it?"

His working companion that day was a chap whose conception of electricity was limited to the familiar explanation that current passing through a wire is analogous to water flowing through a water pipe. He had taken this literally, believing that the cable running across the floor from the starting rheostat to the dynamo actually encased a tangible fluid. Planting both feet firmly on the cable he exclaimed to Baylor, who was about to start a motor, "There! *Now* let's see you make her go!"

The experts spent a month among shop motors. Upon them rested the responsibility of starting the motors before the whistle sounded, morning and afternoon. "Woe betide the expert who was late on that job!" writes Baylor. "It was a well-nigh capital offense. Suspension, following goodness knows what ordeal in the inner office, was the minimum sentence. . . .

"I had quarters almost across the street, and I well recall springing out of bed at the five-minutes-to-the-hour whistle, to race through the check-house with shoe laces flying, collar unfastened, coat on my arm, and buttoning my waistcoat as I ran—breathless and breakfastless."

A vanished expedient, the check-house with its wall-board on which hung the brass check of each employee, was a forerunner of the time clock and the timecard. As each worker arrived, he unhooked his check and dropped it into a box. The instant the starting whistle blew the box was locked and note was taken of the checks remaining on the board.

Relations between the young experts and the company officials were warm. Baylor speaks with appreciation of "the privilege of visiting the home of Mr. Coffin under a standing invitation to the boys of the course to 'come around' Sunday afternoons. Done up in our best, and after painful efforts to make fingernails presentable, we often took advantage of this opportunity to be served with tea by Mrs. Coffin and looked over and 'interviewed' by the great 'C.A.' himself.

"In that way, and by a continuation of the personal touch, augmented by E. W. Rice, Jr., Eugene Griffin, J. R. Lovejoy, and other officials, were sown seeds that have blossomed into a world-wide harvest of loyalty that few men or institutions have ever inspired."

There were occasional nerve-racking occurrences during the testing of new machines. One happened on the day that an alternator with bearings of the self-oiling type was first tested. The engineers had seen a direct-current dynamo so equipped by the Fort Wayne Company, and were captivated with the device. They induced Rohrer to permit the bearings for their own new alternator—a seventy-kilowatt "giant"— to be redesigned. When the day for the test arrived, hope

WHEN THE BI-POLAR WAS POPULAR
View in Building 12 at Schenectady, about 1890.

THE HEYDAY OF THE ARC LAMP
Arc lamps being assembled at the Lynn Works, about 1892.

A FOREST OF BELTS
Machine shop at the Lynn Works, about 1895.

and anxiety alternated like an electric current in the breasts of the engineers.

As the belt was slipped upon the pulley of the dynamo, the armature began to revolve. Then there came a groan, a shriek, smoke—and the belt went sailing through the air. Dependable, self-oiling bearings indeed! They were almost red-hot.

Someone asked the test man who had set up the machine, "How much oil did you put in those bearings?" He looked up with a blank expression. "Oil? I didn't put any in. I was told they were self-oiling."

It took two days for a skilled machinist to work the melted babbitt off the steel shaft. And it was two weeks before the machine could be tested again, this time well oiled and unquestionably successful.

Every dynamo of greater size completed in the shops became a nine-days' wonder. When a new manufacturing tool or shop practice was added to the day's routine, workmen marveled and visitors came to see. The early electric cranes were held in awe at Lynn as well as at Schenectady. The first of these began operations in November, 1888, in Factory K, and had a capacity of twenty tons. Many a week passed before workmen refrained from staring when the crane lifted a load.

When a five-ton electric crane was put into use at Schenectady in 1887, old-timers recall how excursion trains on the New York Central stopped by the Edison works to give passengers a glimpse of the great beast at work.

While these giant industrial "muscles" were lending fascination to the humming electrical factories, Thomson was hard at work in the laboratory giving scientific counsel, and trying out new devices. For several years he had been perfecting his electric meter. Unlike Edison's chemical meter, it measured not only current consumed over a specific time but also voltage, thus establishing a true and equitable means of rendering bills for electric light and power. The meter won fame as the Thomson recording wattmeter.

So urgently had it been needed that within two years a meter department and special shop facilities had to be set up to handle the business. Its ruggedness and simplicity left little to be desired.

There are some who believe that this meter was one of the determining influences in electrical development. It won high honors at the Paris Electrical Exposition of 1890, dividing the prize with a clock-type meter which was more costly to install and required regular winding. A factory, established shortly afterward in France to manufacture the Thomson meter, became the nucleus of the French Thomson-Houston company.

22

New Faces, New Companies

In 1889 A YOUNG MAN left his native country and crossed the ocean to America. His name was Steinmetz. Steinmetz came to an America that was conscious of the new pulse of industrial life and the throb of mighty economic and material energies.

As a young immigrant he entered New York harbor in steerage accompanied by a fellow-student, Oscar Asmussen. Together they stood on deck, gazing at the busy harbor. They saw a multitude of buildings, symbol of a crowded metropolis, of national vigor, of surging life.

The lad's misshapen body and diminutive figure were in odd contrast to his friend's sturdier build. A seeming pygmy, he gazed at vigorous America, preparing to enter the conflict for sustenance and position that was fought daily on those shores. In the air was a newly awakened force, a power that men had aroused from lethargy which seemed to confront them with passive, inscrutable curiosity as if wondering if there were any who would truly master it. On the deck of the steamer, a dwarf in stature, insignificant to his fellowmen, stood one of those masters.

He was not conscious of his destiny and had no intimation that he was to solve some of the riddles of the electrical era. He had no thought, even, of an electrical career.

Since men are human, and hence unaware of the forces of destiny, it was not strange that the immigration officers hesitated to admit Carl Steinmetz upon that June day in 1889. Steinmetz, besides his shrunken body, had a severe cold which had swollen one side of his face. The immigration officers determined that he should be deported.

Then Asmussen took up the cause of his friend. He declared his money was Steinmetz's money, that his home should be his friend's. In brief, he accepted full responsibility for Steinmetz's future.

Thus friendship won for Steinmetz an entrance to his future country. He found himself in the heart of the metropolis—and in the hands of destiny. Events not entirely of his own shaping guided him into his niche in the new world. Of the places where he applied for employment, one gave him encouragement. In the office of Eickemeyer and Osterheld in Yonkers he had a talk with the head of the firm, Rudolf Eickemeyer. There he went to work on the tenth of June as an electrical draftsman, at twelve dollars a week.

Eickemeyer was a manufacturer and inventor, well seasoned by experience and, like Steinmetz, a native of Germany. From him Steinmetz caught the inspiration for putting his great technical ability to work upon electrical problems and through him was provided the most natural outlet for the young man's mathematical talents.

So for a year or two Steinmetz, hidden away in an obscure corner, worked for a modest manufacturer in a humble, unspectacular post. His life was quiet, contented, assiduous. His surroundings were pleasant and wholly untroubled.

Only a few weeks after Steinmetz crossed the Atlantic,

another traveller landed in New York and hurried up to Boston and Lynn. This was Rudolf Langhans, a young German scientist whom Rice had discovered during a trip abroad, and who was believed to have found a way of producing a new filament for incandescent lamps.

He was installed in the Thomson-Houston laboratory, provided with assistants, and given an interpreter. What Langhans proposed to do was to combine pure silicon and carbon in the filament. But pure silicon was difficult to obtain —a fact of which Langhans appeared to be ignorant. The Thomson-Houston chemists discovered that what he was using was not pure silicon, but oxide of silicon.

In the end, Langhans regretfully admitted that his idea was not practicable. He left Lynn, and the attempt to produce a silicon-carbon filament came to an end. Though the Thomson-Houston Company lost $75,000 on the effort, experimental work did not lag. "A better incandescent lamp," was the cry; and it echoed from Lynn to Harrison, where the Edison Lamp Works was wrestling with the same idea.

Looking at the electric light bulb of today, seemingly a device easy to construct, even with its hairlike filaments, one finds little indication of the infinite pains and delicate handling that produced it. So intricate is it that in the early days at the Edison Lamp Works, when a curious soul asked why the various steps could not be done by machines, he was laughed at. The work was far too delicate!

Glass blowing was an old and conservative art, and necessarily slow. Not only the bulb but the glass stem, in which the lead-in wires were mounted, had to be blown. Operators went through months of training, and even then the percentage of spoilage was considerable.

But one change after another affected the shape and size of stems until Edison was able to develop a machine which held the bulb in a horizontal position and, after the filament had been mounted, rotated it in a flame while the stem was sealed in. At Lynn, Branin thought of flaring the stem at one end, so that it could be sealed to the bulb on the flange principle—a process which permitted a more perfect joint, obviated strains in the glass, and caused a saving in glass of half a cent a lamp.

Hand work persisted in such operations as blowing off the lower end of the bulb to a uniform length, and in making an opening in the bulb top through which a tube was inserted for pumping out air. A succession of efforts to produce a satisfactory base culminated in Bergmann's base, which is in use today. The idea for it came to Bergmann while he contemplated the screw-cap on a kerosene can.

But the Edison, Thomson-Houston, and Brush companies were not the only manufacturers producing incandescent lamps. In various sections of the country, particularly in the middle west, small aggressive companies were doing a flourishing business. Lamps manufactured by these concerns were similar to Edison's. The filamentary illuminant in a sealed glass globe from which most of the air had been exhausted was always present. Hence all of these companies, as well as Thomson-Houston and Brush, stood in the precarious position of possible infringers upon Edison's lamp.

They had taken the risk deliberately, because the policy of the Edison Company gave them a feeling of security. Years had come and gone since Edison's lamp appeared, and no steps had been taken to uphold by legal action that valuable patent. But the issue was soon to be fought out at the bar. Preliminary proceedings had been begun late in 1886, although so quietly and after so many legal delays that the sense of security persisted among competitors. They kept on manufacturing and selling.

Within the stately Edison Building, which stood at 16 and 18 Broad Street, New York, the busy organism of the Edison General Electric Company found its brain center. It was an immense corporation for its day, and the forerunner of one still more immense.

Said the *Electrical Engineer* in a special supplement entitled "Edisonia," published with its issue of August 12, 1891:

"One cannot visit the Edison Building without being impressed with the sense of irresistible power that a large, well-knit body in swift, onward motion always arouses. The halls and elevators are thronged, and at every floor one encounters the same bustle and hum of activity. . . . The industry of which these are the headquarters has over 6000 names on its payrolls, and has a monthly income and outgo of a million of dollars. . . . The company has between 4000 and 5000 customers on its books."

Virility was heightened by semimystery. Not yet was the veil wholly drawn so that the untutored public could comprehend what lay back of its electric lights and motors. Edisonia, however, described some of the broad features of the process. "The mere handling of the bamboo, as it arrives in dainty bundles from Japan, tied up in flowery wrappers, and passing from stage to stage, becoming smaller by degrees until at last it is ready for the carbonizing retorts, involves the employment of many sensitive mechanisms and many agile fingers."

Even the tissue-paper squad, smoothing out the used paper for repacking, had its glamor. In that lowly environment lurked the gold nugget of opportunity. Young George Morrison, now a foreman, had started out in the squad ten years before. He was bound to keep on rising, for men still noticed that whatever he did, he did well.

From process to process the visitor continued his rounds,

coming at last to the packing room, "where in huge racks like egg boxes, or in big barrels, the lamps await labeling for the nearest city or for the far ends of the earth." It was a wide practice to ship the lamps in barrels. Says another writer: "A barrel was the *piece de resistance* in a day when all goods were merchandised loosely over the counter, stuffed with excelsior, bound with iron hoops, padded with packing bustles." The barrels were made of the stoutest materials for shipping their delicate cargoes, and "the agent who received a package of lamps had to be a strong and mighty man—and a good feller with a broom."

Barrel shipments were massive in the aggregate, and the capacity of the "huge factory" in 1891 was 25,000 lamps every working day.

"Edisonia" reports of the Schenectady works that they "grow with the rapidity of a western town. . . . These huge cathedral shops, swarming, every one of them, with hundreds of busy artisans and filled to overflowing with machines and tools and labor-saving appliances, epitomize the progress to date both in mechanics and in the arts of dynamoed motor-construction. If you would find the monument of American skill and genius in such fields, look around you." Colorfully the writer describes the production of the Edison tubes, in a building "where huge caldrons simmer and huge piles of black iron pipe rise to the roof, for all the world like exaggerated lead pencils," with an electric drill "pounding away in a ferocious manner at the heart of a block of granite," elbow-to-elbow with "demure young ladies splitting mica."

After the consolidation of 1889, the shops of Bergmann and Company were transferred to Schenectady, and a new group of buildings was set up. Sockets for lamps, switch-boards, and wiring devices were now made at Schenectady. Punch presses hammered and thumped from morning to night in the new section; and the first porcelain shop was there established.

Edison and Villard were frequent visitors at the plant. Their appearance created a general stir. The cry would go up, "Here comes Edison!" and there would be a lively craning of necks. They were an odd pair, Edison and Villard. The financier, his moustache close-cut, was always well-tailored, while the inventor was never mindful of his clothes, usually wearing a shiny Prince Albert coat, and in summer an old straw hat.

In the words of an old darky song, "It must be now de kingdom am a-comin' in, an' de year ob jubilee!" Whatever salvation electricity has brought, its "year ob jubilee" began in 1890. The great formative period of electrical development was at its height.

The nation was passing from one era to another. A new mode of life was emerging from the mists of uncertainty, was adjusting, adapting, solidifying. Industry and commerce, taking shape around a new enterprise, developed with it at tremendous speed.

In the rush and stir of this formative period there arose much confusion in technical and commercial activity and competition among sales agencies. The Edison consolidation set out to minimize this as rapidly as possible by adopting a policy of centralization. Says Edison General Electric's annual report for 1890:

"It was found practically impossible to exercise over so many distinct organizations the close supervision necessary to secure rigid accountability and to conduct the business on an economical basis. It was found further that the prevailing system of allowing commissions on business obtained through local agencies was very expensive, without bringing adequate returns.

"Your board therefore decided . . . to bring about a unification of all the allied manufacturing organizations and selling agencies. . . . It further determined that the entire business of manufacturing, selling and installing should be conducted in the General company's own name, through its own employees.

"The Edison Electric Light Company was excepted from this arrangement, and it remains an active, independent body in all respects."

Vice-President Insull and Comptroller Ord addressed themselves to the task of a complete reorganization. Out of their work came principles of business administration and methods of financial accounting which persist today.

Their salient achievement was to set up a district organization. The United States was divided into seven large areas with a district office in each, and an eighth in Canada. In New England the district office was in Boston; in the Eastern district, in New York; Central district, Chicago; Southern, New Orleans; Rocky Mountain, Denver; Pacific Northwest, Portland; Pacific Coast, San Francisco; Canadian, Toronto.

These were the units which contacted customers. Many departments of the company maintained branches in each district; and each district had its manager. Not the least of their responsibilities was the negotiation of modes of payment for products purchased by customers. In the company's annual report for the following year appears this significant statement: "The General Company could have done a much larger business if it had been willing to accept securities in payment for orders; but . . . a strict rule was adopted of declining all such and doing business exclusively on a cash or short credit basis."

This represented a departure from Coffin's policy of accepting securities of local electric light companies. Securities already in the possession of Edison Electric Light represented more than a million dollars, and gave the parent company a financial interest in more than seventy operating companies. Feeling that its own fortunes were linked too intimately with those of the local companies, the parent company arranged for a specialist to take charge of the financial operations of licensees, appointing Henry W. Darling, president of the Canadian Bank of Commerce.

There was much to be done, for the operating utilities like the manufacturing companies were expanding lustily. The local company in New York erected in 1890 a generating station with a maximum capacity of 200,000 lights, the largest in the country. The report points with pride to the aggregate capacity of all the Edison generating stations in the nation— 1,300,000 incandescent lamps.

All of these operated with direct current, and alternating current was left severely alone. The line of cleavage on this subject between the Edison, and the Thomson-Houston and Westinghouse policies was never more rigidly drawn. From 1889 to 1891 Edison was in frequent controversy with his technical antagonists. Even when his company purchased the American rights to a transformer system invented in Europe, his inflexible position caused the idea of putting the system into practice to be abandoned.

Yet alternating current was the touchstone of the future. Signs proving this were increasing. It was in this same year of 1890 that William Stanley, who had remodelled the Gaulard and Gibbs system for the Westinghouse company, remarked to his young assistant, Cummings C. Chesney, "Let's go off by ourselves and establish a plant for the manufacture of transformers."

Stanley had completed his work for Westinghouse, and he and Chesney went to Pittsfield, Massachusetts, where they succeeded in interesting several capitalists, and on November 1 the Stanley Laboratory Company and the Stanley Electric Manufacturing Company were organized. A small plant was acquired where a force of sixteen men went to work. Within three months the first transformers were designed, built, and shipped.

A year later John F. Kelly joined forces with Stanley and Chesney. From that moment the three constituted a team, whose fame penetrated in ten years to every corner of the electrical realm. Together they originated a complete line of alternating-current equipment, announced and advertised as the "SKC" system—Stanley, Kelly, Chesney. They were an aggressive triumvirate, and their work greatly accelerated the development of the alternating current.

There is no evidence that the Edison company publicly opposed the Stanley company during the "war of the currents." When the Stanley company appeared, the greatest individual issue in the Edison camp was the future of the incandescent lamp, and particularly the validity of its patent.

In 1888 Edison had improved the efficiency of the lamp by coating the carbon filament with asphalt. As a result the lamp consumed only 3.1 watts per candlepower, compared with 7 watts per candlepower in 1880. This efficiency held for fifteen years, even after the "squirted filament" appeared. Efficiencies of 3.5 and 4 watts per candlepower were also supplied in 1890, according to the voltage variation in the circuits of different lighting companies.

Already there had been mutterings of controversy. Feeling which centered around the question of patents bordered on bitterness. Johnson had issued his pamphlet "A Warning from the Edison Electric Light Company." A counter-blast came from competitors, who published anonymously a parody of Johnson's style bearing the title: "E - - - - N Triumphant! An inspirational rhapsody in seven cantos. Translated from the Johnsonese by W. W., poet lariat."

As the 'eighties came to an end, conflict over the Edison lamp patent—No. 223,898—burst in the fury of a legal storm. The future of electricity hung upon the issue; aspirations, labors, fortunes, were at stake.

23

A Famous Fight

IT WAS THE AUTUMN OF 1889 when a group of lawyers met before a court examiner in New York and began taking testimony in the momentous patent suit instituted to determine who was legally entitled to call the incandescent lamp his own invention.

The opponents were the Edison Electric Light Company, complainant, and the United States Electric Lighting Company, for alleged infringement of Patent No. 223,898, granted to Edison in January 1880 and embracing his claims for an electric lamp consisting of a high-resistance carbon filament in a sealed glass container which formed a nearly perfect vacuum. The complainant held that the Maxim lamps, produced by the United States Electric Lighting Company, infringed upon his patent.

A spark of controversy that had lain dormant since 1882, almost hidden from the heedless public, ignored by the electrical interests, had suddenly flamed out.

When the Edison company raised the cry of infringement, other inventors affirmed that his invention had been anticipated, that his patent was worthless. Many testified on the witness stand that others, Hiram S. Maxim in particular, had previously done what Edison laid claim to have done.

Although no evidence was presented in court until October 15, 1889, the Edison company did not delay so long in bringing action against infringements as would appear. The suit was formally begun in 1886, about the time the Edison company realized that other companies could market competing lamps successfully and profitably. Not until then did it cease temporizing and procrastinating. In June 1886 the Edison Electric Light Company filed its amended bill of complaint, to which the United States Electric Lighting Company answered by submitting its amended plea. Preliminary skirmishes occupied the three-year interval.

The trial, when it was finally instituted, occupied many months; the record swelled into many printed volumes of testimony; technical questions were explained, analyzed, interpreted, and legally vivisected; the patent, the grand bone of contention, was systematically picked to pieces, its wording attacked, its validity flouted. It bore the full brunt of battle, and both sides introduced an endless succession of exhibits, physical and documentary.

Richard N. Dyer was the generalissimo who handled the legal artillery for the complainant. His right-hand man was Clarence A. Seward, a keen lawyer. And as advisor to both was Grosvenor P. Lowrey, Edison's veteran legal friend.

On the opposing side was Samuel A. Duncan, shrewd, quick, and thorough, usually addressed as General, chief of counsel for the United States Electric Lighting Company; with his able assistant, Edmund Wetmore.

The defendant's position hinged upon two main points. First, it held that the Edison patent was invalid because the description of the invention would not enable a person "skilled in the art" to make incandescent lamps by following its directions. Second, it asserted that even if lamps could be so made, Edison's work had been anticipated by other inventors who had produced the same sort of electric lamp before the date of the patent.

The defendant introduced the names of five inventors in the effort to prove that Edison was not the first man to bring out a successful incandescent lamp: William E. Sawyer, Albon Man, Hiram S. Maxim, Edward Weston, and Moses G. Farmer. And there was an array of witnesses to testify as experts that an incandescent lamp could not be made by following the directions given in the patent.

The specifications of the patent disclosed how to prepare filaments of a very small diameter out of lamp black and coal tar. To prove that these directions were clear to anyone skilled in the art, the prosecution called upon John W. Howell, electrician of the Edison Lamp Company, to construct lamps by the method described.

Howell made twenty-seven such lamps, and then went on the witness stand and told how he made them. He kneaded the lamp black and coal tar into the consistency of putty and rolled it out upon a plate of ground glass to the hairlike or filament diameter of from six- to seventeen-thousandths of an inch. Short pieces were cut off, wound upon a wooden mandrel into a spiral form, carbonized, and sealed into vacuous bulbs—all precisely as described in the patent.

When they were tested the lamps burned for six hundred hours. The record of the tests, the twenty-seven lamps, and the set of tools which Howell employed were introduced as exhibits. Howell even offered to construct the lamps in the presence of the Court, but this was not deemed necessary.

But the chief battle arose when the complainant called Charles L. Clarke, acting chief engineer of the Edison Electric Light Company up to 1884. He was relied upon to refute

EDISON PAYS A VISIT TO STEINMETZ AT SCHENECTADY

the assertion that Edison's invention was anticipated by others. Clarke took the witness stand on July 21, 1890, and held it almost continually for three months. General Duncan led the charge in an extremely clever cross-examination. He asked the witness nearly six hundred questions, seeking again and again to expose a flaw, a contradiction, an incompetency in his testimony.

The light-giving element of the lamp—what Edison termed the filament—was the storm center of the controversy. Several inventors contemporary with Edison had employed carbon sticks or "rods," which differed only in diameter from Edison's "thread," or filament. The defense contended that both types were in effect the same thing, and that the carbon rods therefore constituted a legal anticipation of Edison's filament.

Day after day and week after week the clash of wits continued. But Clarke's testimony could not be broken down, and he showed such familiarity with a multitude of published articles and books that General Duncan found him a full match for his skillful fencing.

At length Duncan asked the witness if the arc lamps were not, after all, much more efficient than the incandescent lamps, and if they were not so regarded by the "prior art"— the inventions brought out prior to the date of the patent in suit. It was evidently intended as a key question, upon which a sequence of other questions was to depend. But Clarke was not wholly unprepared. The moment the questions was put, Dyer, sitting across the table, turned to Duncan and remarked: "Here is where you are going to get it in the neck!"

Then Clarke gave his reply. He held that the arc lamp was only slightly more efficient than the incandescent and that the prior art so regarded it, citing many authorities on the point. He pointed out the evident conviction among investigators prior to Edison that this margin of efficiency was not so great as to deter them from striving to solve the riddle of a practical incandescent lamp.

The answer checkmated General Duncan. It upset his line of attack and left him taken aback. For several moments he sat silent, stroking his beard.

Dyer at length remarked, "Well, General, why so silent?" To which Duncan replied, "I was just thinking how much I'd like to kick a certain young man."

Finally the time came when the evidence was completed and the case rested in the hands of the Court. The Court's opinion, written by Judge Wallace, was handed down on July 14, 1891. It was a complete victory for Edison.

The defendant appealed, and on October 4, 1892, the United States Circuit Court of Appeals handed down an opinion affirming the decision of the lower court. The patent was sustained.

Judge Wallace looked upon the attenuated carbon burner of high resistance and small radiating surface as Edison's signal achievement. It was this, in the opinion of the court, that turned the incandescent lamp from a failure into a success.

"It was a remarkable discovery," said Judge Wallace, in the opinion handed down, "that an attenuated thread of carbon would possess all the long-sought qualities of a practical burner. . . . The extreme fragility of such a structure was calculated to discourage experimentation with it. . . . The futility of hoping to maintain a burner in vacuo with any permanency had discouraged prior inventors, and Mr. Edison is entitled to the credit of obviating the mechanical difficulties which disheartened them. . . .

"By doing these things, he made a lamp which was practically operative and successful, the embryo of the best lamps now in use."

The higher court, affirming this decision, gave its opinion in part as follows:

"Edison's invention was practically made when he ascertained the theretofore unknown fact that carbon would stand high temperature, even when very attenuated, if operated in a high vacuum, without the phenomenon of disintegration. . . . It was an invention, in view of the teaching of the art as to the disintegration of carbon under the action of an electric current, to still select that substance as a suitable material from which to construct a burner much more attenuated than had ever been used before."

The Court was explicit in maintaining that a carbon rod is not the same as a carbon thread—one of the classic issues in the suit. Said Judge Lacombe of the Higher Court:

"The evidence fails to satisfy us that the prior art furnished any burners less than twice this size. In contradiction to these earlier burners, Edison calls his burner a *filament*."

These judicial statements make it apparent that the reduction of the carbon burner from the diameter of a pencil, or small rod, to that of a thread constituted the germ of a great invention. Judge Lacombe, in deciding that the Maxim lamps infringed Edison's filament, declared that the carbon burners in the Maxim lamps were of threadlike diameter and that they "indisputably lie wholly on one side of the dividing line between rods and filaments."

This opinion is identical with that of the English court which passed on the suit of the Edison and Swan United Electric Light Company brought against Woodhouse and Rawson, in which the Edison English patent was sustained both by the lower and the higher court.

Four courts had agreed that the prior inventors stopped short of success when they failed to cross the significant "dividing line between rods and filaments." When but a few steps from the goal they halted. Edison alone continued to the goal.

Legal triumph meant immediate commercial triumph. Companies desiring to manufacture incandescent lamps were obliged to pay a license fee to the Edison Electric Light Company. But the patent, which had been so dearly upheld, had almost run the course of its life; it would expire in 1894. Hence, counsel for the Edison Company moved as rapidly as possible in bringing injunctions against infringers. And the latter, feeling the pinch of sudden stringency, became extremely resentful. The Edison Company was roundly condemned for waiting so long before bringing suit, allowing the infringing companies to invest large sums of money in their respective enterprises.

But their complaint was well disposed of by the Circuit Court of Appeals in these words:

"Every one of the manufacturing corporations, the competitors of the Edison companies, commenced their operations with a knowledge of the existence of the patent in suit. They were controlled by business men of intelligence and experience. Their promoters and managers may have believed, and probably did, that the patent could not be successfully maintained. But they entered upon the business with an understanding of its risks and of the consequences which would befall them as infringers if the patent should be sustained."

Many of the small lamp manufacturers that had come into existence through the middle and late 'eighties were among those enjoined—the Sunbeam, the Columbia, the Buckeye, as well as the Sawyer-Man Electric Company and its successor, the Consolidated Electric Lighting Company.

It might be supposed that the future now looked bright for the Edison General Electric Company, as smoke of the long battle in the Federal Courts.cleared away.

But the fight left traces of unmistakable bitterness and feeling of apprehension, a sense of insecurity. Electrical men were forced to take the patent question very much to heart. Were they safe in running the risk of infringing other patents held by rival companies? Were they safe even in supposing their own patents valid, in cases where those patents had not yet been tested in court?

The Edison General Electric Company itself shared in this reaction. The suit had been a costly procedure. If other patents should be found to require adjudication, the financial drain might become serious, not to mention the effect upon the public whose own economic well-being was likewise at stake. The prospect, even in the face of so decided a victory, was not bright.

Yet the competing men and their companies were not naturally belligerent. All the Edison Company sought, all that any of them sought, was the chance to pursue their business activities undisturbed; to make and sell articles that they knew the public wanted without fear of legal complications either for themselves or their customers. Such was the simple assurance they desired; and that assurance was the last thing which the future appeared to offer.

But there was a way out in consolidation. The idea was germinating in the minds of officials of the Edison General Electric Company even before Judge Wallace rendered his opinion in 1891.

WILLIAM M. ("BILLY") MADIGAN
The foreman who completed the building of the 1903 turbine on time.

TESTING AN EDISON BI-POLAR DYNAMO

Left to right, Peter Mulvey, Charles L. Clarke, and Ben Helm.

[PART FIVE]

The Formation

of the

General Electric Company

24

General Electric Emerges

TOWARD THE END OF FEBRUARY, 1891, A. L. Rohrer, assistant to E. W. Rice, Jr., at the Thomson-Houston factory, received a telephone call from Charles A. Coffin at his office in Boston.

"Watch for the arrival at the factory of Mr. Lovejoy, accompanied by Mr. Henry Villard, President of the Edison General Electric Company," said Coffin. "Mr. Villard is to be shown through our plant and is to be introduced to Professor Thomson and Mr. Rice. Please see that his identity does not become generally known."

Rohrer hung up the receiver with a tingle of excitement. A visit, with Coffin's sanction, from the head of this great competitor seemed to indicate but one thing.

Mr. Villard was taken around the factory and shown the utmost courtesy. At the conclusion of his tour he departed with an exchange of friendly felicitations. Rice and Rohrer commented on the significance of all this in a guarded manner, which was, nonetheless, privately jubilant. It seemed as if some of their weightiest problems were to be dissipated.

Coffin was no longer the only one to realize the seriousness of patent deadlocks. It was evident to everyone that the burden of heavy license fees disheartened investors who considered buying shares in electrical companies. Natural expansion was threatened by the difficulty of enlisting new capital. There were irritating delays in meeting public demand for electric service, requests for reliable and efficient electrical systems that could not be met—the indefinite postponement of America's complete electrical development.

The Edison patent controlling the incandescent lamp had two years to run, and a two-year handicap was something the Thomson-Houston Company might have difficulty in recovering from. And there were other Edison patents—the feeder patent, the three-wire patent without which direct-current service would be unsatisfactory. Thomson-Houston, on the other hand, held valuable transformer patents, which unlocked the whole field of the alternating current.

The conviction was taking shape that the incandescent lamp and the alternating-current transformer system belonged together, just as did the overhead trolley and the magnetic blowout. The two were complements of each other. Yet they had been kept apart because the patents were held by rival concerns. It was found that no plant could be constructed and no system installed by either company with any hope of rendering efficient service to the public without infringing the rights of the other company. In many of the larger cities two rival electric lighting systems existed. One local company exploited the Edison low-tension direct-current method of incandescent illumination; the other operated the Thomson-Houston high-tension alternating-current arc-lighting circuits and series incandescent circuits.

With affairs in this state, minds in the opposing camps were in a receptive mood regarding consolidation. Overtures came from the Edison Company before the patent suit was settled. They were made through a third party, Hamilton

GEORGE E. EMMONS
Manager of the Schenectady Works for many years.

A BUSINESS OFFICE IN 1902
The Correspondence Department at the Schenectady Works.

McKay Twombley, who was chosen because of his familiarity with the Thomson-Houston Company.

After the visit of Henry Villard and J. R. Lovejoy to the plant nothing was heard about consolidation by the operating officials at Lynn. Months came and went; spring passed, summer, autumn, and winter succeeded each other. The Thomson-Houston people concluded that the project had collapsed.

But conversations were going on at Twombley's residence in Boston, attended by Twombley, Coffin, and Frederick P. Fish, counsel for the Thomson-Houston Company. Difficulties had arisen over the question of terms. Coffin did not consider that the initial proposition submitted by Twombley gave adequate recognition to the record of his company, and he asked for a modification.

It was nearly a year before he satisfied himself that even the revised proposition was suitable for recommendation to his directors. At length, in February 1892, he notified Twombley that he was ready to accept the new terms.

So one March morning Rice entered the factory offices and sought out Rohrer and Knight. They were to go at once to Boston to meet Mr. Coffin at his office. There they found Henry Villard and John Kruesi of the Edison General Electric Company. It was then announced that a consolidation had been agreed to, and that an exchange of visits between officials was to take place preliminary to the signing of the papers and the public announcement of the new company.

Formalities were completed on April 15, 1892. On that day was incorporated the enterprise that combined the wisdom, traditions, and vitality of two vigorous rivals under the title of General Electric Company.

Coffin had insisted upon an equality of treatment between the merging companies and the recognition of certain ideals in undertaking the new organization. He proposed that the new company should consider first the public which it served, and only secondly its own success. He proposed that the enterprise be organized to perform better the task of developing the cornerstone of modern industrial and economic life. Having that for its purpose, the bread-and-butter interest of the new company would never suffer. No other policy, he affirmed, could be regarded as "good business."

Conferences, initiated in the late winter of 1891–92, were concluded nearly a year later. When terms of consolidation were finally drawn, they were laid before the respective boards of directors for ratification. The Thomson-Houston directors met in Boston and the Edison directors in New York. Few doubted that the two boards would act favorably, yet their action was momentous.

So passed into one corporation two great undertakings. In resources and in achievements, the merging companies were almost equal. The Edison company was capitalized for $15,-000,000; Thomson-Houston for $10,400,000. The Edison Company reported a gross business of $10,940,000 for the preceding year; Thomson-Houston showed a gross of $10,-304,500. There were 6000 employees on the Edison rolls, 4000 on the Thomson-Houston. The Edison Company had two manufacturing plants—fourteen acres, forty buildings, and 400,000 square feet of floor space. The Thomson-Houston Company had one plant covering eight acres, with eleven buildings and 340,000 square feet of floor space. Both had between 3000 and 4000 customers each. The Edison Company had approximately 375 central-station companies, and more than 2300 isolated lighting installations. Against this showing Thomson-Houston reported 870 central-station companies, but very few isolated plants. The Edison Company had equipped 180 street railways and 2230 cars; the Thomson-Houston 204 roads and 2760 cars.

To most of the employees of both companies, the consolidation came as a surprise, despite rumors that had been abroad during the preceding year. It was announced to the employees by circular letters posted on June 1, 1892, the date on which the General Electric Company began to operate in its own name.

Before this Thomson-Houston men began to appear at the Edison works in Schenectady, and a general plan of reorganization was introduced. Thomson-Houston ideas and policies were adapted to existing conditions wherever they seemed likely to produce improvement. Otherwise the policies of the Edison Company continued, with considerable readjustment of personnel.

Among the notable group which had created General Electric, Charles A. Coffin stood out by force of personality. Yet his new associates were themselves persons of large affairs and of high administrative caliber.

Distinguished names appeared on the new Board of Directors. Industrialist rubbed elbows with banker, and both shared places with technical and business experts. The eleven directors were: F. L. Ames, Boston financier and business pioneer; Charles A. Coffin; T. Jefferson Coolidge, Boston banker; C. H. Coster, of Drexel, Morgan and Company; Thomas A. Edison; Eugene Griffin, Thomson-Houston official; Frank S. Hastings, Edison official; Henry L. Higginson, of Lee, Higginson and Company; D. O. Mills, New York banker; J. P. Morgan; and Hamilton McKay Twombley.

The representation of two such notable banking firms as Lee, Higginson and Company of Boston, and Drexel, Morgan and Company of New York, later to become J. P. Morgan and Company, gave uncommon financial stamina to the board, which was recognized at the time as probably the strongest brought together for an American industrial concern.

Yet among these exceptional men, there stood out that unassuming and affable New Englander who won everybody's friendship and who thought least of all of his own advancement. To one who met him for the first time, he might not have appeared to be cast for an industrial chief of high position. But his associates knew him for what he was. Without hesitation they selected him unanimously as President of General Electric.

It was a conspicuous position. And its prominence increased with the genuine leadership of the Quaker financier, who twenty years before had been a salesman of shoes.

As its Chairman the Board elected H. M. Twombley. It is striking to note that the Board itself included only one of the inventive geniuses whose achievements had disclosed the possibilities of electrical manufacture to which the company was now dedicated. Edison was the sole representative of this group.

His position on the Board, as the champion of direct current, may seem to have been a difficult one. Henceforth alternating current was to be both advocated and utilized. The new company would recommend for a particular installation whichever of the two types was preeminently fitted for the work to be done. But while Edison did not endorse this policy, it is certain that he concerned himself less and less at this period with manufacturing activities.

It was not Edison, but Professor Thomson, who became the sole member of early electrical inventors to maintain active affiliation with General Electric. Edison retired to continue his independent researches. Thomson continued at work in his laboratory in Lynn. He declined the proffered honor of membership on the board of directors, declaring his dominant interest was to pursue laboratory work unburdened by other demands.

The others of those technical pioneers in the General Electric Succession had gone their several ways. Charles F. Brush had retired, with the sale of his company, and was now concerned with independent laboratory operations. Frank J. Sprague had branched off into the development of electric elevators, and had organized with Edward H. Johnson the Sprague Elevator, and the Sprague Interior Conduit and Insulation companies.

Charles J. Van Depoele died in the very year of this consolidation at the early age of forty-six. Edward M. Bentley had returned to the practice of law. Walter H. Knight, however, came into the consolidated company as one of the Thomson-Houston engineering staff, continuing in electric streetcar development until the middle 'nineties.

When it was at length completed, the organization of General Electric showed a predominance of Thomson-Houston men in the corporate offices. Eugene Griffin (Thomson-Houston) was First Vice President. Second Vice President, Samuel Insull (Edison), soon succeeded by J. P. Ord (Edison); General Counsel, Frederick P. Fish (Thomson-Houston); Secretary, E. I. Garfield (Thomson-Houston); Treasurer, Benjamin F. Peach, Jr. (Thomson-Houston).

Men of tried ability, drawn from both companies, succeeded to the management of the technical and manufacturing interests. E. W. Rice, Jr., (Thomson-Houston) was made Technical Director; John Kruesi (Edison) continued as Manager of the Schenectady Works; and Francis R. Upton (Edison) was placed in charge of the Edison Lamp Works at Harrison.

In commercial organization, General Electric appropriated the best in the methods of both its predecessors. It established four departments, as follows:

Lighting Department, under S. Dana Greene (Edison); Railway Department, O. T. Crosby (Edison); Power Department, J. R. McKee (Thomson-Houston); Supply Department, J. R. Lovejoy (Thomson-Houston).

The scientific factory-costs system of the Thomson-Houston Company and its functional system of factory organization were ingrafted throughout the shops of the consolidated company—introduced gradually, accompanied by education of the men in the new methods and the training of shop foremen.

The nationwide district office plan of the Edison company was made the foundation of General Electric's activities in the selling field.

The personnel throughout was so strong that the prestige of the company was quickly established. Coffin took great pride in the human side of his organization. He wanted fitness and loyalty; but he wanted the loyalty to be spontaneous. He wanted General Electric to give its workers both opportunity and commendation.

The watchdog of economies in all branches of the company was the gruff but painstaking Joseph P. Ord, who served as Comptroller for two years before becoming a Vice President. His business genius was preventing waste of any sort.

Shortly after consolidation, a name was placed upon the rolls which was to assure the future of the new company as the exponent of the intricate alternating current. In January 1892, Thomson and Rice had listened at a meeting of the American Institute of Electrical Engineers to a mathematical exposition which they would not soon forget. The speaker

JOHN MILLER
Millwright of the Schenectady Works for years.

JOHN KRUESI

Foreman of the Edison machine shop at Menlo Park and later manager of the Edison Machine Works at Schenectady.

WILLIAM B. ("POP") TURNER

General Superintendent of the Edison Machine Works at Schenectady.

was an odd-looking young fellow, dwarfed in stature, intelligent in manner, who spoke with a foreign accent but in a manner that carried conviction.

The speaker was Steinmetz, the penniless immigrant of 1889, now, in 1892, revealing new mathematical laws to the acknowledged heads of American electrical engineering!

Steinmetz had distinguished himself in the Eickemeyer factory by making known the mathematics of the law of hysteresis—the law governing losses in the magnetic circuit of an electric motor. It was a brilliant discovery. It threw light into a dark corner of electrical engineering, and simplified one aspect of the art of designing efficient electric power-consuming apparatus.

As it happened, Eickemeyer's work at Yonkers was under scrutiny at that time in the Thomson-Houston offices. His "iron-clad" armature and methods of armature winding had attracted the attention of Thomson and Rice. They discussed the proposition with Coffin of acquiring Eickemeyer's patents. Together with F. P. Fish, Thomson-Houston Counsel, they went to Yonkers to inspect the plant. On their return they agreed that by all odds Eickemeyer's most pronounced asset was the young Steinmetz.

That summer negotiations were opened which resulted in the purchase by the General Electric Company of Eickemeyer's plant, business, and patents.

Rice has recorded his astonishment on his first meeting with Steinmetz, describing his "small, frail body, surmounted by a large head with long hair hanging to the shoulders, clothed in an old cardigan jacket, cigar in mouth, sitting cross-legged on a laboratory worktable." This apparition begins to speak, and immediately his strange appearance is forgotten. "I instantly felt the strange power of his piercing, but kindly, eyes," recalls Rice, "and as he continued, his enthusiasm, his earnestness, his clear conception and marvellous grasp of engineering problems convinced me that we had indeed made a great find. I was delighted when, without a moment's hesitation, he accepted my suggestion that he come with us."

Within a few months Steinmetz left Yonkers to become a General Electric engineer, located in the Calculating Department at the Lynn plant, at the head of which was H. F. Parshall.

Consolidation brought no lag in engineering or sales activities. Nearly all the engineers and sales agents of both companies continued under the consolidated company. Now they worked together instead of in opposition. Some aided in establishing consolidation in the field. None had a larger task of this sort than young Dr. Thomas Addison.

Addison had left the medical profession to devote himself to volts and amperes. He was a salesman in the Thomson-Houston Chicago office, then headed by B. E. Sunny, who sent him in March 1890 to the Pacific Coast, where electricity was one day to go through some of its most dramatic moments. Addison opened a Thomson-Houston office in San Francisco the following May, and in 1892 was authorized to effect a consolidation in Pacific Coast territory. He took over a five-story building and gradually brought under his jurisdiction the commercial and construction activities which agents of the Edison company had been pursuing throughout the Pacific Coast region.

Among these agents was Sidney Z. Mitchell, who had taken to the great northwest a tremendous capacity for fighting against odds. Mitchell went into Seattle, a bold prophet of the electrical day. He wanted $10,000 for a hydroelectric plant, to be operated by a proposed local lighting company.

But the people to whom he talked did not perceive the dawn as clearly as did Mitchell.

Defying fate, he finally secured $10,000, with a towering forfeit imposed by local politicians should his electric plant be not running by a specified time. But Mitchell mastered the situation, completed the plant on time, and saw it become the first hydroelectric generating station on the Pacific Coast. Then he went up and down that country, throughout the great inland empire, promoting, organizing, building, and operating. He was an economic apostle to one town after another, bringing the Edison lamp to brighten the dark shores that bordered the Pacific.

Meanwhile in the East, Hewlett of the New York office of Thomson-Houston was preparing to install new lights on the Statue of Liberty to celebrate, in October, 1892, the quadricentennial of Columbus' voyage. Thomson-Houston incandescent lights were used extensively around New York at that time. Hewlett had put them on several lightships, a line of ferry boats, in Tiffany's store, and had installed them for Paine's fireworks at Coney Island.

A complaint came in one day from one of the ferryboats that the installation was giving trouble. Hewlett went on board and became immediately suspicious when his examination failed to reveal anything wrong. He made a conspicuous mark on the brush holder of the dynamo, so that he could tell instantly if the brushes had been shifted. He showed the engineer what he had done, then got the purser to put up a cot in an empty coal bunker and stretched out for a nap.

At two in the morning, after the boat had stopped running for the night, he went into the machinery room and looked at the dynamo. It was just as he had left it, and, there was

never any more trouble with the lights. His suspicions were
well founded—the engineer, from professional jealousy, had
tampered with the brushes on the dynamo. It was a case of
regulating not the machine but the man.

People living in western Massachusetts noticed during
that summer of 1892 a long shaft of light sweeping the night
sky from somewhere in the White Mountains. The news
quickly got about among the rural communities: an electric
searchlight surmounted the summit of Mt. Washington. It
was the largest unit of the sort then known. The lens was
thirty-six inches in diameter. The volume of illumination was
equivalent to 20,000 candles, and this was magnified to 100,-
000 candles by the use of a Mangin lens. The light had been
manufactured by the Thomson-Houston plant at Middletown, Connecticut.

To get the searchlight in place was a task to daunt the
most determined engineer. A tower fifty-five feet high was to
be built, and it was recorded that gales of over a hundred
miles an hour swept that rugged peak. The Superintendent
of the Mount Washington Inclined Railway wagered the
construction man a silk hat for each one of his thirteen workmen that the tower would not last a year. He lost the bet, but
never paid it.

Watchful, wondering eyes—curious eyes in most cases,
unfriendly eyes in some—observed the formation of General
Electric. It was a "combine," exclaimed the critic, a "trust."
It brought into existence a corporation which was gigantic
for a period when people were alarmed about trusts.

Coffin heard extremists attack General Electric as a monopoly with menacing possibilities, questioning every item
in the annual financial statements over a period of several
years.

Perils conjured up by suspicious folk never eventuated,

nor did the criticisms directed at Coffin and the other officials have any logical justification. The attacks displayed a signal misconception of the possibilities inherent in the electrical business, producing a disquieting effect upon General Electric's finances in the great panic of 1893.

A weekly magazine called *Electricity* made savage accusations against the company's bookkeeping methods and impugned the personal integrity of Coffin himself. Its most frequently repeated charge was that of overcapitalization. In its issue of September 7, 1892, it declared:

"Last week we expressed our belief that the Trust was foredoomed to failure . . . To talk of earning interest on this immense capitalization by honest business methods is nonsense."

Only a total inability to gauge the immediate future could have led to such an assertion.

Far different were the comments of technical men, who have always considered that the merging of Thomson-Houston and Edison General Electric was a move of great benefit to American industry. The Schenectady Electrical Handbook, published by the American Institute of Electrical Engineers in 1904, says:

"Never in the industrial world did organization effect a more magical change in releasing pent-up energy. Guided by master hands, electrical arts leaped into industrial preeminence; the volume of manufacture of appliances, progress of invention, public confidence in electricity, and its general utilization, all took long strides forward."

Whatever the fortunes of other electrical manufacturing organizations, whatever their virtues and achievements, General Electric set for itself certain ideals which, for forty years, have kept it from becoming a "soulless corporation." It had an idealist at its head during its first crucial years. It was to a large extent his vision which gave General Electric the momentum that produced its progress.

From the day of amalgamation, economies were effected. The company found itself with two factories in which incandescent lamps were produced, but it was apparent that one factory would permit of a considerable gain in manufacturing efficiency. Which of the two should be discontinued?

The Thomson-Houston bamboo filaments were treated by the Sawyer process, and the patent covering this process had expired about the time of the consolidation. Whereupon John W. Howell, electrician at the Edison Lamp Works, visited the plant at Lynn to study the treating process. Back in Harrison he shut himself up on the top floor of the factory, started experimenting, and before long discovered a way to simplify the method.

Under the original Sawyer process, a stream of gasoline vapor was drawn through a highly heated bulb containing the filament. Heat decomposed the vapor and coated the surface of the filament with graphite. When Howell perceived that the flow of vapor was too great, causing an unequal cooling of the filament, he diminished the flow a little at a time, and with every reduction found that he obtained a better filament.

While he was experimenting, Rice came out to the factory and announced the decision to maintain a single lamp works. "The factory which will continue lampmaking will be the one at which the best grade of lamps is produced," he said to Howell. "To determine which one that is, we are going to make a test. Your factory will make one hundred lamps, send fifty to Lynn for test and retain the other fifty. Lynn will do the same."

Howell's discovery was in the nick of time. A month later

Rice again visited Harrison and said to Howell, "The Lynn men admit that your lamps are better than theirs, so we will shut down the Lynn factory and the men will come down and work for you."

Howell, meanwhile, kept on with his filament-treating experiments, until he eliminated the flow mechanism, making the apparatus practically automatic. This was the most satisfactory of the filament-treated lamps.

The first annual report of the General Electric Company remarks of the progress of the lamp, that: "The prices at which apparatus and lamps are now furnished by the General Electric Company for the use of such stations (licensees) are, in many instances, lower than those which prevailed prior to the sustaining of the lamp patent, while the quality and efficiency of the apparatus are largely increased. Thus the licensees are enabled to cheapen their production, and their prosperity is greatly enhanced."

There are also to be found in this first report other signs of development: first, generators of larger capacities; second, an innovation in the manner of operating the generators.

"On February 1, 1892," says the report, "the largest power-generator manufactured was of 275 horsepower. Machines of 2000 horsepower are now (February 1, 1893) being manufactured by your company. . . . The largest lighting generators in use on February 1, 1892, were capable of supplying only 2000 incandescent lights each. There are now being constructed generators of the direct-coupled type with a capacity of 12,000 incandescent lights from each engine."

The first use of the direct-coupled, or direct-connected, method was in Edison's Jumbo dynamos. But not until the present period were the direct-connected units started on their commercial career. Their birth meant the gradual pass-

ing of the previous type, the belt-driven generator, except
in isolated individual plants. The change resulted both in
improved efficiency of operation and economy of space. The
forest of flapping leather straps which met the eye in the
larger central stations had always produced friction losses.
These were now avoided by connecting the steam engine
and the electric dynamo on the same shaft.

All this had its effect upon the incandescent-lighting situation. More than 2,000,000 lamps were sold in 1892, and the
annual sale increased steadily. No one but General Electric
could legally market the Edison Lamp from 1892 to 1894.

J<small>UST BEFORE THE CONSOLIDATION</small> an engineer in the Thomson-
Houston Railway Department, W. B. Potter, had a conversation with W. H. Knight, the engineering head of the department, on the subject of the magnetic blowout. There had
been considerable groping about for a better method of controlling the speed of streetcar motors during the starting of
the car, when it was necessary to accelerate the speed
gradually in order to prevent the sudden jerks which would
otherwise occur.

Technical differences had developed in the procedures of
the Thomson-Houston and Edison companies. The streetcar
motors of the former, which were connected in parallel, were
controlled by a rheostat. This device inserted resistance into
the circuit, and as the speed of the car increased, the resistance was switched out a step at a time. Edison streetcar
motors were controlled by changes made during acceleration
in the wiring combinations of the motor's internal field
circuit—commutating the field, as it was termed.

The Thomson-Houston men felt that a master stroke
would be achieved if some way could be found of operating
the motors in series during acceleration and then changing

to parallel connection while the motors were running and after full speed had been attained. The difficulty was the excessive arc in the switch at the point where the circuit was broken, an arc too large for the magnetic blowout, as then utilized, to handle.

Finally Potter proposed that the magnetic blowout should be altered so that instead of a small, intense magnetic field, one of large area should be sought which would draw the arc out to an increased length, making it more susceptible to interruption. Days of study followed, during which Potter drew a rough sketch of motors connected by the series-parallel method to accompany the new form of magnetic blowout. The moment Knight saw the sketch he exclaimed, "That will work—let's try it."

They proceeded to experiment. The control apparatus proved the most baffling factor of all, for mechanical rather than electrical reasons. Finally, Potter worked out a controller, designated as the "J" type, which was an arrangement of plunger contacts, operated in a vertical plane through bevel gearing from either end of the car. It was encased in a long flat box and placed beneath the car body, with a control handle on each of the outside platforms. When the handle was moved, one set of plunger discs was raised until contact was made with a similar set above. The alignment had to be perfect, however, and careless handling crippled the apparatus.

But it worked well enough on early installations to demonstrate the superiority of series-parallel control for streetcar motors. The Hartford Street Railway conducted a comparative trial of this method with the commutated-field method and the resistance method of the Edison and Westinghouse companies respectively. The test, concluded in April, 1892, on the day of the consolidation, showed a saving in electrical energy of twenty per cent by the series-parallel method. Representatives of the competing companies were considerably chagrined. Potter remarked that evening to the Edison Company's man:

"This test gives me a unique satisfaction. Today we have beaten you as competitors; tomorrow we welcome you as associates."

But there was trouble ahead for the "J" controller. Complaints began to come in about the burning out of plunger contacts. The Ninth Avenue Elevated Railway in Brooklyn had ordered a large equipment of the controllers, but only a few had been installed, and they kept a repair force constantly busy.

Eugene Griffin, head of the Thomson-Houston Railway Department, receiving an appeal from the road, asked Potter if he could get the cars running again by July Fourth. Potter said he could. But a brief inspection of the cars in Brooklyn was sufficient to satisfy him that the "J" controller was a failure. He instructed the shop superintendent to take off the "J" controllers and replace them with some of the old resistance rheostats still in stock. So the cars were ready to operate long before the Fourth.

Potter went immediately to the foreman of the model room and said to him, "I see a crash coming on the "J" controller and I want to forestall it. I don't know how many men I shall need, but I'd like to have you put men on the work as fast as I can send you sketches."

Rapidly he evolved a new form of controller. With his draftsmen and the model-room force working like beavers, a model was completed within ten days, the final trick lasting nearly all night. At three in the morning Potter and two shop men carried the model down to the test room for its first trial. It worked to perfection.

Knight was skeptical when he heard the news, and told Potter he wanted to see the new controller after it had been turned on and off a thousand times with the motors running at full load. Potter forthwith assigned a man to carry out the test. He spent the best part of a day turning the controller on and off, on and off. He counted up to a thousand times, and still no injury was done.

This sturdy mechanism was cataloged as the "K" controller. It was of upright cylindrical design, permitting a simultaneous movement of the handle and the contacts. The latter met in the horizontal plane instead of the vertical. What made it particularly simple was the plan to mount it on the motorman's platform, thus eliminating over-delicate mechanisms which had been the undoing of its predecessor. The "K" controller inaugurated a new era of efficiency in electric transportation.

MEANWHILE DOWN IN DIXIE LAND, a region heretofore noted more for agriculture than for industrial ventures, events unfolded which were to bring stationary motors into a white glare of prominence.

Until 1891 installed motors had been direct-current units, not above twenty horsepower in capacity. Thomson's experiments with his first repulsion motor still remained a pioneer study of motors using alternating current. But in 1891 engineers of Thomson-Houston began work on an experimental three-phase induction motor under the direction of H. G. Reist. Most of the later work on this motor was done by W. J. Foster and Dr. Louis Bell, the latter resigning the editorship of the *Electrical World* in 1892 to join the staff of General Electric. Together they worked out the new motor and its generator, conducting a long series of tests.

Two of the units were immediately sold. At the same time

a direct-current generator at Baltic, Connecticut, and a similar machine, used as a motor in the Ponemah Textile Mills four miles away in Taftsville, were proving unsatisfactory. The cost of the heavy copper conductors required for the transmission line was excessive, and the motors did not operate well for constant-speed textile machinery. The new alternating-current generators and motors proved a godsend, and two of each were substituted, late in 1893, at Baltic and Taftsville. A third installation by the Thomson-Houston plant of General Electric occurred in the same year at Redlands, California, later to be described.

But it was in the far south, at Columbia, South Carolina, that there occurred the first historic installation in a textile mill.

From the beginning the Columbia mills scouted the idea of electricity. C. K. Oliver, agent for the mills, and Stephen Greene, his engineer, faced a dilemma. They wanted to employ waterwheels driven by the rapids of the Congaree River, 800 feet from the mills; but a canal for conveying river boats around the rapids interfered with the plan, since it ran between the river and the mills. No feasible plan of mechanical drive could be worked out. Under pressure of dire necessity Greene turned at last to electricity.

He was besieged by salesmen from three electrical concerns. One was Sidney B. Paine, who had put Edison Electric lights in more textile mills than any of his rivals. Now he devoted weeks to urging General Electric motors upon Greene. The cost of an electrical installation seemed prohibitive, and Greene held out until the last shred of hope in some form of mechanical drive had vanished. The three electrical salesmen all submitted propositions, and Paine's bid was the highest—$75,800. Greene dismissed Paine's proposal from the outset, for it covered alternating current, while his competitors advocated direct current at a much lower cost.

"But direct current is not suitable for driving your machinery," Paine told him. Then he compared the two types of electric drive, explaining that machines and lights for the mills would both be supplied from the same compound-wound direct-current generators. When the lights were turned on the voltage of the generators, and hence of the feeders supplying the motors, would be raised automatically, increasing the speed of the motors. Yet to run efficiently, the textile machines required a constant, never-changing speed.

While the issue hung fire, the World's Fair opened at Chicago. One of Paine's competitors invited Greene to attend the exposition as his guest. Paine promptly said, "Very good; now will you return as *my* guest?"

On the return trip Greene told Paine he had made up his mind in favor of direct current. But somewhere between Chicago and Columbia, Paine's arguments took effect. Greene was completely won over.

Now came a struggle to fulfill the contract, which specified fourteen alternating-current motors of sixty-five horse-power each. Thus far the largest alternating-current motors built by General Electric were for slightly more than ten horsepower. It was a tremendous jump.

The contract, following the new routine, went before the sales committee and was approved. Then it went before the executive committee and was there disapproved. It was too radical—too venturesome and hazardous. The committee, however, went to the head technical official, E. W. Rice, Jr., for advice. Rice promptly told them that the thing was perfectly feasible, and the day was saved.

The work of designing the units fell upon Parshall, Bell,

Steinmetz, and the Calculating Department. Parshall was willing to guarantee that the motors would work. The contract, however, required them to be installed on the ceiling of the mill, to operate in an inverted position, and Bell demurred at this. "This is the last application of an inverted motor we'll ever make," he objected. To which Paine replied, "Then it's the last motor we'll ever put into a cotton mill, because there is no room on the floors of these mills for any more machinery."

It was far from the last motor General Electric ever put into a cotton mill. For it was destined to open the eyes of mill owners all over the south and to precipitate an economic step that brought industrial wealth to whole communities.

The generating station began to operate in April 1894, with two 500-kilowatt three-phase generators, water-driven. The transmission line was only 800 feet long. But in the size of the alternating-current motors, their inverted position, the use of both ends of the motor shafts for driving belting, and above all the innovation of subdividing the mill into sections each with its own driving motor, the installation was destined to influence the future equipment of all textile mills.

25

The World's Fair

SUCCEEDING GENERATIONS astound their predecessors. Sons amaze fathers and are themselves dumbfounded by their sons. It was a brief generation that elapsed between the Centennial Exposition at Philadelphia in 1876 and the World's Fair at Chicago in 1893. And the startling contrast between the two was due largely to the magic of electricity.

Spectators at the Centennial marvelled at the interminable lines of shafting which distributed power; at the World's Fair they saw scarcely a single shaft—instead, they heard the purr of motors. At the Centennial they paid little attention to the light of flaming gas burners; at the Fair, the illumination was itself a dazzling spectacle.

General Electric, though only a year old, was able to present at the Fair an almost perfect epitome of the electrical art as it then existed. The great Electrical Building was entirely illuminated by the Edison lamp, and in its center arose a "majestic luminous column," thickly studded with thousands of incandescent lamps. Edison lights also illuminated the Manufacturers and Liberal Arts Building, the "largest room in the world," and General Electric searchlights played upon the illuminated fountains.

Even more famous was the Intramural Railway, a complete electric elevated railroad encircling the exposition grounds, and installed by General Electric. Here was shown the new series-parallel controller in operation; in the power plant was an immense direct-current generator of 1500 kilowatts capacity (2000 horsepower), gloriously hailed as "the largest generator in operation in the world;" and in this same power-house were the beginnings of modern switchboard development. Parshall and the calculating department had designed the big generator; Hewlett and Knight were prominent in devising the switchboard.

A "colossus of industry," a "tamed Titan of traction," this generator weighed ninety tons, while the flywheel of the engine weighed eighty-five tons and was twenty-four feet in diameter. The generator was of the multi-polar type with twelve magnetic poles, and the field frame was sixteen feet in diameter. It was a direct-connected unit, driven by a cross-compound engine, and had a horsepower capacity equal to 250 of the original Edison bi-polar machines or almost 30 of the Edison jumbos.

Parshall said later, recalling the moments of anxiety while the unit was under construction, "The machines were so large and so important, I had the thought in my mind that if I did not get the anticipated result, my job would not be worth having." Many times he rose in the dead of night, turned on the light and went over his notes to be sure he had made no mistake in calculating the electrical constants. These constants were so vividly fixed in his mind that thirty-five years later he could enumerate them!

Another transportation thrill was provided by the motor-driven sidewalk, 4300 feet in length, equipped by General Electric. Its driving power comprised twenty-four railway

TUG-OF-WAR—STEAM VERSUS ELECTRICITY

The electric locomotive demonstrates its power by outpulling two steam locomotives.

FORERUNNER OF THE MODERN ELECTRIC LOCOMOTIVE

A General Electric locomotive pulling a train through the Baltimore tunnel in 1896.

EARLY SWITCHGEAR

Oil switches in the Fiske Street station of the Commonwealth Edison Company.

motors, each of fifteen horsepower, placed at intervals beneath the platform trucks. The latter, 340 in number, were coupled together into one long train, continuously moving in one direction. The sidewalk carried 6000 seated passengers at one time, at the rate of six miles an hour.

On the water, General Electric had its motors in the fleet of fifty electric gondolas that plied the lakes and lagoons. The motors were of two sizes, supplied from Brush storage batteries. In Machinery Hall, General Electric exhibited its electric locomotive, its illumination of the battleship "Illinois," some of professor Thomson's early experimental apparatus, and a pictorial story of Edison's evolution of the incandescent lamp.

A service and repair shop were required to keep dynamos, motors, and lights at top efficiency. Few saw this General Electric shop hidden behind the scenes. Yet it harbored during that summer a future leader of General Electric.

He was a student at Massachusetts Institute of Technology just through his sophomore year. No place in the world looked so alluring to him that summer as did Chicago. He wanted to work there, and he had no fancy notions as to what that work should be. And so a new name was added to the payroll: "G. Swope, helper, per day, $1."

General Electric's principal competitors in that year were the Stanley Electric Manufacturing Company, the Siemens and Halske Electric Company of America, the Brush Electric Company, and the Fort Wayne Electric Company.

The latter two were under the control of General Electric and classified as subsidiaries; the operation of their plants was directed by Rice. Yet both companies were free to compete with General Electric in whatever line of products they were particularly strong. Brush and Fort Wayne salesmen continually pitted themselves against those of General Electric. Coffin and his associates saw an advantage in competition between different General Electric plants, since it disclosed the plant which had the lowest manufacturing costs for a particular product. Manufacture could then be concentrated at the low-cost plant—and low costs meant low prices, more customers, and ultimately greater prosperity for the company as a whole.

There was still much activity by the Brush Company in its own name. Arc lamps were gleaming by the hundred thousand in streets, in parks and outdoor areas, and in large halls. Arc-light generators were brought out in increased capacities, with four poles instead of two and running to a maximum of 7000 volts. To construct such a generator had been dismissed as totally impossible in 1877.

There were still local Brush lighting companies, many of which had added incandescent lighting to their lines. Even in far-away Manila a Brush agent, W. S. Culver, was installing a station equipped to supply 10,000 incandescent lamps and 300 arc lamps.

No less active was the Fort Wayne Company. McDonald had remarked to James J. Wood that he considered the Slattery alternating-current system out of date and proposed that Wood design a new one. Wood immediately set to work. He was able and unusually diligent as a mechanic and designer. His apparatus was noted for its simplicity of construction, his models had the appearance of finished machines, and he usually brought out a product not costly to manufacture, yet possessing great efficiency.

Wood's alternator proved all that McDonald could wish for. Its maximum internal temperature was considerably lower than that of the Slattery machine. It rose to this temperature quickly, however, while the temperature of the Slattery machine rose more slowly. The Wood machine weighed about two-thirds less and ran at a slower speed, although its output was the same.

The first central station engineer to encounter the Wood alternator remarked, "These little machines will never do the work the big ones did. And they get so hot you could fry eggs on 'em!"

Wood hastened to the station and succeeded in convincing the engineer that the heat losses in his machine were less than in Slattery's. The egg-frying test was not resorted to.

The Stanley Company at Pittsfield, Massachusetts, was devoting itself exclusively to alternating-current problems. They were first and foremost transmission engineers. Stanley was the trail-breaker, never defeated, never down-hearted, alive with ideas. Kelly, on the other hand, was phlegmatic, contemplative. He had unquestioned inventive talent and a prodigious memory, so that whenever Stanley or Chesney thought of something new they laid the idea before Kelly, who could usually tell if anything of the sort had ever been done before. Chesney was the detail man of the group, who kept the routine going—the production engineer who got inventions through the drafting room and shop and out upon the market.

When in 1892 a delegate to the National Electric Light Association asserted that transformers of greater capacity than five kilowatts would never be practicable, the "SKC" men smiled, for at that moment they were building transformers of twenty and thirty kilowatts capacity for commercial use.

In constructing these units, they established an efficient practice in the insulation of transformer coils, first by treated cotton cloth and later by an impregnating process, a compound being forced into the coils until wires and compound together formed a solid mass.

Stanley was satisfied in 1892 that he had built a transformer of high efficiency. His data were corroborated when the department of electrical engineering at Cornell University tested a Stanley transformer of seventeen kilowatts capacity and found it to be 96.9 per cent efficient.

Transmission lines at that time usually used single-phase current of 133 cycles. No satisfactory motor for such circuits seemed to be forthcoming, and the Stanley company began to agitate for polyphase circuits of lower frequencies. It boldly designed a polyphase alternator having a stationary armature and a revolving field, but for either 66 or 133 cycles, and for any voltage up to and including 12,000. This was first used for long-distance transmission in 1893 at Housatonic, Massachusetts. Current was carried to Great Barrington, seven miles away. The transmission line—impressive in length for those days—was mounted on poles and insulated with porcelain insulators and iron pins, both imported from England. This was one of the first instances of polyphase transmission, vying with those at Taftsville and Redlands.

Meanwhile the Siemens and Halske Company of America had been developing business in the Middle West and creeping outward from Chicago over a constantly widening radius. Much electrical apparatus had been imported from Germany and placed on the American market. Early in 1893, however, the company began manufacturing at Chicago its "inpole dynamo," in which the field and field poles were inside the armature. The capacities of these machines ranged from about 50 to 1500 kilowatts; they were direct-connected to the steam engines which drove them.

At first the personnel was almost entirely German. Later a

Charles G. Curtis

William Le Roy Emmet

THE MEN WHO MADE THE CURTIS STEAM TURBINE A REALITY

FORERUNNER OF THE GIANTS
The first Curtis steam turbine, built in 1901 for experimental purposes.

few Americans were taken on, and effort made to introduce American methods and policies.

These, with the Westinghouse Company, were General Electric's competitors. All of them met on a competitive basis at the World's Fair in Chicago in 1893.

26

Coffin Faces the Panic

UNDER THE SOMBER CLOUD of the financial panic of 1893 General Electric's future suddenly darkened. Throughout the greater part of the World's Fair, depression was deepening.

The actual money stringency lasted from early in April until the middle of September, but it was the aftermath which proved hardest to bear. It was then that the pinch of hard times was felt by the majority of people.

Buffeted by this economic storm, General Electric needed a stout heart and a steady hand at the wheel. It needed especially a calm, intrepid mind to chart a course of safety, let the winds howl as they might.

The corporation had had but a year in which to gather strength to face the trial. Coffin, though still in the leadership, was no longer dominant as he had been in the Thomson-Houston organization. There were new members on the Board of Directors, critical New York financiers, who were not always disposed to concede his soundness of judgment.

One of their first proposals was the setting up of an executive committee to pass upon Coffin's plans and policies, and even to override him, should it seem desirable so to do. Under this committee were departmental committees, which supervised the conduct of affairs in their respective spheres of activity—the manufacturing committee, the sales committee, the engineering committee.

Coffin was still adjusting himself to the unfamiliar curbs upon his administrative powers when the panic came. Business fell off abruptly during May and June.

General Electric had to pay unheard-of rates of interest for money with which to meet its pay roll week after week. Few knew the burden with which Coffin struggled. Yet there was a problem with a more menacing outlook for the Quaker business man. Its roots went beyond the panic; but because of the panic, the life of General Electric was threatened.

On July 31, 1893 the financial reports submitted to Coffin showed that the total indebtedness of the company was $10,028,000. This consisted of $4,446,000 in notes payable, $1,579,000 in accounts payable, $609,000 in dividends, and $3,394,000 in paper discounted under endorsement. Cash on hand amounted to $1,294,000, making the net indebtedness $8,734,000.

Direct indebtedness—the company's own notes and accounts payable—was troublesome enough at such a time. But the situation was aggravated by indirect indebtedness, the notes of other companies, chiefly customers, which bore General Electric's endorsement and had been discounted under that endorsement for ready cash.

These notes were eloquent of the way in which electricity had taken hold. Enthusiasm in starting local light and power companies had often outrun capacity to finance the enterprise. Local companies required equipment and frequently purchased from General Electric apparatus for which they could not pay in cash. Such purchases they financed by obtaining bank loans, then offering these loans in part payment.

General Electric, believing in the future of the electrical business, required only that men of integrity and ability manage the business, and on this condition accepted and endorsed their notes. This was the Coffin policy. It was his way of giving local companies their start and had advanced business in rapid strides. Yet it became a boomerang when the panic broke.

General Electric's endorsement made the corporation liable for repayment of the loans should the original borrowers (the local companies) prove unable to pay them off at maturity. Because of the panic, the local companies proved unable to pay the notes, and banks began to clamor for repayment of their loans.

That was the prospect General Electric faced as the summer of 1893 wore on. Having encouraged a vast economic movement during its incipient stages, the company found itself travelling a thorny path. And the end of the path, unless an immediate way out could be found, was bankruptcy.

Particularly critical were the New York bankers regarding Coffin's policy—which had been so vital in the development of both Thomson-Houston and General Electric. It was no secret that New York banking circles believed General Electric could not survive. It is even said that Twombley, Chairman of the Board, was openly twitted regarding his connection with the "defunct General Electric," and that this had something to do with his eventual resignation from the board.

But Coffin did not falter when criticism of his methods was outspoken and sharp. He did not for a moment repudiate his actions or deny his responsibility for the existing situation. He stood unflinchingly and faced the issue, even though he is reported to have said, years later, "There were months that seemed like scalding centuries."

He had one carefully considered plan, one hope of averting disaster. Without delay he laid it before his associates on the board for their scrutiny.

The proposal was to liquidate, even at substantial loss, the stocks and bonds of local companies which had accumulated as an outcome of the same business policy and which represented millions in ultimate market value. These securities had come into Thomson-Houston hands in part payment for the purchases made by customers, and Coffin had always succeeded in converting them into ready funds through the United Electric Securities Company. Some of them had come from the old Edison company, which received them from its customers in payment of license fees.

The total amount of securities was reported in the balance sheet of January 31, 1893, at a book value of $9,173,251, par value of $16,220,391. Some day these stocks and bonds would be of immense value. But in the great panic they could scarcely be sold in the open market. The most attractive of them would hardly have brought twenty-five cents on the dollar.

Coffin listed the best of these stocks and bonds, a list showing an approximate par value of $12,200,000, and proposed to offer them to the stockholders of the company on the basis of thirty-three and a third cents on the dollar. The stockholders had the opportunity to purchase the securities as soon as the panic passed; meanwhile they were to be deposited with trustees. Bankers interested in the company were to be asked to underwrite the eventual sale, which meant an immediate advance by the bankers of about $4,000,000 in cash.

It was a great sacrifice to make, but desperate times require desperate measures. Nor was the proposition coldly received. Lee, Higginson and Company stood behind Coffin from the outset and promptly agreed to the plan.

But what would the New York bankers say? Morgan, who held the determining vote, was at his summer home in Maine. The plan was forwarded to him for scrutiny. His reply was anxiously awaited. For Coffin, it was one of those months in his life that "seemed like scalding centuries."

Jesse R. Lovejoy, manager of the supply department, who knew in a measure what Coffin was passing through and what he hoped to accomplish, inquired one day, "Is everything going through all right, Mr. Coffin?" To which Coffin replied, "Everything is either going through or falling through by tomorrow morning."

The crisis was at hand. The silence from the Maine coast had grown ominous. Coffin made plans to catch the next train for New England to urge the plan in person. Action of any sort was better than the tension of waiting.

Opening the door of his office, he nearly collided with a telegraph messenger. Morgan had accepted the plan without reservation, and another "scalding century" had come at last to an end.

Thenceforth future endorsements of customers' notes were based on a more conservative policy. "Today," says the second annual report (with what a feeling of relief hidden between the lines!) "no paper is under discount except such as it is believed will be paid by the makers; consequently the indirect obligations of the company are nominal rather than real."

Other evidences of caution are to be found in this report of January 1894:

"While the liquidation of the debt has been going on, the company has also readjusted its basis for sales, either to cash or to short credits to desirable customers. . . . It is believed that your company has lost little legitimate business in consequence of its curtailment of credit to customers. It intends to confine its business to this basis."

The panic had burst upon General Electric before it became a smooth-running personnel operating at maximum efficiency. A problem still unsettled in the spring of 1893 was the status of the district offices, many of which were working with such a degree of independence as to be almost separate concerns. However, the necessary reorganization was, if anything, hastened by the severe lessons of the panic. It brought to the district offices a realization of the value of centralized control, of having back of them in times of stress the seasoned board of General Electric.

It was only a matter of months before Coffin, with characteristic tact and firmness, transformed these independent district offices into branches of the general office, cemented into the general organization and responsible to central officials. It was an arrangement that permitted efficiency and economy and definitely contributed to the slowly returning tide of prosperity.

Meanwhile, at Fort Wayne the panic had brought developments which concerned General Electric. The Fort Wayne company suffered severely, and at the beginning of 1894 had financial obligations which it appeared unable to meet. McDonald exerted every effort to obtain the required funds, but with only partial success.

Of the capital stock of $4,000,000, General Electric, the largest stockholder, held $1,137,000. Coffin and his associates advised McDonald that they favored a reorganization which would allow the plant to be operated on a sound basis. McDonald hurried east for a conference with Coffin, and on his return to Fort Wayne he petitioned the Superior Court for the appointment of receivers and the liquidation of the company's affairs. This petition was granted. Almost simultaneously, McDonald organized the Fort Wayne Electric Corporation, with capital stock of $1,500,000, which forthwith contracted with the receivers to continue the business of the company.

By this time—the middle of 1894—business was slowly improving. In General Electric shops the six-day week had returned. The home office was transferred upstate from New York.

Orders from every part of the country began to come in. Much of the increased business originated with the local companies, which were thus building up a strong and durable new prosperity for General Electric. To them the Coffin helping-hand policy, despite criticism and misgiving, had imparted a renewed vitality. And that policy, once the great panic passed into history, began to pay dividends.

THE FIRST OF THE GIANTS TAKES FORM

The first large Curtis steam-turbine generator being installed in the Fiske Street station in Chicago.

THE "MONUMENT TO COURAGE"

The Fiske Street turbine soon after it had been brought back to Sche-nectady and mounted in Works Avenue. Left to right: E. W. Rice, Jr., W. L. R. Emmet, Thomas A. Edison, George F. Morrison, Charles P. Steinmetz, and H. F. T. Erben.

PART SIX

The Development
of Big Generating Units,
Beginning of Hydroelectric Projects,
Expansion of Systems
through Transmission

27

White Coal

THE TALK AMONG ENGINEERS in 1893 and 1894 was all of alternating current and transmission—the two developments that represented a new technical era. The foundations of General Electric's work were laid in the early experiments of Professor Thomson, but the influence that was to bring General Electric into leadership in the field was the brilliant mind of Steinmetz. The moment he joined the staff the mathematics of the law of hysteresis and of the alternating current became available at first hand to General Electric engineers. Into their midst came the master of these intricate methods to explain his equations in person.

One of the trials of electrical engineering was the task of applying mathematics to the phenomenon of alternations, cycles, and phases. It was being done by slow, complicated methods. But the young mathematical genius had discovered a method so simple that the formidable difficulties of the alternating current were forever eliminated. It meant a saving of years, perhaps of generations, in the electrification of American life.

But the Steinmetz formula was not easy to comprehend.

Even experienced engineers had to be instructed, and they became students of this odd young fellow with the hunched shoulders, the jet-black hair, the keen eyes.

This period of classroom engineering, begun in the old Calculating Department at Lynn, continued and expanded when the department moved to Schenectady in 1894. At the time of that transfer Parshall went abroad, and into his shoes as Head Engineer stepped Steinmetz.

This happened at the very time when the period of power and light together was beginning to succeed the period of light. Lines already established to furnish light by night offered a new source of revenue if they could also furnish power by day. The growth of the systems was inevitable. But if they used direct current, the only way they could expand without an exorbitant investment in copper wire— augmented by losses in the conductors—was to establish a great number of generating stations.

Alternating current solved the perplexity. With the invaluable transformer the current could be sent economically for long distances; lights and motors could be operated from the same circuit; and economical transmission meant flexible systems, capable of immense expansion.

In Yonkers, a stone's throw from the Eickemeyer and Osterheld factory, where Steinmetz began his career, the Bradley Electric Power Company in 1893 was built around an invention which meant almost as much in the development of the alternating current as did the transformer. Charles S. Bradley was one of Edison's pioneers. He had later developed a mechanism which permitted electrical energy, transmitted as alternating current, to be converted into direct current. Trolley lines, which invariably employed direct current, and the direct-current lighting lines already in existence, could thus become part of the unified system.

THE BIRTH OF ELECTRIC RAPID TRANSIT
Sprague (in white suit) demonstrates his multiple-unit control on the test track in Schenectady.

A BOOM IN REAL ESTATE

*The transformation in Manhattan brought about by the electrification
of the Grand Central Terminal. These two pictures were taken from
almost the same spot, the upper one in 1906, the lower, down modern
Park Avenue, in 1929.*

In his laboratory at Yonkers Bradley worked out a rotary converter, or synchronous converter, having a revolving field and a stationary armature. It was so designed that it would receive alternating current at one end and change it by a commutator into direct current, to be drawn off on a working circuit at the opposite end.

After the converter, the next step was the substituting of polyphase for single-phase systems. Polyphase systems proved far better adapted to light-and-power work. General Electric in its polyphase service preferred the three-phase, as used in the first induction motors at Concord, Taftsville, and Columbia. But the first commercial polyphase system built by General Electric was at Redlands, California, and it was the first such system in the world.

The problems presented at Redlands would seem amusing today but at that time they were gigantic. Redlands was the nucleus of what finally became one of the largest central-station service systems in the west—that of the Southern California Edison Company.

The town in 1895, a community of 4500 inhabitants whose chief occupation was growing oranges, was lighted by oil, except for a few private plants. Manufacturing of any sort was at a premium, for coal cost eleven dollars a ton. Alert citizens felt that electric power would insure for their town a bright future. In 1892 they engaged as consulting expert an electrical engineer, Almarian W. Decker. Decker investigated the field and reported favorably on a plan to locate a hydro-electric generating station on Mill Creek, a branch of the Santa Ana River. He prepared specifications and corresponded with four electrical manufacturing companies, including General Electric, to secure bids for the equipment.

Then the hesitancy and caution that were characteristic of the period came to the surface. It was essentially a transmission installation, and transmission was a new departure. The manufacturers expressed doubts. One was unwilling to try three-phase machines, which Decker had specified. Another insisted upon direct current.

Even General Electric did not bid on generators to operate at 5000 volts, as Decker originally demanded. It offered to install two three-phase generators rated at 250 kilowatts and 2400 volts. But it won the contract on the basis of its three-phase plan.

So to that picturesque region under the snow-crowned Sierras went two of the first polyphase generators that General Electric built.

They were trucked up the creek from Redlands by teams of horses and installed under the supervision of Fred Barber, General Electric's versatile sales agent and field engineer in that section. The construction work was in charge of young Albert C. Jewett, later to make a reputation for getting things done against staggering odds. The generators were driven by one of the first of Lester A. Pelton's impulse waterwheels.

While the station was building, the Redlands Electric Light and Power Company was hustling for business. The Union Ice Company became its first large customer, buying electric power for its plant at Mentone, not far distant. So cheap was the cost of power that the ice company could ship 7000 tons of ice per year to Los Angeles, at two dollars a ton railroad freight, and still sell ice in Los Angeles fifty cents a ton cheaper than anyone there could manufacture it. Electricity was becoming an economic revolutionist!

On November 7, 1893 the Mill Creek Power House No. 1 began to operate. Dr. Louis Bell undertook to synchronize the two motors, as specified in Decker's contract, with an acoustic synchronizer. Two diaphragms of sheet iron, each connected to a phase of the two generators, were encased in a brass cylinder with an opening in its center. Bell expected the diaphragms to vibrate in harmony when the generators were in unison. The men at the power house dubbed the contrivance the "growler," a term which proved to be far too mild.

As the generators hummed, the vibrating diaphragms set up a din. A scrambled medley of sound issued. Bell with tingling ears backed rapidly away from the listening hole in the cylinder. Neither he nor anyone else could learn by acoustics when the generators were in unison. Eventually the problem of synchronization was adjusted by other means.

Thus the birth of transmission work for General Electric occurred more than three thousand miles away from Schenectady. But it did not outgrow infancy for some years, even in California, for three limiting factors delayed progress: the size and insulation of transmission cables and their protection from lightning.

MEANWHILE, OBSERVE NIAGARA! Majestic, sublime—and useful.

For generations Niagara appealed only to esthetic instincts; then in almost an instant its practical aspects were realized. Poets, won by the beauty of the spectacle, were replaced by economists and engineers who saw it as a potential empire builder. Their aspirations to harness its energies formed a strange contrast to the early superstitions that haunted the cataract.

Indians worshipped Niagara as an embodiment of the Great Spirit, offering human sacrifices to the thundering, mist-veiled cataract. Every year the tribe which dwelt beside the Onigara (Niagara) placed its fairest maiden in a birch canoe loaded with flowers and fruit, and pushed the little craft into the boiling current.

From the riverbank the redskins watched unmoved as the

maiden swept through the upper rapids and shot over the curving crest of the falls. She was a sacrifice to Onigara, a hostage to security and prosperity.

Of a different breed was the white man of modern times, whose thought lay along another pathway. His ambitions were not to make war across Niagara's rushing flood, nor to walk tightropes, as did some of his ancestors, above its thundering sweep, but to apply its giant strength to machines that would increase mankind's material prosperity—a far different sacrifice.

He came not to worship Niagara, but to tame it. Niagara inspired him to exploits as thrilling as those of the adventurers of early days and awakened in him as much imagination as it did in the poet.

In 1845 canals and mechanical waterwheels were first proposed for utilizing this concentration of natural force. Not until the early 'eighties was an installation of any size made. By that time from 5000 to 10,000 horsepower was harnessed through canals and waterwheels to the machinery of a group of mills.

At that time electrical men were awakening to the possibilities of the giant working in their whirring dynamos. They were fascinated by the scheme of making Niagara turn dynamos, of causing Nature to pay the power bills, of capturing some of the "white coal" that wastefully plunged itself "from a rock taller than the tallest pines."

Although they knew there was no prospect of utilizing all the power of Niagara, they calculated what the aggregate might be. Estimates ranged from four to seven million horsepower, though Steinmetz, years later, placed it nearer nine million.

Many ways for harnessing this power were studied; thousands of dollars were spent. Compressed air had its proponents, as had hydraulic pipes, and a system of manila or wire ropes. It was even proposed to stretch a steel shaft the length of New York State to enable factories within reach to attach belts and gear wheels and secure as much power as they needed!

Not until 1892 were bids asked from electrical concerns. A power-house of three generators was specified, each of 5,000 horsepower. It was the first large waterpower installation to be proposed and promised to add a new chapter to the glamor that was Niagara's. The best brains of General Electric went to work on the problem. S. Dana Greene handled the commercial aspects. Rice, Parshall, and Steinmetz addressed themselves to the engineering problems. In December 1892 General Electric sent in its preliminary proposition, and submitted a final bid early in 1893. It was an exhaustive array of data, contained in sixty typewritten sheets accompanied by twelve exhibits, blueprints, study sketches, and photographs. It was said that of the five bids none was more thorough than General Electric's.

On May 12 the Cataract Company notified the bidders that it had rejected the three-phase idea in favor of two-phase, and had decided to have its own engineers prepare plans and specifications for the generators. Rice, Parshall, and Steinmetz inspected these plans, and then prepared a new proposition based thereon. But they found it necessary from professional conviction to depart from certain technical features laid down by the Cataract technicians.

All bids were now in, and the days of waiting began. On October 27, 1893, President Edward D. Adams of the Cataract Company notified General Electric that the contract had been awarded to a competitor.

It was one of the fortunes of war, but for General Electric it proved a spur to keener endeavor. Such stamina as this was no mean asset. For there were other laurels to be won at Niagara. Again General Electric leaders went to work. And this time they were successful.

The proposition submitted on July 23, 1894, was accepted. It was a transmission job, to send power from Niagara to Buffalo over a line twenty-six miles long, at a potential or pressure of 10,000 volts. In the Niagara Falls power station electricity was generated at 2000 volts. This current was to be passed into General Electric transformers which were to subject it to a double process. They would raise the voltage from 2000 to 10,000, and at the same time change it from two- to three-phase.

Into a substation at Buffalo current at 10,000 volts passed, after its transmission over a bare copper cable supported on several thousand wooden poles with porcelain insulators of a special type. In the substation it was stepped down by companion transformers to the original voltage of 2000.

Some of the current at that voltage went direct to synchronous motors, driving dynamos in an electric-light station; some of it supplied motors in a city pumping station at 110 volts; some went to a general lighting system at 110 volts; and some to a set of rotary converters into which it entered as alternating current at 370 volts, emerging as direct current at 500 volts to operate the Buffalo street-railway system.

Here was an example of the flexibility, versatility, and practical usefulness of an electric service system. It was Niagara at work a score of miles distant from the thunder of the great falls. It meant a total of 30,000 horsepower in transformer capacity.

Around the new powerhouse of the Cataract Construction Company began to rise factories on land leased to them by the power company to use the power it sold. The first two were the Pittsburgh Reduction Company, manufacturers of aluminum, and the Carborundum Company, manufacturers of carborundum. Both ordered transformers, rotary converters, and special voltage regulators from General Electric.

From 1894 on, the field work of General Electric at Niagara was in charge of W. L. R. Emmet, the former field engineer of the old Sprague Company, now engineer of General Electric's Lighting Department, and a student of the alternating current.

Nor was this the end of General Electric's work at Niagara. Shops at Schenectady were to contribute other and larger halters for the taming of the cataract, the harnessing of this greatest source of "white coal" in America.

So THEY'VE GOT Mr. Edison's electric lights in the city now? Got 'em in all the big places, have they? New York, Boston, Chicago? Well, that's fine, but guess we'll keep on with gas light for a while."

So spoke many a sturdy citizen to the wife of his bosom during the hard times that reigned after the panic. Electric lights were too expensive, thought the average man, for those who had to figure carefully over ways and means. A pretty penny to put into wires, not to mention the little bulbs with the red-hot hairpins!

It was the alternating current that was soon to send the little hairpin-container into just such modest homes to replace the open gas burner that had already been replaced in the big houses. Hand in hand with the return to more prosperous days went the transition from direct to alternating current, reaching further and further into the homes of the common people.

This was in 1894–95. The Pearl Street Station now served 5000 customers. Electrical lines were crawling northward toward the Harlem River and into the Bronx. Service circuits, however, did not extend beyond Sixty-third Street. People living farther north began to agitate for light and power, so the New York Edison Company leased property at Fifth Avenue and Seventy-second Street for a substation. It was the task of the Stanley Company, contractors, to lay out an alternating-current underground transmission line at 2400 volts between these two stations. The current at this substation went into a motor-generator set, the alternating-current motor operating a direct-current generator. The direct current was distributed upon the customers' service circuits.

This method was later superseded, almost everywhere, by substituting a Bradley rotary converter for the motor-generator equipment, thus realizing Bradley's prediction that the converter could be made the "heart of a system." The first use of this converter was made by General Electric in Chicago in 1897.

In nearly all its installations for central station companies General Electric now put in alternating current. Motors and lights came into use upon the same circuit and expansion to the lively growth of demand was made possible. Communities could be served by distant waterfalls or from generating stations in other towns. And all because men like Elihu Thomson and William Stanley had developed an ingenious agent called the transformer.

Professor Thomson obtained a patent in 1887 on his discovery that a pure mineral oil not only insulated, or confined, the voltage but also carried off the internal heat of the machine. It was not easy, however, to induce customers to employ oil-immersed transformers. They objected that the oil added to the cost, and constituted a fire risk should it leak through the case. General Electric engineers sometime in 1893 discovered through a series of tests that the oil-immersed transformer could work at much greater capacities than transformers insulated otherwise. Thus the oil, in addition to insulating and cooling, was proved to permit greater operating loads; and since transformers have no moving parts, they lend themselves perfectly to oil insulation. This made possible the eventual discontinuance of air-blast transformers, and constituted a significant step in transformer development.

28

The Skilled Workman Appears

BACK IN THE SPRING of 1891, "Pop" Turner, the horny-handed superintendent of the old Edison Machine Works, saw a young chap coming between the shops with a handful of tools and called him into his office.

"Lad," he said, "I want you to take charge of 10 tomorrow. Take off your overalls."

The mechanic was a foreman in charge of experimental work in Building 10. Sometimes he knocked elbows with Edison when work brought the great man to the Schenectady shops. He could keep up with the "wizard" when it came to long hours and little sleep, but he was nonetheless astounded at Turner's words. To "take charge of 10" was a supervisory position of a high order, such as only master mechanics could aspire to hold. General foremen, then as now, did not wear overalls nor handle tools with their men. They were shop executives of intelligence and pronounced mechanical and technical skill.

William Madigan obediently doffed his overalls and set to work. One could see that the smell of the shop, the scent of lubricated metal, and acrid machine grease carried a tang to his nostrils. "Pop" Turner knew, if "Bill" didn't, that he was ripe for running the principal shop of the plant.

It was imposing to the dynamo builders of that day, Building 10. It purred and hummed from morning to night and was cluttered with electrical machines in all stages of manufacture. Madigan, who loved to see a piece of metal machined true to a hair, delved into the task of turning out fine work and turning it out on time. He watched fondly over the old Edison bi-polars and the stolid Sprague motors, and no less fondly over the later Titans.

The shop had only one crane, a small affair, but a wonder to those who compared it with the ungainly yard derricks. There was a planing machine which would take a piece of work twenty feet long, and a ten-foot boring mill. Both were considered monsters of their kind.

Bill McCool, one of the millwrights under Turner's direction, handled the placing of all machinery which went into the plant. McCool once needed an extra man for a few days, and John Miller of the carpenter's gang was detailed to lend a hand. Miller never again wore a carpenter's apron. He stepped into McCool's place when McCool went elsewhere, and was to move forward, little by little, into the post of Chief Millwright of the works.

Miller petted every new machine that came in; he and his men eased them off the freight cars, coaxed them through doors, and swung them by derrick and crane into place. Sometimes they took them in piecemeal, put the intricate parts together, and set them running, with never a hitch or a miss. As much as Madigan loved to make them do good work, so Miller loved the machines for themselves. Soon he was speaking of them with a touch of pride as "*my* machines."

He had been through some experiences with them, he and McCool. Once the Mohawk River, transformed into a

flood by melted ice and spring rains, poured over its low
banks and spread across the "big flat." The Edison works
was soon under water—three feet deep, which rose to the
level of shop benches and office desks.

Everybody went to work mopping up. Miller put in 120
hours in one week. He and some of McCool's gang made a
raft at the gate of the plant and poled their way among the
shops, rigging tackle with which to lift machinery out of the
water, to dry it and clean off the mud. Kruesi, the Works
Manager, waded about in hip boots, his coattails dragging
on the surface of the flood.

Some of the office force rowed in a boat to what is now
Building 6. H. L. Baltozer went in through a window, made
steppingstones of bookkeepers' stools, and climbed over
them to the safe to get out the books.

A year later a fire broke out in Building 11, where underground tubing was produced. Six hours later Rach, the General Foreman, Kruesi and Turner stood surveying the hot
ruins while a crowd of smoke-grimed workmen went on
playing streams of water into the shell that remained.

It was at the height of a busy season for underground tubing. Said Rach to the two bosses, "If you'll give me all the
men I need, I'll be running again within a week."

"A week!" cried Turner, "Chris, you're crazy."

But Kruesi gave him the men and Rach went to work while
the ruins were still ablaze. He laid out the work without a
moment's hesitation, giving each man a particular job and
making sure he understood it. Then they started to clear out
the debris.

Men went into the ruins with ropes which they attached
to the ends of smoking beams and ragged corners of hot
metal. Hoses were played on the beams as they were jerked
free.

The men worked in shifts with no cessation, day or night. As soon as the charred shell was cleared out, rebuilding began. The works lumber mill, in Building 4, hummed twenty-four hours a day to keep pace with construction. Masons, working under canvas covering because of a siege of rain, rebuilt the brick walls and the ovens used for baking insulation. Rach slept in snatches until Thursday night, when he collapsed. But the following Monday morning, almost a week to the hour, he closed a switch that gave the new shop its working power—and production at full tide went on. There were orders to fill and promises to keep, new designs to be placed in production.

A few months later the pall of the panic set in. But the skeleton organization of foremen—the Madigans, the Millers, and the Rachs—carried on. With fresh zest they entered the new burst of activity that began with the closing years of the nineteenth century.

In the "New York Shops" other developments were coming to a boil. Equipment for Niagara and Buffalo, and shortly after railway apparatus for New York, raised the inevitable problem of insulation. Not a mile of line, not a switch could work at high voltages without proper insulation. How William Cermak, the veteran porcelain maker of the old days of Bergmann and Company, wrestled with the problem. He had made good electrical porcelain in small pieces, for sockets and small switches, employing what was known as the dry process. But insulators that would withstand 10,000 volts were another matter.

Experiment after experiment was made. Scores of insulators were designed and tested, only to go to pieces under less than 10,000 volts. Loads of broken porcelain were hauled from the scene of the struggle. It was a nerve-racking period. At length Cermak and the transmission engineers produced the well-known "petticoated" insulator, a succession of out-spreading ridges, like the old-fashioned hoop skirt done in flounces—which stood every test up to and beyond 10,000 volts.

These insulators for the moment kept the spectre at bay. But it was yet to be completely vanquished. Cermak and the factory heads moved heaven and earth to do it. Cermak well understood that it was his task, that if he could not measure up to it the works would get someone who could. But the factory heads had not the slightest idea where such a man was to be found. Yet, unknown to all of them, he was in the Schenectady works at that time in the person of Edward M. Hewlett, whose great contribution will be discussed in later pages.

Many a service record of which the possessor is proud was begun by young mechanics shaping themselves into artisans in those transition days. It was monotonous, winding armatures and field magnets, yet it was work for skilled hands to do. If the winding was done carelessly, there would not be room on the shaft for the bearings and the commutator. There were nice calculations to be made to insure proper clearance between the fields, maintaining the air-gap, and to insure proper connections and the adequate number of turns for the machine's capacity. An Edison motor of ten kilowatts required over sixty pounds of wire for the windings, and took three men twelve hours to wind.

About this time there appeared at the Schenectady works a man short in stature with black, well-trimmed beard and keen, pleasant eyes. He was seen going and coming in the office of John Kruesi, whose assistant he had been made. This was the same George Emmons who, in the days of the American Electric Company, had astonished his roommate, E. W. Rice, Jr., by sitting up half the night to locate an error of three cents in his trial balance. Rice had sent for him a few years later when the Thomson-Houston Company wanted a man to keep track of its costs. He was then appointed Factory Auditor, and, under General Electric, Plant Manager at Lynn.

Kruesi had laid a solid foundation for the growth of the plant at Schenectady. Emmons was made his assistant, and through the following year they gauged together the needs of the thriving factory and planned its future. Then Kruesi was appointed consulting engineer, and Emmons succeeded him as Works Manager.

To every man his profession. That of George E. Emmons was originally the study of costs. But from this scrutiny in business, and especially in industrial business, Emmons worked out policies directed toward developing economy. This took him into the domain of management, where his executive qualities came to the fore.

When he came to Schenectady, Emmons applied the Thomson-Houston cost system and functional plan of factory organization to their utmost. As Works Manager, he had un-restricted authority to build slowly, soundly toward his ob-jective—an efficient factory, conducted on scientific princi-ples of management and cost.

Before long it was apparent among the shop force how well Emmons understood men, and how completely he represented the cooperative conception of industry. All, himself included, were working together for industrial achievement.

Before long he had an extensive acquaintance among the men. He had a habit of greeting everyone he passed, whether he knew their names or not. He had a way of swiftly looking a man over as if to place that man in his mind; yet his glance seemed to carry the assurance that they were brothers in a common task. After awhile a quaint phrase grew up among the men of the plant. They alluded to Emmons as the "little man." It was a token of respect. Sometimes there were differences of opinion or definite disagreements between Emmons and the workers; but that sense of personal relationship between them was never lost. They called him the "little man" even when problems were knottiest and opinions most divergent. They still felt confident of fair treatment at his hands, and they knew that his first concern was the efficiency of the plant.

That efficiency did not come easily. It meant the substitution of new methods. It meant putting factory work on a planned schedule, and creating a system of reports by means of which the factory heads could tell the daily status of a specific piece of work; such innovations as assigning each man a permanent place in the shop—a practice which saved much confusion and valuable time.

Good business came back to General Electric. New shops sprang up. Machines grew to giants, and with them grew the problems to be faced. Emmons and his men became the veritable giant killers of their time, for every problem had its gigantic aspect.

But the problem that never stayed killed was that of keeping manufacturing facilities abreast of commercial demands. The rush of orders was ceaseless. For a while neither the Schenectady nor the Lynn plant could handle them.

So it happened that despite Emmons' efficiency, the Schenectady works toward the middle of 1895 found itself ten weeks behind in deliveries, and customers became querulous. Every effort was made to relieve the congestion. Several lines of products were transferred bodily to Lynn. Langdon Gibson, taking up the task of Production Manager, worked out improvements in the shipping routine which permitted faster

THE CRADLE OF G-E RESEARCH

The barn on Liberty Street, Schenectady, where General Electric's Research Laboratory was founded.

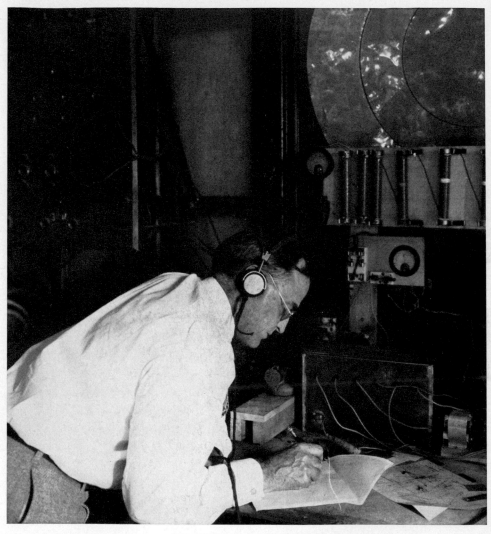

DR. WILLIS R. WHITNEY
The founder of the General Electric Research Laboratory.

shipments to be made. And Emmons was on the firing line from early morning until after dark.

The situation was closely watched, too, by the indefatigable Coffin, by Rice, now Vice President in charge of Engineering and Manufacturing, and by Eugene Griffin, Vice President in charge of Commercial Operations. Griffin's department was directly responsible for the inrush of new business. Of the salesmen at work under him, there was none more zealous than the department chief. Griffin believed in the electrical revolution, heart and soul. He was so full of his subject that to meet him was to become immersed in an atmosphere of confidence. Few prospective customers could resist the contagion. Local leaders considering the organization of an electric light and power company could entertain few doubts of the future after Griffin had enveloped them with his enthusiasm. The result was more orders, busier shops, a swifter pace.

Griffin went to Coffin one day, considerably perturbed. "We're in a pretty fix!" he said. "The Lynn factory cannot turn out more than forty motors a week and I have orders for a hundred."

Coffin chuckled. "I wouldn't mourn over that, although I appreciate your predicament and I'll see what we can do. I'd feel a lot more distressed if the factory were able to turn out a hundred motors and you had orders for only forty."

J. R. McKee, Manager of the Power and Mining Department, had told the sales committee recently that the possibility of electric motors for operating large mills was attracting more attention every day. Frequently he had impressive summaries to present of industries which had turned to electric power, and he issued a weekly bulletin describing the installations.

A second textile mill in the South, at Pelzer, South Carolina, was about to undergo electrification. Even yet, the owners required courage to sign a contract for electric motors
rather than for a form of mechanical rope drive. In Charles-
ton, where most of the capital stock for the Pelzer Mills was
subscribed, the news that the electric drive was going in
caused the stock to drop $25 a share. The mill hands pro-
tested flatly, "The mill never will run with those little wires
to pull it." On the day the mill started operation, a kind
friend approached Captain Smythe, who was responsible for
the contract, and offered his condolences on the failure of
the electrical transmission system. "I've watched those wires
all day," he said, "and they haven't moved yet."

Twenty-five General Electric motors drove the spindles
in that mill in 1895, and now one textile mill after another
sent in orders. In one week of that year, McKee's bulletin
reports that motors were sold for use in mines, shoe factories,
yarn mills, tanneries, powder mills, watch factories, and even
for blowing church organs.

Meanwhile, the annual sales of the incandescent lamp had
reached the six million mark, despite the fact that the Edison
patent expired in the previous November. The directors, in
their annual report for that year, outlined their policy as
follows:

"Your company will chiefly rely upon the high quality of
the lamp manufactured by it and its facilities for manufacturing at a low cost to maintain its commanding position
in the lamp business, irrespective of patent control. Lamp
prices have been greatly reduced. While the volume of this
important part of your business will without doubt be largely
increased in the future, the profit thereon will be less."

This amounted to an announcement that General Electric
intended to hold its own in competition for business by sheer

efficiency of methods. Competition was quick to show itself. The independent lamp manufacturers who had been forced to discontinue their infringing lamps now swarmed into the field.

Local light and power companies equipped by General Electric in 1894 aggregated nearly 1,500. They still had financial problems, and the parent company still accepted, to some extent, negotiable paper in lieu of full cash payments, especially in the form of bonds of the local companies. This revived the need of an agency for handling the bonds as they accumulated, and so there was organized in 1894 the Electrical Securities Corporation. It bought from General Electric the bonds of local companies—which were not readily marketable—and issued against them its own collateral trust bonds.

Almost completely had the memory of the fearsome days of 'ninety-three faded from the minds of men. The manager of the Metropolitan Telephone Company in New York reported that more telephone messages were handled daily for General Electric than for any two other concerns in the city.

About this time Coffin proposed to Griffin a trip to the Pacific Coast. "But think of the expense," protested Griffin.

"I think it would be worth while," said Coffin, thoughtfully. "I should like to show you what we are doing on the coast, these transmission enterprises, the outlook in that region."

And so a cross-continent trip, which causes so little concern to business today, was carefully weighed and pondered by the leaders of a young industrial concern. Indeed, there were events of vast significance taking place on the coast, among the foothills of the lofty ranges where a giant's energy awaited the harness of the pioneer.

Into the mountain hinterland of California went this new

explorer, the electrical engineer, making his way into regions where human habitation was scant or nonexistent. Miners had already discovered gold in those heaved-up mountains. But the new explorer sought treasure of a different sort, though scarcely less valuable than the metal for which the forty-niners struggled. It was treasure as old in the ranges as gold, yet more difficult to extract—white coal.

This treasure, too, had its boom, when the mining camp of other days gave place to the bustling construction camp of hydraulic engineers. Invasion of the mountain solitudes went on without cessation. The initial project at Redlands was scarcely in operation when the city of Sacramento sent engineers to the falls of the American River, twenty-five miles distant, to prospect for a waterpower site. In the power-house erected by the Folsom Falls, General Electric installed four generators, each of 750 kilowatts capacity, producing three-phase alternating current, to which the company had now committed itself. Over the intervening miles a transmission line was built to Sacramento and energy was first delivered in that city on July 14, 1895, at 11,000 volts. Electric streetcars, a city-wide system of arc lights and incandescent lights, and a variety of motors for stationary power drew energy from the falls at Folsom.

The Sacramento *News* proclaimed jubilantly: "The Folsom power is here! It came early yesterday morning, and a hundred guns awakened the town, proclaiming the glad news. . . . The Sacramento plant is the most extensive yet put in place anywhere. . . . No event ever occurred in Sacramento that has been heralded to her greater advantage than the splendid industrial feat of yesterday."

Thereupon one after another of those western white coal centers yielded up its energy. Competition among the electrical companies was keen. General Electric, in the following

year, built an 11,000-volt line from the Kern River fourteen
miles to Bakersfield; another extending fourteen miles from
the Big Cottonwood River to Salt Lake City to work at 10,-
000 volts; and a third from the Ogden River thirty-six miles
to Salt Lake City, at 15,000 volts. In 1897 a transmission
project of eighty-one miles and 33,000 volts was undertaken,
the longest commercial electric power transmission system
and the highest voltage yet attempted. It stretched from the
Santa Ana Canyon to Los Angeles and Pasadena.

Triumph indeed. Yet in the midst of it the *Journal of
Electricity,* under date of May 1897, noted that all was not
yet under full control. "Not to that trustworthy servant, the
transformer, may the present limitations of electric transmission be ascribed," it said, "the barrier is embodied in
the insulator alone. In addition to being a practically perfect
nonconductor, the insulator should be wind, rain, snow, sleet,
dust, and insect-proof. . . . Truly may it be said that unlimited reward awaits the inventor of a perfect high-tension
insulator."

Nevertheless, General Electric struggled along with the
insulators that were at hand—and transmission and voltages
in California crept slowly upward. The fight for the business
grew intense. And those bold specialists, the SKC trio, shone
in one of the daring projects of the white coal region.

DEVELOPMENTS AT SCHENECTADY now shift our scene from
the far west to the city of Washington, where smart naval
uniforms color the streets and the corridors of the federal
buildings. In the office of the Bureau of Ordnance, United
States Navy, early in 1894, Captain W. T. Sampson, head of
the bureau was talking to Lieutenant Bradley A. Fiske and
an associate. Sampson suddenly inquired, "Do you think you
could turn gun turrets by electricity?"

Lieutenant Fiske, already a successful inventor, had his doubts. But the problem interested him so much that he accepted the assignment, established headquarters in New York, and began to consult with various electrical manufacturers. He spent some time with J. W. Kellogg, Commercial Manager of Marine Work for General Electric, and other members of the staff. These men showed him a scheme of motor application and control known as the Ward Leonard system and built by General Electric under license from its originator, E. Ward Leonard. Fiske decided to try the system and experiments were begun in adapting it to gun turrets on the cruiser *Brooklyn*, then under construction.

After two years Lieutenant Fiske finally worked out a plan that made the whole scheme practical. He took out a covering patent and sold it to General Electric.

Then came the task of convincing the ultra-conservatives that electricity for turning turrets was superior to steam. The naval constructors who were officially sent to Schenectady to examine the apparatus sent in an unfavorable report. Lieutenant Fiske suggested that two of the *Brooklyn's* turrets be equipped with steam and two with electric machinery, so that the systems could be compared under identical conditions.

The Bureau of Construction and the Bureau of Steam Engineering opposed the proposal. General Electric then offered to stand the entire cost of the installation should the tests prove a failure. The question reached the desk of Secretary of the Navy Hilary A. Herbert, who, although quite impartial, was unversed in the technical phases involved. Accordingly General Electric sent two of its executives, S. Dana Greene and J. R. McKee, to take up the fight. Dana Greene is said virtually to have lived in Washington for months. McKee appealed in person to Secretary Herbert to permit the test to be made "so that this administration would go into history as the one identified with inaugurating this forward step."

Finally the Secretary was won over. "On his own orders," writes McKee, "and against the recommendations of the Navy Department's bureaus" he ordered the four turrets equipped.

The test was conducted toward the close of 1896, in the presence of a board of officers. In Fiske's own words, "No triumph could have been more complete. The forces of ultra-conservatism were utterly routed, and a most important step in the forward progress of the Navy thereby permitted. The . . . system . . . was adopted by the Navy and was one of the important reasons for the improvement in gunnery which afterward resulted."

The board of officers reported of the test that: "The electric-controlled turrets could be turned . . . and brought to rest with the object previously selected between the cross hairs of the sighting telescope with great facility, the turret having a smooth and regular motion. While it was possible to arrive at the same result with the steam-controlled turrets, it was only done with considerable difficulty."

These were fifty-horsepower motors, and McKee calls their adoption "the real beginning of the use of electrical apparatus on naval vessels," although General Electric had, a year or two previously, put seven-horsepower motors on a cruiser and three battleships for operating ammunition hoists. General Electric also installed the first electric motors for deck winches on two battleships, as well as on two grain-carrying vessels. But the turret equipments were functioning in ample time to take their share of the glory that came to the *Brooklyn*, as one of the fleet under command of former Captain Sampson, in the battle of Santiago less than two years later.

29

The Steam Locomotive Challenged

A NEW DAY HAD COME for the traction motor. Its years of trial and tribulation had vanished. Within five years of the struggle at Richmond it had fulfilled aspirations that would have dazed the staunchest railway men of a decade earlier. The traction motor had leaped from the streetcar tracks of the teeming cities to the railroad tracks of trunk-line systems, and was challenging even the province of the steam locomotive.

Before the consolidation of 1892, the Baltimore & Ohio Railroad was confronted by a problem which steam locomotion only aggravated. In Baltimore the road was building a tunnel more than a mile long with an appreciable grade. A considerable saving in running time of trains was effected between New York and Washington, but the smoke and coal gas of the locomotives in the confined space were unendurable.

In their dilemma the railroad turned to the Thomson-Houston Electric Company, asking if an electric locomotive could be built for service in the tunnel. Knight and Potter promptly replied in the affirmative. The railroad began negotiations for three such locomotives, which were eventually contracted for by the new General Electric Company.

The engineers who had bargained to move heavy railroad trains by electricity were not entirely actuated by over-confidence. They had tried their hands at the electric locomotive of thirty tons which was exhibited at the World's Fair, and had also designed the Cayadutta, which weighed thirty-five tons and became a "yarder," or light-service locomotive. But the big fellows for the Baltimore tunnel weighed ninety-six tons, and their gearless motors, four to each locomotive, were rated at 360 horsepower. They could make fifty miles an hour by themselves, and could haul thirty freight cars at fifteen miles an hour or ten passengers at thirty miles—including in each case the steam locomotive, which was left coupled to the trains.

These big fellows operated with never a hitch or a failure. Actual service began on August 4, 1895, and one "monster" made a name for itself by hauling forty-four loaded freight cars and three steam engines up the grade of the tunnel at a steady speed of twelve miles an hour. "Not a sputter, spark, or slip of wheel indicated the tremendous energy which was developed by the locomotive," said one of McKee's bulletins.

Old railroad men, raised in an atmosphere of steam, scarcely realized what this meant. It was the formal introduction of a new locomotive power.

The division superintendent of the Baltimore and Ohio could not believe the electric locomotive had a drawbar pull equal to that of a steam locomotive. Potter suggested that he apply any sort of test he desired, whereupon the superintendent rode on one of the electric locomotives to see what it could do.

The rule had always been followed of accelerating gradually the speed of the train in leaving Camden station, and the

motorman was proceeding in that manner when the superintendent asked him why he didn't "pull her wide open."
The motorman demurred. The superintendent told him to do
as he was told, and the controller was turned clear around to
full speed. A shout went up from the train crew. The sudden
surge of power had pulled the end out of a boxcar that was
loaded with oats. The track was knee-deep in loose grain. By
the time the mess was cleaned up the division superintendent
was satisfied as to the pulling power of the electric locomotive.

All this time the traction motor for streetcar operation was
by no means standing still. Toward the end of 1893 appeared
the G-E 800 motor, which incorporated most of the merits
and avoided most of the errors of the early motors which
General Electric had inherited.

One significant feature of this motor was the appearance
of the Eickemeyer method of winding. This consisted of
separate coils of copper bars, all alike, bent so that they could
be inserted in the slots of the armature core until the surface
of the core was a solid mass. This allowed for the removal
of any individual coil, in case it became defective, so that a
new one could replace it. The problem of insulation was also
simplified. The process of manufacture was both accelerated
and standardized because the coils could be made and the
insulating tape wound upon them by machine. Farewell at
last to the laborious hand-winding.

Motors at this period became more workmanlike in appearance. But they were still intricate. The G-E 800, for merely
insulating purposes, contained such a variety of substances
as Irish linen, oiled pressboard, oiled cotton, mica, asbestos,
hickory, Japan pressboard, canvas, and tape.

It was the G-E 800 that was placed upon the cars of the
Metropolitan Street Railway Company in New York when

that road finally adopted the underground conduit for its Lenox Avenue line in upper Manhattan. Determined to discover what the best method of motive power might be, the directors of the road offered a prize of $50,000 for a practical and economical mode of traction. They were immediately swamped with suggestions. Three thousand applicants submitted ideas.

One inventor would have placed small windmills on the roofs of the cars; another would have harnessed the tide at Sandy Hook; a third wanted to hitch each car to a balloon! The prize was never awarded. The directors, almost prostrated by the multitude and variety of the proposals, decided to save their money, which doubtless went in 1894 toward paying the expense of the conduit electric system put in by General Electric. The five-mile line, subject to construction conditions peculiar to a great metropolis, cost more than $100,000 per mile to build.

In Chicago, the demonstration at the World's Fair had won over the Metropolitan West Side Elevated Railway to the idea of electric instead of steam operation. General Electric also equipped the Lake Street Elevated, and for this worked out a new style of motor rated at 160 horsepower. It had a box frame devised by E. D. Priest to solve the difficulty of fitting motors of increasing size into the small space beneath the cars.

In the same year, 1895, the New York, New Haven and Hartford Railroad wanted electric equipment for a branch line running to Nantasket Beach. The G-E 2000 motor, a heavy-duty unit, went in, and traffic increased 300 per cent.

Fast-flying years! Old equipment disappearing as new came in. Potter, succeeding Knight in 1895 as engineer of General Electric's railway department, wanted to locate one of the old Van Depoele cars, with the motor on the platform and a chain running to the axles, to have it preserved as a relic. Not one of the old cars was to be found anywhere! They had disappeared completely, even from the carbarns and the scrap yards.

"Somebody once asked, 'Where do the pins go?' What I'd like to know is, 'Where do the trolley cars go?' " said Potter as he abandoned the search.

30

Campaigning for Candlepower

IN THE OLD DAYS electric lighting stations required a great array of dynamos, for each dynamo supplied only about fifty lamps. In the larger cities, the arc light generating stations needed a battalion of dynamos. The Chicago Arc Light and Power Company in 1893 had fifty-six dynamos, serving 2242 arc lamps, or about forty lamps apiece.

One of the rotating giants which the nineties ushered in could equal in performance many of the old-time midgets. The battalion gave way now to a corporal's guard, or even a lone soldier. It was a time of replacement; equipments became obsolete rapidly; space was conserved.

The local companies were rapidly combining. Edison and Thomson-Houston licensees were merging in each local community—for two electric lighting companies in one town had come to be as undesirable as two telephone companies. But there was a delicate problem involved in these mergers: the question as to which company in each town should preserve its identity. It was natural that Charles A. Coffin wanted the Thomson-Houston licensees to dominate the local consolidations. But he was too astute to adopt such a policy. He appre-

ciated that it was the incandescent lamp—Edison's lamp—
which guaranteed the electrical future. And how potent was
the name of Edison! From motives of justice, of sentiment,
and of commercial value, Coffin felt that it should be perpetuated, so he championed the name of his former competitor.
Soon the entire country was·dotted with utilities bearing the
name of Edison.

So the time came when one electrical company served a
single town, generating only alternating current. Yet for
street lighting purposes, arc lamps on series circuits were
essential. To change the original street-lighting systems to
multiple circuits, corresponding with the incandescent-lamp
circuits, meant a large investment in labor and in copper
wire. Special circuits would also be needed if the street lights
were to be turned on and off from the central station. Otherwise each lamp would have to be turned on and off indi-
vidually, and the "limping lamplighters" would be recalled
to the streets. Independent operation, so vital to the incandescent system, in the case of arc lamps was an actual
disadvantage.

Something new was needed, a regulating device to control current in the circuit after it had left the generator, something functionally like the transformer and the rotary
converter. And it was Professor Thomson's constant-current
transformer which met the situation. Here was another
contrivance for making electricity its own regulator with
greater than human precision.

Existing series circuits, on wires that had been put in years
ago, could now be connected to the secondary coils of the
constant-current transformers. The series circuits were kept at
constant current, though street lights were part of a city-
wide electric system of multiple circuits at constant voltage.

And the arc-light circuits could be enlarged whenever growth demanded it.

The arc lamp itself was moving toward greater efficiency, as was the incandescent. Until 1893 the arc, although protected from the weather by a globe, had been exposed to the air, and the carbon electrodes had been consumed so rapidly that almost daily replacements were necessary. L. B. Marks, an illuminating engineer of New York, devised an enclosed arc lamp and sold his patent rights to General Electric in that year. The electrodes lasted for days without trimming, and the life of the lamp was ten times prolonged.

The volume of illumination, however, was not so great, and some of the larger cities continued using the old-style open-arc lamps. The new style lamps, however, were designed for operation upon every existing type of circuit. Yearly General Electric put out 100,000 arc lamps, and more than half of them were of the enclosed type. It came eventually to be the most widely used of all types, and was used for illumination even in the larger stores.

While the arc lamp and the alternating current were getting acquainted with each other, the incandescent lamp continued to thrive. Where the arc lamp was called for by the thousands, the incandescent was turned out by the millions. The hope of the Edison Lamp Works was for machines that would replace the painstaking work of glass blowers.

Edison had already made a beginning, and others were at work on new experiments. If bulbs could only be blown in moulds! Once or twice it was tried. It *could* be done—but the stem still had to be sealed in by hand, and bulbs made in moulds were not much of a gain if they must immediately go through the uncertainties of hand operation. Then about 1895 two inventors of the Buckeye Incandescent Lamp

Company of Cleveland, Spiller and Massey, brought out a sealing-in machine, and Howell, at Harrison, began improving it. This machine sealed the glass stem and the glass bulb together in an air-tight joint. Edison had worked out a similar machine, which was unsatisfactory because the bulbs were rotated in a horizontal position and repeatedly lost their symmetry; the Spiller and Massey machine rotated the bulb in a vertical position, insuring perfect symmetry. Almost at the same time there came an improvement in the tubulating machine, which pierced the top of the bulb and attached a glass tube through which the air could be pumped from the globe. A high vacuum could now be obtained more easily and more quickly than before. Hence bulbs blown in a mould, instead of free-blown, were again attempted, this time with success beyond all previous experience.

The Edison Lamp Works could now supply yearly the million lamps that had become the demand of the American public. General Electric was producing almost half the number itself while independent lamp companies were turning out the remainder.

In the midst of this promotion of electric incandescence, there appeared one man, D. McFarlan Moore, who took his stand as the proponent of artificial illumination by chemical gases. These gases became radiant when placed in a vacuum and made to conduct electric currents. Moore had been with Edison and later with General Electric until 1894, when he obtained the financial backing to organize a company of his own to experiment in the field of gaseous conduction. He remarked to Edison that he hoped to produce an imitation of daylight.

"What's the matter with my light?" Edison inquired.

"Too small, too red, and too hot," replied Moore.

Eventually Moore produced a lamp, tubular in form like

"Dad" Vinal's crew takes time out for lunch.

One of the motors installed.

THE STEEL MILL MOTORS AT GARY

"THESE ARE PROUD MEN—ARTISTS"

the mercury vapor lamp of Peter C. Hewitt, which imitated daylight so closely that it found immediate use for color-matching. But it was far from acceptable for universal lighting, in the home or elsewhere, because of the high voltage required to operate it. It was the incandescent lamp, small, red, and hot as it was, which multiplied its radiance in homes and business buildings the country over.

The early lamps had lasted as long as 3000 hours, giving neither brilliant nor efficient illumination. After a few hundred hours, candlepower dropped. In 1893 the Edison Lamp lasted for 1200 hours, but it burned at 80 per cent or more of its rated candlepower for scarcely more than one-fifth of its life. Yet the lamp consumed electric current during the inefficient four-fifths of its life for which the customer paid. He was plainly not receiving full value for his money. Illumination cost him more per candlepower than if the lamp lasted for a shorter period, retaining more of its efficiency during the entire time.

By 1895 General Electric had produced lamps designed to give better light for a shorter period. With a total life of 700 hours they gave at least 80 per cent of their rated power for more than half their life. As the lamps of later years continued to improve, the consumer profited by getting more illumination for the same amount of money.

Perhaps the most important contribution to lamp manufacture at that time was the use of red phosphorus vapor in producing the vacuum. It was a process discovered by an Italian engineer, Arturo Malignani. The news that lamps were being exhausted without the use of mercury caused a stir at Harrison. The factory heads sent for John W. Howell. "We want this invention," they told him. "Go over there and buy it for us. Catch the first boat."

Howell was about to be married, and the invitations were

ready to be mailed. There was a hasty scratching out of dates
and writing in of earlier ones. It was a rapidly married couple
that caught an early boat for Italy. They were still out of
breath when they found the inventor, Malignani, in a tiny
Alpine village. Howell bought the American rights to the invention, stopped in England on his way home to order a
special pump required by the new process, and returned to
Harrison triumphant. That was the end of the mercury-
exhaust process, and the sale of the discarded quicksilver
paid practically the entire cost of altering manufacturing
facilities for the phosphorus exhaust.

This was the most important change since the treated filament. It reduced the time required to secure a vacuum from
half an hour to less than a minute; it created a far higher
vacuum; and of great importance, it removed the danger of
mercury poisoning.

Howell could not see a new apparatus without looking it
over for possible improvements, so that before long he hit
upon a weak point in the Malignani process. The lamp was
connected to the exhaust pump by a glass tube, which was
painted on the inside with the phosphorus. After the pumping
was completed the phosphorus was vaporized, and to insure
the vapor's passage into the bulb and not into the pump, the
connecting tube had to be closed. This was originally done by
a glass-blowing process, but Howell inserted a section of
rubber tubing which could be completely closed by a pinch-
cock pressed upon the rubber before the phosphorus was
vaporized.

This eliminated one glass-blowing step, and permitted
more exact control of the vaporizing. Finally, Howell and
William R. Burrows devised an apparatus for performing the
complete exhaust process upon ten lamps at a time.

In 1894 the famed bamboo filament was replaced by the

squirted filament. Under this procedure cotton was dissolved in zinc chloride, and the cellulose mass which resulted was squirted through a small die into alcohol or water to harden it. Then it was washed, dried, shaped, packed into crucibles, and carbonized. This type of carbon filament was more uniform and more homogenous in structure than the carbonized bamboo. It required less labor and less material to produce. It made longer filaments possible, and a more uniform distribution of the light was obtained by making the filament more oval and steadying the middle loop with an anchor.

This was the efficient lamp of the middle and late nineties —the lamp which would produce economical illumination. It was a product calculated to build good will. At the time it appeared, the Edison central station companies, comprising the Association of Edison Illuminating Companies, led the way in urging the policy of renewing customers' lamps as soon as they grew dim.

Consideration of customer needs was one of the ideals upon which General Electric built. It was a policy that Thomson, Rice, and Coffin had woven into the fabric of the Thomson-Houston Company and then transferred to General Electric. Because of this policy, a field of service, as yet unsuspected, was brought into existence.

THERE WAS AN OLD-TIME "EXPERT" of the Thomson-Houston Company named Walter D'Arcy Ryan, who was convinced that electric lighting was being applied by careless methods. No scientific study was made of lighting projects, and lights were put in by guesswork. Inevitably, thought Ryan, that sort of thing is costly. And to whom? To the users of lights— the customers of General Electric.

And so he conceived the idea of putting electrical illumination upon a scientific basis. Careful studies of a customer's premises would form the basis of recommendations for scientific illumination. This would be done without consideration for the business which General Electric would derive from the installation.

It was a new proposition. Ryan went to E. W. Rice, Jr., Technical Superintendent of the Company. And there his idea met with a friendly reception, for Rice authorized the necessary appropriation, though largely as an experiment.

Thenceforward, customer needs received special study and expert recommendation. The objective in every installation was the correct volume of light from the most efficient equipment. As the practice extended, the laboratory grew. Customers realized a saving in money. And General Electric was proving again its principle of service.

In 1902 the laboratory, now officially designated the Illuminating Engineering Laboratory, was transferred to Schenectady, and Ryan received the title of Illuminating Engineer. From this laboratory, in 1903, came a concentric light diffuser, a type of reflector which produced evenly distributed rays of light throughout the illuminated area. New instruments were brought out for demonstrating what the scientific analysis and measurement of lighting could be made to accomplish—the spectrophotometer, the luximeter, the luminometer, and later a line of devices for studying the effects of light on colored materials.

THE PREDICTION OF CALVIN A. RICHARDS, the old-time horse-car man, was reaching fulfillment; electricity had grown from youth to manhood and was fast becoming the "giant of the future." Day and night without a lull, energy in such volume as the great pioneers had never dreamed of issued from a multitude of rotating monsters that whirred and hummed, making and distributing the electric current that meant light, power, and heat over a spreading network of cables and wires.

But energy uncontrolled is not only useless but perilous. It must be mastered after it is brought into existence. And this mastery involved the problem of the electric switch. The future of electric power depended upon the invention of switches capable of controlling a titanic energy. If greater switches could not be developed, the trend toward generating stations of greater capacity would be halted.

In the midst of their early work with switchboards, General Electric engineers perceived this problem drawing nearer and taking shape.

In the electric switch two contact points are drawn apart, and an arc is produced in the gap, growing longer and longer as the gap lengthens, until it breaks and the circuit is interrupted. The procedure lasts but a fraction of a second. In some of the tests that Rice and Hewlett conducted, the arc leaped a dozen feet before it broke. They agreed that no one would want to handle a switch that created such formidable arcs. But there was one remedy possible—mineral oil. If the arc were produced beneath the surface, the oil would smother it.

The oil switch succeeded. It became the "H" type, famous for its perfect work and its high capacity. In the generating station at Ninety-sixth Street, New York, these switches proved a perfect complement to the big generators. Within a few years the Manhattan Elevated, transformed from steam to electric operation, installed these switches in its power house, as did the Interboro road and later the New York Central. This was the only type of switch that could handle properly the volume of energy now speeding forth upon the circuits of electric service lines. It was to go down on the books, not as a switch, however, but as a circuit breaker.

Meanwhile a race of midgets was growing up to join the

circuit breakers in their task of controlling the energy of the rotating giants. For potent as they are, the relays are indeed a race of midgets.

The relay is a collection of metallic parts without life or consciousness, yet it is eternally on guard; devoid of human faculties, it is yet a sentinel more dependable than humans.

Edward M. Hewlett, the premier designer of switches and switchboards, fathered the relay. He both fathered and nurtured it; and all the while urgent men were bringing new switchboard problems to his office, and the five major departments with professional insistence dinned their needs in his ears and consumed the bustling energies of his little staff.

Hewlett experimented with dashpots, with pendulums, with clockwork. Finally he turned to air pressure for retarding the movement of the solenoid core. He undertook to introduce an air cushion by means of a little sack of leather. But he found that a special grade of leather was required, a leather that was both dense and flexible.

He visited leather factories to discover the differences in grades and to study samples. He finally settled upon a type of kangaroo leather, and with this he originated the bellows relay. In this the plunger rod, or solenoid core, in attempting to rise under the magnetic influence of the solenoid, pushed against the bellows; it could not complete its movement and close the circuit contacts until the air had been pushed out of the bellows, a matter of several seconds. By that time, if the short circuit had been slight, the trouble would have passed; the excessive current, magnetizing the solenoid, would have ceased, and the plunger would have dropped back to its original position.

Meanwhile, on the Pacific coast, the electrical engineer was tussling with the great mountain ranges, planning a hydroelectric project among the rugged Sierras. The distance of transmission would be greater, and hence the voltage higher, than any previous system. They would have to transmit at no less than 40,000 volts. The organization of the Standard Electric Company was begun, and through the self-confidence and technical originality of John F. Kelly, the Stanley Electric Manufacturing Company finally won the contract.

To those who said it couldn't be done, Kelly remarked that it depended upon the size of the transmission cables. Two generating stations were immediately begun, one at Colgate on the North Yuka River 142 miles from Oakland, the other at Electra (Blue Lakes) 149 miles from Oakland in the opposite direction. Kelly went into the mountains to the site of the Colgate powerhouse, lying far north in the Sacramento Valley. He rode along a precarious mountain trail that climbed and wound through defiles and skirted sheer cliffs— the road over which all equipment and every item of supplies was laboriously carted to make that power-house a reality. It was thirty-five miles from the nearest settlement, but an eight hour trip.

On the Yuka River, winding through a great gorge in the wooded mountainside, Kelly and his men put in their cumbrous electrical machines. They stretched transmission lines upon poles that were perched on the shoulders of the mountains, and fixed their insulators upon crossarms that projected into dizzy space.

The insulators were a problem in themselves. They had been made at first either of glass or of porcelain, but later only of porcelain. Their function was to keep the high-tension current from leaping off the transmission lines and through the supporting poles. Mechanical requirements demanded that the insulators should be small, strong, and of simple construction; electrical requirements demanded that they be extremely large, complicated, and built of porcelain, a substance particularly fragile. They had of course to be non-conducting, and their surfaces had to be kept dry and clean. Yet they were perched upon a succession of poles deep in the recesses of the hills, out of sight and care of men.

Nonetheless the line from Colgate crept toward the distant city; and to meet it there crept up from the south a twin line from Blue Lakes. At last they met at Oakland, 152 miles from Colgate and 147 miles from Blue Lakes. The former line was that of the Bay Counties Electric Company, the latter was built for the Standard Electric Company.

Blue Lakes and Stockton, fifty miles apart, were connected in 1897 and operation begun, three years before that span of the system crept on to Oakland. The Bay Counties Company in 1899 began delivering electricity at 40,000 volts as far as Sacramento, seventy-six miles from the powerhouse, thereby reinforcing Sacramento's service from the Folsom plant which General Electric had equipped a few years before.

General Electric engineers were constructing an eighty-mile line to supply Los Angeles at 33,000 volts, and they too experienced difficulties with the paradoxical demands of the porcelain insulators. But all activities in their company were overshadowed by events in the East which had suddenly come to a climax. It was a situation again involving patents, the immense volume of which was now underlying the whole electric service systems of America.

EDISON ONCE SAID that a patent is an excuse for a fight. Yet the United States Patent Office has been one of the sources from which has sprung the greatness of America. When the Japanese government sent a special commissioner to Washington in 1899 to study the American patent law, he was asked why the Japanese desired a patent system. He replied that Japan had been striving to emulate the acknowledged great nations of the world, among them the United States. Then he added:

"We said: 'What is it that makes the United States such a great nation?' We investigated and found that it was patents; so we will have patents."

Back of this naive explanation there is much truth. The assurance of definite legal protection as a reward for contributing something new and useful to society has encouraged innumerable inventors. Yet, stimulating progress as it unquestionably does, the patent system has also come close at times to threatening it—another paradox.

In the twenty years since 1876, there had been issued thousands of patents covering the adaptation of electrical energy to the needs of man. Keen minds thought of the same ideas, made the same discoveries. Many controversies were fought out in the patent office; others went through the courts.

Companies could not offer perfect electrical systems unless they held patents covering all their equipment. As rival companies frequently each held patents vital to competitors' systems, neither could offer the perfect system with legal right and safety. True, both could "muddle through" until the patents expired. But letters patent in the United States are granted for a term of seventeen years, and it was a dismal prospect to think of suspending progress for such a period.

New patents came out faster than old ones expired. Litigation swelled, and executives mopped harassed brows. It was a situation which had tormented Charles A. Coffin as President of Thomson-Houston and which precipitated the mergers finally resulting in the General Electric Company. But in 1896 the ramifications were wider, and threatened with a more sinister aspect the public weal. For electrical systems were large, prosperous, and indispensable, with millions of dollars invested in them and millions of people dependent upon them for a necessity of modern life.

Inextricably enmeshed in the patent deadlock were the two largest electrical manufacturers in the United States—General Electric and the Westinghouse Electric & Manufacturing Company. Competitors for years in every type of electrical enterprise, each held a multitude of patents, many of them deadlocking in their effect upon the rival manufacturer, many of them infringed, either deliberately or unconsciously, by the other company. Westinghouse held the patents of Sawyer-Man, Maxim, Weston, Tesla, Stanley, and many others; General Electric held those of Thomson, Brush, Edison, Sprague, Van De Poele, Bradley, and others. And the customers of both were doomed to share the resulting enormous burden.

Coffin did not propose consolidation now. In the advanced and more intricate form of the industry, consolidation did not seem practicable.

Instead, a working agreement was proposed, providing, in essence, that each of the two companies should license the other to manufacture under its patents. The agreement was signed on March 31, 1896, when a Board of Patent Control, representing both companies, was set up with headquarters in New York, a central clearinghouse for handling licensing procedures.

This agreement insured freedom of action in the legal relations of the signatories for a period of fifteen years. Instead of lessening commercial competition, it stimulated it, for both companies were now free to manufacture and sell in competition with each other all essential equipment required by their customers. The merit of each company's product governed the amount of trade and the range of prices which it could obtain—and neither of them controlled the market.

PART SEVEN

The Development of Steam Turbines, Start of Industrial Research and of Commercial and Financial Expansion

31

Courage—and Grime

IN HIS QUIET EXECUTIVE OFFICE in New York the Quaker president of General Electric was reviewing the year's events. It was nearing the close of 1896, and Coffin was preparing his annual report to the stockholders.

A memorandum lay before him: in all more than 9,000 generating machines sold—their total capacity representing 400,000 horsepower. That would contribute a pretty volume of illumination to the continent. Six thousand railway motors marketed, and 8,000 horsepower in stationary motors. In what new way was electricity next to work? Coffin thought of what his lieutenant in all things technical, E. W. Rice, Jr., had told him. There was a man trying to interest the Company in a new form of steam drive—inner wheels with curved blades, to be whirled at high speeds by the force of steam. It was a new form of turbine, distinctly different from the Parsons turbine already in use in England.

The new year was still young when a tall young man, quick in movement, entered Rice's office in Schenectady. He announced himself as Charles G. Curtis, of New York, and in his travelling bag he brought the plans and the description of his steam turbine, for which he had unsuccessfully sought a market in the city.

The men to whom Curtis talked were open-minded. They were interested when he told them he proposed to build a new kind of wheel with a succession of concave steel blades, technically known as buckets, around its circumference; and to revolve this wheel by the force of steam striking against the blades.

Rice had the imagination to believe that it could be done. He analyzed, appraised, examined drawings. And at last he told Curtis that General Electric would make an agreement with him. He was to have the best facilities of the Schenectady Works to carry on the experiments necessary to make the turbine practical, in return for which General Electric was to be allowed to purchase the patent rights in case the turbine proved a commercial success.

In the factory yard a pit was excavated, in which was placed a small, crude model of a turbine. The revolving parts were metal discs to the rims of which were riveted the buckets. There was a boiler, and from it the steam passed into a steam chest. It was then shot against the blades of the wheels from nozzles.

Gingerly the shop crew worked over this modest affair, which was to revolve at such high speed that the more fearful believed it would fly apart. Curtis was assisted in the work chiefly by John Kruesi, now Consulting Mechanical Engineer. He had been assigned by Rice to report upon the progress of the experiments, making his own recommendations.

There were trying days when the revolving discs gave trouble. Their dimensions had to be exact to a hair, and this called for shop precision of a high order. Curtis made test after test, with the wheels dangerously near the casing of the turbine.

Problems sprang up one after another. When after two years of experimenting, Curtis had given several demonstrations, Kruesi sent in his final report to Rice, and gave an adverse verdict! He recommended that the tests be abandoned.

Engineering heads conferred in considerable consternation. The tests, aside from the period of time consumed, had meant a large financial expenditure. Rice turned in his dilemma to a man who knew nothing of the turbine experiments, who was disinterested and reliable in judgment. William LeRoy Emmet, Engineer of the Lighting Department, had distinguished himself by his handling of the problems of alternating current. Rice asked Emmet to investigate Curtis' turbine and study the results of the tests.

Emmet conceded that the tests did not show a performance comparable with the ability of reciprocating engines, but he saw something in the turbine that made him think that it required further experimenting to bring out unsuspected possibilities. If turbines could be made to work efficiently, he reasoned, their mechanical simplicity and economy of manufacture would prove of vast importance. Emmet recommended that two machines be built for commercial usage, one of 500 kilowatts capacity and the other of 1500.

Rice called him in for consultation. "Would you take charge of the design and manufacture of the trial turbines?" he asked. "If you would, I'll authorize their production."

Emmet, having had no experience with turbine principles, said that he would. Within twenty-four hours he was down in the shops, immersed in the tremendous question of the future of the new turbine.

What Emmet saw in Curtis' steam turbine was the principle, in embryo, of the great steam turbines of today; wheels revolving upon a common shaft and jets of steam blowing with terrific force against their blades. There were the noz-

zles from which the steam, starting from the steam chest
under high pressure, was expanded to a lower pressure, to
acquire velocity before it was applied to the blades of the
moving wheels. There were guides for the steam, channels
which received the jets and passed them on so that they
struck the next wheel from exactly the same direction as their
impact upon the preceding wheel.

It is a tempestuous journey that the steam experiences
inside that immense iron jacket, squat and black, which en-
closes the vitals of the modern steam turbine. Superheated
to a high temperature and acted upon by tremendous pressure, it crowds its way into the steam chest, surging irre-
sistibly toward any available outlet. Through valves into the
nozzles it flings itself, is immediately expanded to a lower
pressure, and hurls its energy at tremendous speed—in some
turbines more than sixteen miles a minute—against the first
revolving wheel, escaping instantly between the blades into
the first set of stationary buckets. There it changes swiftly
to its original angle of impact, strikes the next revolving
wheel, and shoots into the succeeding stationary buckets. At
the end of the first stage it is caught in a second set of nozzles,
which expand it to still lower pressure, giving it renewed
velocity for the increased diameters of the next wheel. In
the far end of the turbine, at reduced pressure, it is condensed
in a vacuum chamber.

Emmet felt that Curtis' first turbines should be redesigned
in order to perform efficient work. He investigated and experimented. Presently he made changes in detail. He studied
especially the arrangement of the buckets and the proportion
of bucket rows to the number of stages. Here was the man
who had redesigned and reconstructed some of the early
Sprague railway motors until they gave such service as simi-

"AS METICULOUSLY ACCURATE AS A FINE WATCH"

Despite their size, huge turbines must be built and assembled with unbelievably close accuracy.

"THEY HAVE A KEEN SENSE OF THE ROMANCE AND ADVENTURE OF WORK"

This motor, built by workmen at the Schenectady plant, was at the time of its construction the largest electric motor in the world. It develops 22,500 horsepower.

"THAT VAST TABERNACLE OF BRICK AND STEEL"

Building 60 at Schenectady. The size can be judged from the figures of
workmen in middle foreground.

lar motors on other roads could never produce. He had found again an opportunity to exert his peculiar genius.

In 1900 two turbines had been jointly designed by Curtis and Emmet. The smaller turbine had a capacity of 500 kilowatts and a speed of 1800 revolutions per minute. Curtis designed the buckets and the nozzles; Emmet designed the general mechanical construction and the arrangement of parts; Emmet, in conjunction with H. G. Reist, designed the generator which the turbine was to drive.

Shop process was slow and laborious, as the shop men for the most part knew nothing about turbines. The only experienced men were a crew of thirty-six mechanics, all of whom had been wrestling with Curtis' first small units for three years or more, and now formed the nucleus of a turbine-shop organization.

Within a year the first Curtis-Emmet turbine was complete and ready for testing under service conditions.

It came up to every expectation. A few months later the 1500-kilowatt unit was well advanced. Emmet and Curtis next designed a vertical 5000 KW turbine, and offered it to Samuel Insull who was now president of the Commonwealth Edison Company of Chicago. He was building a new generating station on Fiske Street in Chicago.

Rice had his hands full to win the Board of Directors to an undertaking so beset with difficulties. But he did it in the end. And all the while Emmet was busy with engineering data, which he finally took to Chicago to lay before Insull. Assured by Emmet that the turbine was possible, Insull staked his business reputation and designed his new station for it.

That was in 1901. The Fiske Street Station was to begin operating in the fall of 1903. Emmet, confident and optimistic, hastened back to Schenectady, and the executive offices hummed with the news he brought.

Bill Madigan was directing the activities of Building 10. Again and again Emmet came to him with turbine parts to be machined. And Madigan, watching the turbines develop, discovered points about them that appealed to him as a connoisseur of machines.

The year 1903 dawned, and with it came anxiety and apprehension for General Electric. Chicago began to ask when the first factory test of the big turbine would be made—Insull and his engineers wanted to be present. A tentative promise was given. It had to be postponed, then postponed again.

A whisper went around, especially among the makers of reciprocating engines, that General Electric was having trouble with the turbine. Perhaps their engineers had been a little too cocksure.

Then Coffin, who understood the selling power of good will, wrote to Rice that the turbine *must* be built on time! Rice called in Emmons, the "little man" who was giving the Schenectady works an *esprit de corps* to be proud of.

A few hours later Emmons had assembled all the factory superintendents in the plant. He put to them one question, "Who, among our general foremen, is one hundred per cent qualified to complete the building of that turbine *on time?*"

A ballot was taken. Only one name on the list had one hundred per cent marked after it by every man in the meeting. The name was Madigan's.

The next day—it was early in February, 1903—Emmons sent for Bill Madigan, and when the friendly mannered foreman appeared, Emmons instructed his secretary to admit no visitors. Madigan felt the tenseness in the air before a word was said.

"Bill," said Emmons, "do you want to make a change?"

"Which way?" said Madigan promptly. "Up or down?"

"Up, if you can swing the job. The story is this, we're in hot water over that Chicago turbine. We've promised to have steam in her by March, and she's nowhere near ready. The company's reputation depends on keeping that promise. We've picked you to swing it. Think it over and give me your answer."

"I don't need to think it over," Madigan replied. "I've been watching the turbine job, and I'd like to tackle it."

The following Monday the new foremen of Building 20, where the big turbine lay almost finished but unassembled, began laying out his work. Early as it was, Emmons was there before him. All the resources of the plant were placed behind this pleasant-spoken, quick-moving master mechanic.

The parts of the turbine were scattered all over the shop, and scarcely another man in the plant knew how to assemble them into a finished machine. Two wheels were to be machined over again because of flaws. Everyone who looked at those wheels shook his head and said, "Six weeks at least." Madigan said nothing, but as he studied the job his fighting spirit rose to the challenge.

Like a general he marshalled his men, organizing their different operations. He kept the work going without pause. Repeatedly he stepped in and worked with his own hands. Everything he did was planned ahead.

Emmons came down to the turbine shop day after day. "When will you steam her, Bill?" he asked.

"March 7th," was the reply.

"You're too optimistic," said Emmons. Those to whom he repeated this promise said, "Madigan's crazy!"

Nevertheless word was sent to Chicago that the turbine would receive its factory test on March 7, and Insull made his plans accordingly. By that time the turbine builders were working at all hours in Shop 20.

March 1 arrived. Rice came down and asked when the turbine would be steamed. Madigan, grimy with dirt and grease, replied, "On March 5!" His eyes were red from lack of sleep, but his head was as clear as ever, his smile as reassuring. The big turbine was almost assembled, a mammoth towering four times as high as a man. A few more days of intensive, unflagging work and on March 4, three days ahead of his first promise, Madigan told the test men to let in steam.

The turbine performed excellently for President Insull at the official test of March 7th. The good name of General Electric had been saved!

The turbine-generator which Samuel Insull ordered from General Electric required only one-tenth of the space and weighed one-eighth as much as the reciprocating engines it replaced. But Emmet's problems were not yet settled. The unit in the Chicago powerhouse had still to be installed. For months things kept going wrong. Construction men had to stay there and watch the turbine as it ran. They fairly lived in the generating station. Whenever the turbine ran well, General Electric stock seemed to rise; when it ran poorly, the stock sagged.

But at the end of three months no more unfavorable reports were received. The turbine ran steadily day and night, month after month. And Emmet busied himself with new experiments and new designs, for a clamor was going up from central station executives for turbines of their own. None were ever demanded that Madigan couldn't build, though he remarked years later that he never enjoyed anything so much as that first "scrap with the turbines."

Other turbines were already on the market but not yet in as large sizes. The DeLaval, and the Parsons, in the hands of

Westinghouse, were from the first great competitors of the Curtis turbine.

As the General Electric shops hummed in the effort to supply the turbine demand, its engineers improved both turbine and generator year after year, eventually reverting to the horizontal type, until the machines grew in efficiency beyond the rosiest dream. But their biggest selling point, in a period of rapid expansion, was economy in space. The capacity of plants could be expanded without adding a square inch to the buildings already in existence. More kilowatts without laying a brick! And the cost of a turbine-generator unit was one-third that for a reciprocating engine and generator.

Curtis' relations with General Electric continued to be active, although the purchase of his patents had been concluded. Under the contract finally entered into he received $1,500,000 for his patent rights in the invention. The contract permitted him to develop on his own initiative turbines for marine applications in all cases where the mode of propulsion was other than electrical. But it left General Electric free to put the turbines on ships if they were electrically run. The possibility of propelling a ship by electricity was something that no one as yet took seriously. But Rice believed in it, and he saw to it that the clause went into the contract. Most electrical scientists, in 1900, dismissed the idea with the remark that to drive an ocean liner by electricity, the generating plant would have to be so large that it would sink the ship! Rice was looking fifteen years ahead in inserting that clause, which was one day to play a leading role in the destiny of the Company.

For the time being General Electric was busy supplying the light and power companies with turbines. In 1909 the original unit at Chicago and a duplicate unit subsequently installed gave place to two larger sets. These were rated at 12,000 kilowatts, more than twice the capacity of the old units. Yet there was so little difference in their dimensions that the new machines were placed upon the original foundations and supplied with steam by the original boilers.

Six swift years had passed. None of those who had borne a hand in the turbulent production of the first Chicago unit was likely to forget the experience. Hence it was proposed that this first large turbine should be taken back to Schenectady, the place of its birth, and set up as a perpetual monument to an industrial victory. There the old pioneer stands today, on the main thoroughfare of the General Electric Works, just outside an enormous building where its own titanic successors, now far more powerful, are carefully assembled and shipped. Madigan himself was there until his retirement.

So was launched the turbine era. Meanwhile, other events were at work shaping the career of the turbine's guardian Company.

Ronald McDonald, the eccentric genius of the Fort Wayne Electric Corporation, died in 1898, whereupon the following year General Electric purchased it.

Four years after this, in 1903, General Electric purchased the Stanley Electric Manufacturing Company at Pittsfield. The Stanley Company had brought out its inductor alternator, and its transformers had reached a point of great efficiency. General Electric could not offer to its customers complete electrical systems without this progressive concern. In 1900 the Siemens and Halske Company also sold its business to General Electric.

32

Magic Comes to Manhattan

THOSE WERE EXCITING DAYS for General Electric's commercial men. Particularly exciting, perhaps, for the selling experts whom Coffin had taken into his organization from other lines, such men as John R. McKee, the former boot and shoe wholesaler of Indianapolis, William J. Clark, the erstwhile coal dealer and postmaster of Birmingham, Connecticut, and many another. Both these men had vindicated Coffin's judgment by rising to high departmental posts; McKee became manager of the Power and Mining Department, and Clark of the Railway Department.

McKee always valued his breaking-in days with the old Thomson-Houston Company, grubbing in the coal mines with young fellows fresh from college, trying to make practical the Van De Poele electric mine-digger. Now he was pushing the electrical idea for coal and metal mines for all he was worth, and motors for almost every use under the sun.

"We are biting into the mining business," he said to Coffin in the summer of 1895, and produced the latest issue of his sales bulletin to verify the statement. The superintendent of the Berwind-White Coal Mining Company, of Osceola Mills, Pennsylvania, announced in that publication that he had a mine "turning out over 11,000 tons of bituminous coal per month, and not a mule about the place."

The Eureka Colliery never had a mule from the day it opened. A rough track, a generator, and a two-ton, ground-hugging electric locomotive did the pulling. The locomotive was like a flat box on wheels. It was small indeed for a loco-motive—ten feet long and five feet wide, and so low that the overhead conductor was less than thirty-six inches above the rail. It was dubbed the "turtle-back" because of its slop-ing, rounded top, and it had the pulling power of many mules.

A few weeks later McKee was describing a power plant at Scott Haven from which electrical energy was supplied to several mines. "A central station in mining work," he re-marked to his colleagues of the sales committee. But McKee had little time for waving the feathers in his cap. Sales op-portunities poured in upon his staff.

In those stirring, strenuous days many an epic was related at the meetings of the sales committee. There was the mis-sionary motor at Middletown, Ohio, which was given only "tolerance room" in a bicycle factory by the skeptical own-ers; but it was soon being "tolerated" to such an extent that the owners ordered eight others like it.

There was many a tale of being marooned overnight in the sort of hotels that make men dream of home. W. J. Han-ley, who was ranging the region south of the Great Lakes with an energy that was to turn him one day into a district manager, had one such experience when a window broke and the snow of a blizzard whirled in over his bed all night. Later in the same winter in a temperature fifteen below zero he had sold an electrical outfit to a snowbound miller. He made a dash to catch a freight train in an open cutter with part of his pajamas wrapped around his head to keep his ears from freezing. He caught the freight, and clambered over the rocking cars in pitch darkness to ride on the locomotive, which carried him to his station.

McKee's salesmen of the Power and Mining Department and those of S. Dana Greene, of the Lighting Department, thought themselves thoroughly conversant with modern electrical machines. Then Coffin announced the patent agreement of 1896 with Westinghouse, which permitted General Electric to handle the Tesla type of polyphase induction motor. Again the commercial personnel studied charts and digested test reports between sales, until they were able to present the virtues of this new type of motor as wholeheartedly as salesmen should.

The motor sales went well over twelve million dollars in 1895, and reached seventeen million dollars in 1899. A yearly increase in total orders of twenty per cent was not uncommon. The Supply Department, under Jesse R. Lovejoy, reported an annual increase running from 20 to 24 per cent, and incandescent lamp sales were swelling yearly by leaps varying from 23 to 25 per cent. Total orders in 1900 stood above twenty-six million dollars.

At Lynn, where doubts had once been expressed that the business would occupy an entire three-story building, the buildings were now numbered by the score. A new plant had arisen upon the flats along the Saugus River. Begun in 1892, halted by the panic of 1893, resumed in the middle nineties, the future River Works was outstripping even the original factory on Western Avenue, where the Thomson-Houston Company had struggled in the optimistic eighties.

The inroads made upon the conservative railroad business were slower in taking shape, despite the electric locomotives of the Baltimore and Ohio. Then in 1898 came an opportunity. Clark and his men were soon beaming over the railway outlook as were McKee's power salesmen over the sales of motors. They had a customer in the Hoboken Shore Road, which operated a two-mile freight terminal line from Weehawken to Hoboken, where the docks of the North German Lloyd Steamship Company were located. To handle this haulage a stout two-truck locomotive of 540 horsepower capacity had been built, with an expected speed of eight miles an hour under load.

This installation, though not large, had great missionary value. It was close to New York, and when its trial trip took place railroad officials from every road that served the metropolis were watching closely as it pulled its load of nearly 300 tons.

From the center of Manhattan Island there once arose in pre-electrical days a pall of sooty smoke that rolled up incessantly. Its lower depths were shot through with white, fanlike billows of wind-blown steam. At night lurid shafts of firelight pierced the ascending vapors; and infernos of flame could be seen down in the darkness of the pit.

Fifteen blocks through the heart of the metropolis and thirty or forty acres of high-priced real estate were occupied by this blanketed area. It seemed one of the inevitable burdens of modern metropolitan life, a grimly exacted penalty.

To this spot there came every twenty-four hours, loudly puffing and panting, seven hundred steam locomotives and 30,000 persons riding in the trains they hauled. The marvellous steam toilers could be seen moving up and down that vortex with easy effort and murky breath, hundreds of lusty locomotives, each one adding its hissing voice to the deafening chorus, as if exulting in the superhuman power with which human brains had endowed them.

Such was the passenger yard of the Grand Central Terminal at Forty-second Street as the nineteenth century closed. Stretching northward was its one outlet into the north, the Park Avenue tunnel, where passengers and crews endured the nuisances and dangers of smoke in the narrow tube.

These conditions had existed for years, and on the Manhattan Elevated Railway snorting little steam locomotives were pulling the crowded "L" trains. Each of them consumed its quota of bituminous coal and gave back in return not only useful hauling power but low-trailing clouds of smoke. For years attempts had been made to replace the little steam locomotives with electric motors. Public campaigns favoring the change extended back into the eighties. But in twenty years no day had dawned when the smoke had not filled the lungs of patrons.

If the passenger yard of the Grand Central Terminal was a smoking pit, the Manhattan Elevated was a smoke-belching serpent twining the length of the island metropolis. Thus it remained when Sprague, last of the hopeful demonstrators, withdrew his electric motors in defeat. After the merger of 1889 which added the Sprague Electric Railway and Motor Company to the Edison General Electric, Sprague struck out again for himself with an idea that had germinated in his mind some years before. The Sprague stationary motors were winning friends in Massachusetts through the agency of George F. Steele and the old New England Electric Company. One day Steele heard of a new type of motor which had given a startling demonstration of speed in lifting an elevator. He talked with its designer, a young Boston mechanic, Charles E. Pratt, and notified Sprague, who became interested at once in Pratt's accomplishment. Sprague and Pratt finally decided to join forces, and early in the nineties the Sprague Electric Elevator Company was organized.

Sprague understood perfectly what electricity could do in the operation of elevators, from the days when his stationary motor had run scores of belt-driven elevators. But, invading a domain already in the possession of the hydraulic elevator companies, he met with intense opposition. Working steadily against it, he obtained his first promising contract in 1892. The Postal Telegraph Building in New York purchased six Sprague-Pratt passenger elevators. But in so doing they demanded a cast-iron guarantee that in case of failure of the electrical method the Sprague Company would install any hydraulic system the customer might select.

These hydraulic systems never had a chance. Sprague ran four of the electric elevators at a speed of 325 feet per minute with a "live load" of 2500 pounds, and the other two at a speed of 400 feet per minute with a load of 1800 pounds. So came into existence the modern high-speed electric elevator, driven by directly connected motors, with a control system expressly adapted to such work. From the status of pioneer, Sprague rose to that of leader in the field. T. Comerford Martin spoke of him years later as "the father of electric transportation, horizontal and vertical."

Sprague continued to experiment with the motors in the Postal Telegraph Building. He connected the individual control circuits to a master control switch so as to operate all the elevators simultaneously. They responded, but their movement was far from synchronous. For some time he pondered the experiment. There was something about it that haunted him. Then came the swift inspiration that trains of cars could be operated by the inter-control, master-switch plan which he had tried with the elevators.

It was the golden key to a hundred problems of traction. Sprague visualized the application clearly. He was able to design that system almost at a single sitting. It became the multiple-unit method of train control—a method that proved to be the final step in the practicability of electric trains on elevated roads, in subways, and even on electrified main railroad lines. No other schemes of train operation approached it in simplicity, flexibility, and effectiveness.

In its perfected form, multiple-unit control permitted assembling into trains, with control from any point in the train, any number of cars each with its own motors and controllers. The electrical units were connected with each other and with master controllers by a "train line" which produced unison in the motive power provided by each car. The number and sequence of the cars was immaterial; they could be operated in any combination.

What feats were not made possible—quick control, rapid acceleration, fast train schedule, short intervals between trains, and easy adaptation of train lengths to fluctuations of traffic! It was the solution of operating problems in congested city areas, with their recurring rush hours and expanding populations.

Sprague thought at once of the Manhattan Elevated Railway. A year later, in 1896, and again in 1897, he sent letters to the officials of the road describing his multiple-unit idea and offering to demonstrate it with their trains at his own financial risk. When nothing resulted from these proposals, Sprague went back to his elevators.

Two years went by. Then out of a clear sky Leslie Carter, President of the South Side Elevated Railway of Chicago, known as the "alley L," wrote to Sprague asking if he would serve as consulting engineer in the electrification of that road.

Sprague was in the midst of an ambitious elevator project; and he was on crutches as well. During his convalescence after a bad fall, John McKay, the largest stockholder of his company, had suggested that Sprague go to London to secure a tempting contract which involved half a million dollars— a proposed elevator installation for the Central London Tube Railway.

It was the largest installation yet attempted. There were to be forty-nine elevator cars. Sprague assembled data and prepared drawings, planning to sail the last of March. It was then that he heard from Leslie Carter, and the engineers of the Chicago road called upon him with the plans for its electrification.

This was the opportunity Sprague had been waiting for. He explained his idea of multiple-unit control to the engineers and to William J. Clark, manager of General Electric's Railway Department, who accompanied them.

Sprague delayed his sailing for a month. His bid for the electrification contract he submitted purely as an individual, with no company back of him, and in competition with General Electric, Westinghouse, and the Walker Company. Sprague not only stood his ground with these organized concerns, but entered into a lively contention to prove to Carter that an eighteen-mile schedule, as proposed by one of his competitors, was unsound engineering, and that his own recommendation of fifteen miles an hour should be adopted. He and Carter spent several hours one day in April talking by telegraph over an open wire, each standing at the elbow of an operator, totally oblivious of the swelling telegraph tolls.

The day before Sprague was to sail for Europe he received word that he had been awarded the contract, one of the conditions being that he put up a $100,000 bond as a guarantee of performance. Sprague wired that he would furnish the bond upon his return from London.

So he departed on April 29, 1897, facing a tremendous

task to be carried through in a conservative country, and leaving behind him a situation that bristled with problems.

In London Sprague felt as if he were trying to straddle the Atlantic, with one foot in England and the other in the United States. He must work fast with his London prospect, yet he had arrived in the midst of the Whitsuntide holidays. He must protect his interest in the execution of the Chicago contract, yet all he could do was to cable instructions and rely upon the judgment of his assistant, McKay, who was to sign the contract under power of attorney.

It did not ease his mind that one of the stipulations in this contract was the guarantee of a demonstration of multiple-unit control by July 15th. It was then the first of May. Multiple-unit control existed only on paper, and he had no idea how long he would be detained in London.

One encouraging thing happened during those first two weeks with the arrival of William J. Clark, sent by General Electric to get the sub-contract for the 240 electric motors to be installed on the South Side Elevated. After Clark got his contract, Sprague obtained through him the use of General Electric's experimental railway track at Schenectady. Sprague had assumed the obligation of providing the track, the railway furnishing the cars.

Meanwhile things were dragging in London. Sprague had a full-size controller equipment and a typical elevator car safety mechanism set up in the basement of the Cecil Hotel for demonstrations, and had submitted his bid for the contract. But he could not get the Central London Tube Railway to come to a decision. He guaranteed that the cost of operating the elevators would not exceed one pound per thousand single trips of 67 feet rise, regardless of the size of the cars. But still they hesitated.

Time was passing and he had to get back to the United

States. In a last effort to clinch the matter, he offered to proceed with the contract staking all his prospects in the London elevator project unreservedly upon the performance of trial elevators in one shaft, Sir Benjamin Baker, the railway's engineer, to be the judge. Upon this basis he was awarded the contract.

Sprague sailed for New York on June 16th, landing three weeks before the date on which he was required to demonstrate multiple-unit control. He found that some beginning had been made, guided by what meager instructions he had been able to send by letter and cable. But a colossal task remained, and no one but a man with driving willpower, unsparing of himself, could hope to swing it.

Sprague did not spare himself; and he did not hesitate to spend money. He worked day and night, and on July 15 he was in Schenectady with multiple-unit control installed upon two cars of the South Side Elevated Railway. He operated those two cars himself the following day, and saw his idea admirably vindicated.

Within a year after the tests at Schenectady, the South Side road was fully equipped and multiple-unit control was in service on its first installation. Almost at the same time, Edward H. Johnson sought another business alliance with his former associate, and early in 1899 the Sprague Electric Elevator Company merged with the Interior Conduit and Insulation Company, which Johnson had organized, to form the Sprague Electric Company.

Fresh from his success on the Chicago line, Sprague turned again to the New York situation. He had long advocated before the Rapid Transit Commission an electric underground transportation system for the city. Now he renewed his campaign. He also wrote repeatedly to the officials of the Manhattan Elevated, and published a number of news-

TRIUMVIRATE OF SCIENCE
Dr. Whitney, Dr. Coolidge, and Dr. Langmuir, of the General Electric
Research Laboratory.

CAMPUS OF "THE UNIVERSITY OF LIGHT"
The General Electric plant at Nela Park, Cleveland, Ohio.

"AMERICA'S LARGEST ELECTRICAL WORKSHOP"
Airplane view of the Schenectady Works

paper interviews describing the virtues of multiple-unit control. It seemed to be effort wasted. There was no interest from 1897 to 1900.

In another quarter, however, the importance of Sprague's system was more fully appreciated. Electric train control was an issue with the General Electric engineers. They were working on various ideas, and believed they had found the most reliable method in a contactor form of the series-parallel control system, which embodied the work of Elihu Thomson, William B. Potter, and Frank E. Case. After seeing Sprague's tests of 1897, they considered the application of their contactor type of apparatus to Sprague's multiple-unit system.

When the Manhattan Elevated finally began planning electrification in 1900, negotiations had been begun by Coffin for the acquiring of Sprague's multiple-unit patent. These were completed in 1903, and General Electric acquired the Sprague Company; the contract for the electrification of the Manhattan Elevated had not yet been closed. The question of what the road should pay for the equipment resulted in a deadlock, and the commercial men could do no more. They perceived that a master hand was needed, a final, diplomatic, understanding word. When the situation was presented to Coffin, he went alone to the office of the Manhattan Elevated Railway to speak the word that no one else could speak. He brought back with him one of the largest contracts in months, representing more than a million dollars and involving the initial installation of nearly 1700 motors.

Electric service on the road began on December 20, 1900, and the first ticket for passage on an electric train in New York was sold at 11 o'clock that morning to a woman at the 92nd Street Station.

Meanwhile the situation at the Grand Central Terminal was approaching a climax. As trains fought their way through the smoke of the tunnel, the firemen in the locomotives were obliged to lie on the floor of the cabs and peer beneath the swirling vapors to read the signals and guide the engineers. Sentiment was so strongly awakened that the city authorities adopted an ordinance permanently banning the operation of trains into the city by steam power. Thereupon the New York Central appointed an electrical commission to undertake a study of electric power. And the commission discovered that electrification would mean a saving of hundreds of thousands of dollars every year!

A project was launched for making over the great terminal station at a cost of some forty million dollars. The station was to accommodate 200,000 passengers a day instead of 30,000; the great passenger yard would handle 3000 trains a day instead of 700.

And what was to become of the smoking pit, with its dark vapor-cloud? It was to be concealed from sight beneath the city. Above it, forty acres of real estate would be created in the heart of the city that was hungry for more space.

By 1908 the program was under way. General Electric locomotives hauled trains through the northward tunnel in clear, clean air, and for thirty miles to Croton, and twenty-five to White Plains. Originally there were thirty of these clean, quiet, but no less powerful locomotives. Designed by Asa F. Batchelder, the motor armatures were mounted gearless upon the axles and the field magnets embodied in the mechanical structure of the locomotive. This line, built in the Schenectady shops, was introduced by historic old "6000." Each unit weighed ninety-four tons complete and had four driving motors. They were the first gearless locomotives of General Electric make since those designed for the Baltimore and Ohio Tunnel, but were more sturdy and simple in form. Pulling with 2800 horsepower, they were as powerful as the steam monsters they replaced. By means of the multiple-unit system two of them could be coupled together as a single unit of double power, and as the *Electrical World* put it, could "dally lightly with the biggest trains the Central system has ever known."

They drew their power from steam turbine-generators in a distant powerhouse. Eight turbine-generators, 60,000 horsepower all told, supplied the energy. And it was there, where they were not a menace, that the smoky vapors now rolled skyward.

The Interborough Rapid Transit Company soon followed the Manhattan Elevated in determining upon electrification. General Electric designed a new type of motor expressly for use on this road and sent two trial units to appear in the competitive tests. After they had been delivered, it was discovered that a certain change in the internal design of the motor would greatly increase its efficiency. To conceal from the competitors what was in the wind, one of the two motors already installed on an Interborough car was changed over night. When the comparative trials took place, this motor out-performed any of the others, and General Electric was awarded half of the entire motor order in addition to the whole order for control equipment.

33

A Venture Into Research

THERE HAD BEEN A PROBLEM in the back of Rice's mind since the expiration of the Edison incandescent lamp patent in 1894—how to increase the lamp's efficiency. One day toward the fall of 1900 the door of Rice's office opened to Charles P. Steinmetz, now becoming famous as a mathematical engineer, and with him, Albert G. Davis, manager of the Company's Patent Department.

"Mr. Steinmetz and I," said Davis, "believe it would be an excellent idea to create a laboratory where scientific investigations might go forward on the incandescent lamp and other problems. We should like to recommend such a step for your serious consideration.

"To improve electric lighting is our foremost thought," he continued, while Steinmetz, leaning in characteristic pose on a corner of Rice's desk, nodded assent. "I personally feel, and Mr. Steinmetz endorses my views, that the electric light has a future more brilliant than its past. We should not like to assert that the carbon filament lamp is the best lamp we can have. There may be a better type of electrode for arc lamps than the carbon electrode. These things cannot be determined properly without research."

Research! It was what Rice himself had been thinking of, Yet hardly another executive in the country in those days was considering such a step.

The three entered into an analytical discussion of the question. They all agreed that the proposed laboratory at Schenectady should be entirely separate from the factory and the sales branches, a place where all talk of sales should be out of order.

Dr. Willis R. Whitney, of the Massachusetts Institute of Technology, was finally engaged for the post. In order to start working at once, Whitney agreed to take advantage of a laboratory which Steinmetz had established for his own use in an old barn that stood in the rear of the rooming house occupied by Ernst J. Berg, Eskil Berg, and himself on Liberty Street. There in 1901 Whitney came for three days a week to work on preliminary problems, usually with assistance from Steinmetz. The entire staff consisted of Whitney and a young assistant, J. T. H. Dempster. But that little barn was the cradle of General Electric's Research Laboratory.

COFFIN REALIZED AS FEW OTHERS DID the role of the incandescent lamp as the herald of the electrical idea, the first contact which many thousands of people had with the electrical way of doing things. If it made a good impression, electric service in general would benefit by the resultant good will. So Coffin's policy of helping the independent companies to improve their product, either with or without amalgamation, was pre-eminently sound.

Among the independents there was one man who held the key to the problem, Franklin S. Terry, proprietor of the Sunbeam Incandescent Lamp Company of Chicago. This unpretentious company was established just about the time of the great lawsuit over Edison's lamp. Terry had found himself restricted by the infringement actions, but after the patent expired in 1894 he had slowly built his business anew, watching with wary eye the progress of his big competitor. Shortly before 1900 Terry began talking consolidation with some of the other independents. One evening in 1901 he sat next to B. G. Tremaine at a jobbers' dinner in Chicago.

"I tell you, Tremaine, we've simply got to combine!" he exclaimed. "If we don't we'll never get anywhere and General Electric will get everywhere."

"What have they been doing to you now?" said Tremaine.

"Taking business away from us," snapped Terry. "We had a big prospect in sight and submitted samples of our lamps. So did the Edison Lamp Works. Then they proposed to the prospect that he test their lamps and ours. Even provided the equipment for the testing. Of course they won. Why? The old story—a better lamp. We can't stand that sort of thing."

Slowly, as they talked, the virtues of consolidation assumed clearer outlines to both of them and a plan suggested itself—a plan for merging the independents as actual competitors of General Electric and at the same time obtaining from General Electric adequate financing to assure success in operation. It was a bold plan.

But General Electric was prepared to accept the proposition. They knew that Terry and Tremaine's interest would stimulate their activities, and they were confident that these men could be relied upon to do a good piece of work. It was not the first time that General Electric had acquired control of an enterprise and vested full executive management in the men already operating it. It was men—always men—that Coffin sought, the driving force behind all enterprise, the dynamic source of all progress and all success.

Let Terry and Tremaine have full play! If they developed new ideas, excellent. There was no doubt that General Electric would share in these, just as the National Association would be allowed to share in new ideas emanating from the Lamp Works at Harrison.

And so, before 1901 drew to a close, the National Electric Lamp Association was created, without a General Electric man in it. By 1904 the National Electric Lamp Association was in full operation. In all essential respects it was an active competitor of the Edison Lamp Works of General Electric. In the Cleveland factory of the Association on 45th Street had been organized such service departments as cost, sales, and advertising analysis, credit systems, production methods, and engineering and scientific research. Each of the affiliated companies was termed a "lamp division." They were fully autonomous and so nearly independent that, although authority centered in Cleveland, it was seldom apparent. Expert aid, such as they could never have afforded by themselves, was quickly available when needed.

As time went on, it was repeatedly demonstrated that leadership in the manufacture of incandescent lamps was not to be wrested from the veterans at Harrison. Notable improvements still came, for the most part, from the Edison Works.

Amazing and brilliant work was being accomplished, between 1900 and 1910 by William R. Burrows, once a Thomson-Houston apprentice, and John W. Howell, the veteran Edison lamp engineer. Burrows had devised a machine which accomplished the double weld process automatically and made use of a smaller size of platinum wire than an operator could hold in his fingers. The first reduction in the costly amount of platinum used in the lamp came with the invention of the double weld process.

Platinum was used originally because it is the only metal which expands and contracts at the same rate as glass, so that during the cooling of the stem seal, containing platinum wires embedded in the glass, the airtight joint was not impaired. Around 1912 research under Howell's direction developed dumet wire, which consists of a core of nickel-iron alloy within a thin shell of copper. Dumet wire shrinks at the same rate as glass, and by its use platinum is avoided.

So platinum had gone the way of the bamboo filament. But no one was satisfied yet with what had been done to this tiny globe of glass.

Burrows set to work to devise an automatic filament-cementing machine and an automatic exhaust machine in which the air was pumped out of the bulbs and the exhaust tube sealed off from the bulb at the rate of several thousand lamps a day—lamps far superior to any that had been produced by hand methods of exhausting. A similar machine was developed about the same time at Cleveland.

Already bulbs were blown in moulds instead of by hand. But now came the remarkable bulb-blowing machine, known as the Westlake machine. It was devised by August Kadow of the Libbey Glass Company, and purchased by General Electric in 1917. Nothing like the automatic glass blower had been seen before. It did what generations of hand blowers had never believed possible—it produced symmetrical, moulded bulbs of glass automatically.

Lower factory costs meant lower selling prices. The National Electric Lamp Association, because it was part of General Electric, was able to share in these cost-reducing innovations. The effect of the trend in "co-operative competition" between the two establishments made itself apparent in the greater number of lamps annually purchased.

34

Steinmetz and the Arc Light

STEINMETZ HAD THE CREED of a searcher. He was never tired of laboratory work. That was where happiness lay for Steinmetz. He lost himself for long hours, for half a night, in his private laboratory in Schenectady, and what he did there he never alluded to as "work."

When he joined with Davis in recommending the experimental laboratory which Whitney was beginning, Steinmetz endorsed Davis' views of the need of applied electrical science. Already there was the carbon-filament lamp (incandescent), the carbon-electrode lamp (arc), and the carbon brush of the direct-current motor and generator. Electric light and electric power had really passed through what might be called the "carbon era."

Was carbon the ultimate medium for all these products? Steinmetz would not be satisfied to say that it was. And so he bent his scrutiny upon the arc lamp. The arc lamp had not changed in essential character since the evening in 1808 when Sir Humphry Davy of the Royal Institution produced the first electric arc, with the aid of a battery of 2000 voltaic cells. Two electrodes of carbon were used on that night, and had been ever since. Changes were all concerned with the manner of producing the current that passed through the electrodes, the mode of connecting the lamps to the circuit, and the method of regulating the length of the arc by magnetic mechanism. These were the contributions of Brush, Thomson, Wood, and the rest. Davy had contributed the light source; the others had contributed the various means of utilizing that light source for practical illumination.

At night, absorbed in the enthralling search, Steinmetz was to be found in his laboratory. By day he pursued his mathematical engineering and his consultation work at his office at the General Electric plant. People passing the new Steinmetz dwelling on Wendell Avenue, unfinished in 1900, could see shining from the windows of a long, low structure in the rear electric lights of an intense bluish-white radiance. More and more frequently as the weeks slipped into the year 1901 were those lights seen. They were an illuminated gauge of the progress the black-bearded little man was making in his search for something that would supplant Sir Humphry Davy's arc-lamp electrode.

Toward the end of 1900 all his experiments centered upon a type of electrode composed of magnetite—an oxide of iron —mixed with a proportion of titanium. The resulting light was far more brilliant than that produced by the carbon electrodes. But only long investigation could determine the quantities of magnetite and titanium that would work best together. Both substances had drawbacks. They must be combined in the one ratio in a thousand which would succeed in allowing their advantages to outweigh their objectionable points.

To assist him Steinmetz called upon the new General Electric laboratory which now, after its first few months of existence, was located in a small wooden building at the

General Electric Works, designated then as Building 10. There and at the Steinmetz laboratory on Wendell Avenue the study of the magnetite-titanium electrode went on, until its brilliant future was at length assured.

The new lamp had peculiarities of its own. The arc instead of springing forth pointed at both ends and bulging in the middle, as did the arc of the carbon electrodes, became triangular, spreading in both directions from the tip of the upper electrode and coming to a point at the tip of the lower. In the second place, the illumination originated in the arc itself, whereas in the carbon lamp the illumination was caused by the incandescent tip of the lower electrode, heated white-hot by the arc.

These were advantages that caused Steinmetz and Whitney to watch their laboratory lamps with keenest attention, and to consider it only a minor episode when they discovered that after the current had once been turned off they could not reproduce the arc!

They saw at once that when the current ceased to flow, the upper electrode dropped against the lower, as in the case of the carbon lamp, and owing to the melted magnetite both stuck together, so that when the current was again turned on the control mechanism could not pull them apart. Current flowed through the two electrodes without encountering the break in the circuit on which the arc depends. Magnetite has a lower melting point than carbon, so that this difficulty was not encountered with the carbon lamp.

Steinmetz soon had another disciple in the person of C. A. B. Halvorson, one of the most active engineers at the River Works at Lynn, where arc lamps and their auxiliary equipment were manufactured. So active a disciple had he become, as the problem of the magnetite arc lamp came to a focus, that it was soon apparent that he might do for

Steinmetz's discovery what Wood and Brush and Thomson did for Sir Humphry Davy's—put it into practical working form.

Halvorson succeeded in designing a control mechanism which would keep the two electrodes apart when the current was off, and would automatically move them into the correct relation to form the arc when the current came on again. Then the melted magnetite caused more trouble. Globules of molten iron, instantly solidifying, dropped from the upper electrode and smashed through the glass globe of the lamp.

Again and again it happened. Globe after globe was broken, and at the end of each day the janitor was swamped with the job of sweeping up glass fragments. Hundreds of globes were broken before it was reluctantly admitted that magnetite could not be used.

After more experimenting, Halvorson tried pure copper for the upper electrode, retaining the magnetite-titanium combination for the lower. Here was the great solution. The difficulties of melted magnetite were eliminated, and the brilliance of the arc retained, despite the fact that only one electrode was active. The copper was permanent to an unusual degree, requiring renewal only about once in three years. This electrode, however, had to be encased in a steel shell to prevent undue oxidation.

A fresh difficulty now arose from fumes and vapors given off by the magnetite under the heat of the arc. The vapor, thick and brownish, settled on the globe, obscuring the arc. A number of expedients were tried, but Halvorson finally placed inside the lamp a smoke outlet or chimney constructed of wrought-iron pipe. This drew the vapor into the outer air, and a small cap with lateral openings allowed it to escape without being blown back into the chimney by the wind.

At length the new lamp was ready for quantity manufacture, and ready to face manufacturing problems, now that problems in design had been met and defeated. The magnetite electrode consisted of a tube into which the magnetite and titanium, in powder form, were forced under pressure. The two kinds of powder had to be uniformly distributed throughout the tube, and it was impossible for anyone to do this with such speed as to allow quantity production.

Again Halvorson attacked the problem, while the work of preparing the new lamp for the market was suspended. He was completely baffled, until one day, walking along the shore, he noticed how closely the sand was packed by the action of the waves. A solution came to him in a flash. He got back to his office as rapidly as possible. There he worked out his scheme for subjecting the electrode tubes to a constant gentle bumping as the pressure was applied. The uniform distribution of the powder was assured, and the whole process could be performed by a machine.

Early in 1903 most of the new lamp's advocates had given it up in despair. Someone suggested that a batch of fifty of the lamps should be manufactured and presented to Dr. Steinmetz, and that the undertaking should then be considered closed. The fifty lamps were sent over to Schenectady, and Halvorson went along to install them. About half of the lamps were put up on poles around Steinmetz' new house and along the adjacent streets. Steinmetz was delighted. He had no inkling of the skepticism at Lynn or of the virtual rejection of his arc lamp in that quarter. He believed in the lamp, never doubting that its day of practical utility was close at hand. As he and Halvorson stood in the picturesque grounds surrounding Steinmetz's home and watched those lamps flash their blue-white brilliance, they knew that this was the arc lamp of the future. It still had its imperfections—but it would not fail!

Yet this ceremony, planned as the funeral of a tremendous project, proved to be a celebration of its success. Halvorson was able to obtain operating data from the installation that indicated readjustments and refinements in the lamps. The Lynn men were bowled over by the news that the magnetite lamp was a practical success and was to go on the market forthwith!

Out of an odd, almost Bohemian environment came the magnetite electrode. No workshop in America, perhaps in all the world, had quite the bizarre atmosphere of Steinmetz's laboratory during those years when the new century was coming in, and with it the gleaming, blue-white lamps.

In that environment the study of all the problems of commercial introduction and operation of those lamps went steadily forward. Research and science were mingled with the informal housekeeping of a bachelor menage. There were ordinarily two persons in the establishment, Steinmetz and his general assistant, J. LeRoy Hayden. They lived and worked in the laboratory while the new house was being built, for Steinmetz refused to leave his beloved paradise.

Hayden had come up from the General Electric works to take charge of the power plant adjoining the laboratory, where a Brush arc-light dynamo generated direct current for the twenty-five magnetite lamps of the outdoor exhibit. Steinmetz offered him quarters in the laboratory to save the long trip back to his room in downtown Schenectady. Hayden was only too glad to accept, little supposing that it was the beginning of a working combination that was to last twenty years, or that he was to become Steinmetz's most intimate friend. He moved his personal effects into the laboratory, sleeping in the room next to Steinmetz's on the second floor, and eating the generous meals that Steinmetz cooked on a little gas stove.

It was a necessary evil, the business of eating, but Stein‑ metz took the burden upon himself, and he cooked not as a chef but as a chemist. He was partial to all shades of yellow. Eggs were consequently a staple of diet, varied, when he could get his mind off his favorite color, by beefsteak and boiled potatoes.

The two ate unceremoniously, did their chores on a co‑operative basis, and hurried to the test room and the glowing bulb, while day vanished and the hours of the night marched on. Neither thought of sleep until late and yielded to it only with regret.

Halvorson and others of the engineering group frequently visited Steinmetz who offered them the hospitality of his laboratory. They sat in faded, threadbare parlor chairs or on a horsehair lounge that stood amid a maze of laboratory apparatus, as talk drifted to the magnetite lamp.

"But it works only on direct-current circuits," one salesman complained in dismay, for there were not many direct-current circuits in existence.

"That only means," said Steinmetz, in his characteristic way, "that we must have some way of changing current from alternating to direct. In our laboratory Dr. Weintraub is experimenting now with a tube in which an electric current is changed from alternating to direct by means of mercury vapor."

Dr. Ezechiel Weintraub, who had discovered that mercury vapor will permit the passage of an electric current in one direction only, was a physicist in the General Electric Research Laboratory. He made the discovery in a mercury-arc lamp of fair illuminating properties but cursed by a ghastly greenish tint.

Peter Cooper Hewitt, son of a former mayor of New York, was following the same line of experiments in Newark. He, too, had invented a mercury-arc lamp of brilliant, greenish light, which he was attempting to market in long tubes. He, too, brought out a mercury-vapor rectifier. Inevitably the claims of the two inventors clashed in the United States Patent Office. To clear up the situation, General Electric made an offer to purchase Hewitt's concern. Accepting the offer, the Cooper Hewitt Electric Company thereby joined General Electric, and the latter marketed Hewitt's tubular mercury lamp, which developed a special field of usefulness in photographic studios.

In the meantime Steinmetz had adapted Weintraub's mercury-arc rectifier for commercial work in connection with the magnetite lamp. After several changes in the design of the tube, he substituted this convenient device for the bulky and costly rotating machines which had hitherto performed the converting function.

In Jackson, Michigan, magnetite lamps first went into commercial use in 1904. The interest of electric light men all over the country was focused upon that city. The new lights were given the trade name of "luminous arc lamps," and their merits were so apparent that scores of orders materialized.

Then Boston demanded a street light of even greater brilliance than the luminous arc lamp as yet supplied. General Electric engineers set to work to raise the capacity of the lamp from 300 to 500 watts, and to increase the proportion of titanium in the electrode. It was no simple task. Day and night for almost three months Halvorson and his assistants worked with an isolated lamp in the outskirts of Boston. Then they installed twenty-five lamps on Huntington Avenue with a success which amazed the Boston engineers. Four thousand of these lamps eventually supplied the entire area of Boston proper.

EDWIN W. RICE, JR.
President of General Electric from 1913 to 1922.

THE MACHINE THAT MADE RADIO HISTORY
Dr. E. F. W. Alexanderson and his high-frequency alternator.

In 1902–03 General Electric built searchlights with lenses thirty-six, forty-eight, and sixty inches in diameter. Most of these were ordered by the Army and the Navy, which were engaged in extensive maneuvers to test the coast defences on Long Island Sound and Casco Bay. The naval craft were attempting, theoretically, to get past the coastal fortifications by night. Searchlights were set to work to hunt down the "enemy." The first 60-inch light was placed in Fort Wright, on Long Island Sound, and a battery of 36-inch lights was set out in other forts around New London. Unwaveringly the powerful beams "protected" New York from the attack. Not a vessel escaped detection.

One 80-inch monster was built by General Electric in 1904 and sent to the St. Louis Exposition—the only one of its size ever built. The handling of this great projector was a construction job in itself. A stationary steam engine, rigged to a block and tackle, was required to swing it up the side of a building to its resting place. It was not the sort of thing that anyone would expect to get lost—yet that is what happened. General Electric never knew what became of it after the exposition ended. A rumor drifted in some years later that the big light was sold to the Russian government when the Russo-Japanese war opened, and that it joined in the defence of Port Arthur on the coast of Siberia.

These multifarious developments were of necessity the work of a highly specialized personnel. Technical problems were most frequently mastered by technical men, but not always. Now and then an idea emanated from the shops. Such was the case when, in preparing for a railway motor test, Peter J. Mulvey, foreman of the test, contributed a notable improvement to the carbon brush.

A dozen years had passed since the carbon brush was applied to the infant street-railway motor, in which time it had stood the burden well. But the increasing capacities of traction motors proved greater than the brush in its original form could handle. In the electrification of the Manhattan Elevated in 1901, the motors were rated at 153 horsepower, and the carbon brushes sparked alarmingly when current was applied. The engineers tried to lubricate the brushes by dipping them in oil, but the sparking continued. The problem became a thorn in the side of "Pete" Mulvey, then spending his tenth year in the plant.

The boys who worked for Mulvey on the railway motor test—college graduates fresh from the campus—were great admirers of his sagacity as foreman, his knowledge of electric motors, and his open-handed manner. They found him not only fair in his dealings, but a jolly fellow in a crowd and one who appreciated a joke. They were delighted when the news swept their department late in 1901 that Pete had solved the problem of lubricating the carbon brush that Van De Poele had invented a few years earlier.

Various accounts tell how he turned the trick. The version most generally related, even by Mulvey himself, attained in time the dignity of tradition. The story went that Pete had become so annoyed one morning over the obstinacy of the carbon brush that he flung it the whole length of the shop and saw it vanish in a bucket of oil. Repenting of his impulsive conduct he rescued the brush, took it home that night, dried it out by baking it in the kitchen stove, and discovered the next day that it worked with complete freedom from sparking.

What Mulvey actually did was a trifle different, though he achieved the same results. Experimenting on his own account, he immersed brushes in oil, then subjected them to repeated bakings, with an interval of time between each baking. That was the secret of the lubricated brush. The lubrication was so thoroughly baked in that the brush would transmit a heavy current without danger to the commutator from sparking. Later the Research Laboratory devised a self-lubricating brush, and reduced the costs of manufacture.

An entire shop at the Schenectady Works was now devoted to carbon products, including brushes, and 2,000,000 pieces were manufactured there annually. The period of tremendous expansion in the shops was then at its height. And John Miller, the weather-beaten millwright who so dearly loved his machines, was encountering tight situations in equipping the spacious new shop buildings. A big building, the present Building 16, was completed in 1899 and into it went a huge sixty-foot boring mill. To handle this mass of metal, a steel casing twelve feet in diameter had first to be sunk thirty-five feet in the ground to contain the operating mechanism and the spindle shaft on which the bed of the boring mill was to revolve.

35

Brains and Brawn

THE RESEARCH LABORATORY was thriving in its new home in Schenectady, having graduated from the one-story shed-like structure to Building 19. In its deep cellar Whitney and his few assistants had carefully collected their stock of chemicals and mechanical appliances in the spring of 1901. That was a high-water year for the impetuous Mohawk, which overflowed its banks and poured into the cellar of Building 19, setting afloat all the supplies of the laboratory. The place was converted into a lake clinking with bottles and jars afloat.

Before another spring the laboratory had been moved, and in 1904 was lodged in Building 6. Whitney's staff now consisted of three chemists drawn from the Massachusetts Institute of Technology. Various enterprises were afoot and more men were being required. Whitney's own work resulted, before the end of 1904, in the development of a new type of electric resistance furnace.

In subjecting various articles to the heat of the furnace, Whitney was amazed at the effect which the heat had upon carbon filaments. Analyzing and testing the filaments inside incandescent lamps after this high-temperature treatment, he realized that the very nature of the carbon was changed. It now behaved in a way characteristic of metallic substances.

These metallized carbon filaments were a new step in the line of Edison's original objective, which was to utilize a high-resistance filament. When the new lamp was finally ready for commercial usage, it consumed only 2.5 watts per candlepower and yielded nearly 300 candles per horsepower. It represented an increase over its predecessor of twenty-five per cent in candlepower for the same volume of energy.

This new type of lamp, known by the trade name of "Gem," was the final achievement of the long carbon period in incandescent lighting. It was recognized as the greatest single improvement of the entire span of development and was in itself a justification of all the efforts expended in the research institution.

Two years of study and experiment were required before the manufacture of the new filaments was possible commercially. They were more expensive to produce than the old-style filament. But in 1907 the sales of "Gem" lamps approached four million, and in 1909 they leaped to ten and a half million, outdistancing for the first time the unmetallized-filament lamp.

Yet the carbon period in incandescent illumination was fated to pass. Even as Whitney was making ready to turn his lamp over to the factory, a newcomer was being heralded from abroad.

In Germany, under the encouragement of the Siemens and Halske Company, Dr. Werner von Bolton had been experimenting with the hard, brittle metal tantalum, which he had purified until he was able to render it ductile, or pliable, so that it could be drawn out into a flexible wire. Incandescent lamps with filaments made of tantalum wire were of even greater efficiency than those with the metallized filament.

There was a fresh stir in electric light circles. General Electric obtained a license to manufacture the lamp in America, and it was commercially introduced before the close of 1906. The tantalum lamp consumed only two watts per candlepower and yielded 370 candles per horsepower, which was about twenty per cent better than the metallized carbon lamp.

But the tantalum lamp had a great drawback; it was confined almost entirely to direct-current circuits. When connected to alternating-current circuits, its life was curtailed because of the crystallizing of the tantalum. Nevertheless, sales rose as high as twenty-seven million a year by 1913.

Invention is like lightning. It strikes none can tell where or when. Nor does it always require the man of broad technical schooling to work its will. While Whitney in his laboratory was firmly fixing the principle of research in General Electric's program, at the opposite end of the works brawny John Miller, the millwright, was turning things upside down to contribute an unheard-of idea to the development of mechanical processes.

Direct-current motors as they came into extensive use gave rise to many months of searching for noiseless gears and pinions. The strain upon gear teeth, meshing together with great force one moment, stopping entirely the next, caused them to wear out rapidly and unevenly. Most of the gear teeth in the thousands of motors that were driving machinery underwent a constant banging action. In the days of belts and shafting, such shocks were absorbed by the belting, but those days had passed. And the noise of the gears was nerve-racking.

Miller spent some time experimenting with many kinds of gears. He tried bronze, but it was too soft to last. He tried hard steel, but it made such an uproar that it was out of the question. He tried rawhide, but it did not stand the strain. The same was true of leather. He tried copper, laminated iron, wood, compressed paper; all in vain.

"The gear we want is a gear that will wear smooth," he told himself, watching the punch and shear. "These teeth are wearing unevenly, some places giving out faster than others. What we want is a gear that wears evenly, all over its surface, so that it continues to mesh perfectly even while wearing."

A few days later a thought occurred to him while he was gazing at a shiny spot on his coat sleeve.

"Worn smooth!" he exclaimed.

With sudden inspiration he secured some buffing wheels from one of the shops, wheels made of cloth sewed together in layers and used for polishing the finished parts of machines. He took these to his own shop, pressed them together between clamps, cut out gear teeth and mounted the cloth gear upon the hack saw. Then he started the saw going and watched it closely.

Two months slipped by. The cloth gear seemed to be standing the test. It was silent in operation. And it was wearing smooth and shiny like Miller's coat sleeve. It was getting hard as well, so that one could scarcely tell it from metal. Convinced that he was on the right track, Miller took the gear to John Riddell, the mechanical superintendent of the plant.

"There's a gear made out of cloth," he announced with pride.

"Out of cloth?" exclaimed Riddell. "I'm afraid you're going crazy!"

Miller took him down to the shop and let him watch the construction of another cloth gear. Riddell became half convinced. He notified the Patent Department, but he took precautions to make light of the story and even drew a humorous sketch representing General Electric scouts foraging among neighboring clothes lines for raw material for the "lingerie pinion."

But the cloth pinion was no joke; the Patent Department, the engineers, and even Riddell himself, were soon taking it seriously. Miller soon had a cloth gear and a cloth pinion on the punch and shear, where they worked both silently and successfully for three years. The best previous gear on that machine had given out in a week.

So it was that General Electric manufactured and marketed cloth gears. The first step in preparing the original type involved placing cotton cloth under enormous pressure, and from this it was termed Fabroil. A later adaptation, known as Textolite, made its own place in the world in the timing mechanism of automobile engines.

Again hard times came "a-knockin' at de door," and American business and industry were forced to stop and listen. It was the financial stringency of 1907. But this time General Electric did not suffer. Though its sales were curtailed, its supply of available cash was abundant. It was better off than scores of contemporaries, large and small.

What gave it such a financial advantage at a time of crisis was the financial genius of a man who had an extraordinary capacity for appraising the trend of business developments.

During the first six months of 1907, when orders received by General Electric increased twenty-two per cent over those of the corresponding period of the preceding year, General Electric issued bonds to a total of nearly thirteen million dollars. The interest rate was five per cent. It was the first extensive financing the company had undertaken in more than ten years. Again and again the annual report had contained such paragraphs as these: "During the past year the company has not borrowed money or incurred obligations." General Electric had lived within its income.

But as the second half of 1907 set in, there appeared the stringency which Coffin had sensed. From August 1, 1907 to January 31, 1908, General Electric's orders declined twenty-three per cent over the corresponding period of the preceding year. Business was dull, work slackened, markets wavered or went to pieces. Money became scarce and rates rose alarmingly. Business houses on every side were paying ten or twelve per cent for what cash they could borrow—and the supply of cash was limited.

Through it all General Electric sailed on an even keel. Although its factories were compelled to slow up, as the tide of orders ebbed to a slender stream, its executives were undisturbed about meeting payrolls or financing current obligations. Indeed, Coffin was able to help some of his large public-utility customers, loaning them thousands of dollars from the funds accumulated by his issue of bonds. And that stored up in turn a fund of future good will which gave General Electric salesmen a golden advantage year after year when the skies had cleared.

LATE IN 1907 a construction foreman left the Chicago office of General Electric and jolted over rough, sandy roads to the wild southern shore of Lake Michigan, where a steel company was fashioning a new community. The foreman was O. B. Vinal, experienced as a mechanic, capable in handling men, brusque yet kindly in manner. He could mix with any crowd, live under any conditions. He had the pioneer spirit.

The town smacked of the early gold-rush days in California or the oil-boom period in western Pennsylvania. A single street of swirling sand, churned ankle-deep by traffic; a straggly line of shacks that were lodging houses; brawny, sun-browned fellows of the construction gangs and erecting crews, who formed nine-tenths of the population; a constant rattle of explosive language as man and beast toiled daily through the sand dunes or shivered in the gales; and sand fleas everywhere, burrowing and biting, day and night—that was Gary, Indiana, when Vinal and his men first arrived in November 1907.

The great steel mill was under construction while the big motors were going in. The salamander stoves, scattered about in those drafty interiors, flung their warmth hardly beyond an arm's length against the cutting winds.

The men of the General Electric crew bunked two in a room in the one substantial hotel, where all united in a cease-less warfare against the fleas!

"Dad" Vinal was boss of the cuisine, general manager of the hotel, fatherly preceptor to his sixty huskies, and general construction foreman on the motor-assembly work. By one means or another he kept up morale through months of grind in a backwoods environment.

Slowly the huge motors were machined to precision meas-urements and their ponderous parts fitted together. They were bulky driving units, those motors, towering nearly thirty feet above the mill floor. And they had never been com-pletely assembled before, even in the factory.

The great flywheels were shipped in sections which the construction crew had to machine, mount, and bolt in place; the face of the rotors had to be pared down, so that the air gap would be two-tenths of an inch across; and four hundred tons of sheer weight for each complete unit had to be lifted into place. All this with the knowledge that the motors were to be tested, for the first time, while steel men from all the districts looked on.

Time pressed, and the sand fleas stuck as relentlessly to their task as did the men to theirs. Questioning letters came from Schenectady, and Vinal wrote back reassurances, though himself not altogether reassured. It was an exhausting life but no one was idle, and excitement added its spice.

What the construction men did not know—though the engineers at Schenectady did—was the skepticism among steel-mill operators over the mammoth motors. There had been but a few instances of steel-mill electric drives, all on a comparatively small scale, and there were none in which the steel mill was entirely and continuously run by electric motors. Hence the predictions up to the day of operation that the motors would never deliver the required power. Back in Schenectady the young designing engineer, Howard Maxwell, held no doubts, for he had designed these motors to deliver as much as 20,000 horsepower in case of need.

On the day of the test, January 17, 1909, Vinal looked a good deal calmer than he felt. Steel men by the score had gathered, and competitors of General Electric, not to mention General Electric's own engineers, led by E. W. Rice, Jr. Vinal moved the handle of the pole-changing switch which regulated the speed of the steel mill, a speed that was double that of any previous mill. Hewlett had designed that mechanism which controlled current at 4000 volts, and had heard the critics predict its failure.

There was a precipitate backward movement among the crowd as the motors started a tremendous droning song. The steel mill was in operation! Vinal and his crew withdrew and left the big motors to themselves.

PART EIGHT

Spectacular Applications and
Discoveries, Continued Expansion,
Birth of Radio, Major Achievements
—Marking the End of the
Pioneer Period

36

The Romance of Work

In the early years of the new century, an epochal struggle was developing. It dealt with transmission. How could current be transmitted without undue loss? Unless this question were solved, transmission distances would be forever limited.

The thing that held them back was nothing other than the insulators on the poles. Queer-looking tyrants they were, imitations of "a lady with an umbrella and a variety of petticoats." Some of them by 1902 stood as high as a table, were as plump as a barrel, and weighed nearly sixty pounds. They were constructed of fragile porcelain, difficult to transport, to erect, and to replace without breakage. Yet these delicate, unwieldy objects, weighty as they were, had to be mounted upright upon the crosspieces of every transmission pole, held in place by long vertical pins, and there support the swinging cables attached to their topmost points in spans varying from 400 to 500 feet between poles. To go beyond 70,000 volts, they would have to be too enormous either to manufacture or to handle.

What tales the linemen could relate of getting these insulators up intact. How difficult the task of replacing one that had been smashed. They made wonderful targets for thought-less youngsters and sharp-shooting cowboys. And replace-ments had to be made immediately to avoid interruption in current, no matter how the gales might howl. Insulators were then selling at $3.50 apiece, and systems of size re-quired from 5000 to 20,000 of them.

Harold W. Buck, electrical engineer of the Niagara Falls Power Company, who had started with General Electric, was reflecting in 1905, as was every other transmission engi-neer, upon the things that could be done if electricity could be transmitted at more than 70,000 volts. At that moment he had a project in mind that hinged upon the possibility of transmitting at 100,000 volts.

He had asked the switch engineers of General Electric if they could construct oil switches for controlling energy at such a voltage, and they had quickly answered "Yes." But no one could guarantee him a practical insulator; his plans were halted there.

Buck pictured his dilemma to Hewlett, General Electric's veteran switchboard engineer. It was an appeal for help. And Hewlett was not the man to dismiss a challenge. Together they discussed problems and sketched ideas.

Buck suggested insulators made of hickory sticks and im-pregnated rope, inserted in the transmission lines between the dead ends of the cable. Hewlett suggested distributing the insulation over a series of units. Then he asked why cables could not be attached to insulators that were sus-pended downward instead of mounted upright, and why there could not be a unit type that could be made up into strings as desired.

Hewlett returned to Schenectady and Buck to Niagara, and both began to experiment. Out of this there came the suspension type of insulator, Hewlett's conception; and its

ELECTRICITY OPERATES THE PANAMA CANAL

*The development of control equipment for the Canal was one of the
most important achievements of the early part of this century.*

ELECTRICITY CONQUERS THE CASCADE MOUNTAINS

A transcontinental passenger train on the Chicago, Milwaukee & St. Paul being pulled by an electric locomotive.

complement, the strain insulator, which was Buck's. They obtained a joint patent in 1907.

Broad, flat discs of corrugated porcelain were suspended from each crossarm in strings one beneath the other, like Chinese gongs, the bottommost disc supporting the transmission cable; this was the suspension type. A severing of the cable, the insertion of a section of nonconducting material uniting the severed ends yet itself attached to the crossarm of the pole, and a swinging loop of electrical conductor hung from one dead end of the cable to the other to furnish a path for the high-voltage current; this was the strain insulator.

Between them they carried the day. The nonconducting function of the insulator, distributed between those several discs, could be increased as the line voltage was raised by adding more discs. The strain insulator, which was mounted only on certain of the poles or towers, took up at regular intervals the mechanical strains which were imposed upon the transmission cables.

Steel towers were replacing the less substantial wooden poles. Since they were more expensive, they were placed farther apart, and the spans swinging between them were lengthened to seven, eight, and nine hundred feet. The cables themselves grew in less than twenty years from the thickness of one's little finger to the size of a shovel handle. But the two new insulators sustained those weights with both mechanical and electrical success.

One of Hewlett's engineer friends asked him as time went on, "Just where is the limit in all this?" To which Hewlett replied, "I don't know, it's not in our department." And so it appeared. From 70,000 to 110,000 volts in one leap meant expanding two and a half times the area which an electrical system could serve.

Fʀᴏᴍ ᴛʜᴇ ᴘᴇɴ of Chester T. Crowell came a description of a visit to Schenectady. In telling of his impression of the great turbine shop, he said:

"An enormous door rolled back on little wheels . . . My first impression was that we confronted miles and miles of roofed space. Sunlight, filtering through windows placed fifty or sixty feet above ground, showed that far away in the distance there was a rear wall. One saw it through a haze— not of smoke or steam, but just distance . . .

"The mechanism of a steam turbine is as meticulously accurate as that of a fine watch, but the delicate measurements are applied to pieces of metal so large that a dozen men working on them look like ants. These are proud men—artists. Watch their sensitive fingers caress that steel eggshell. Watch them measure distances as they signal to the ponderous crane. What pride shines in those faces as ten tons or more of machinery silently meets the floor, every corner in place.

"These are not horny-handed laborers . . . their features are keen and sensitive; brawn is not a premium here . . . They are working on what will eventually be one of the world's great power plants; they are working under the direction of engineers and scientists whose acquaintance is an honor . . .

"I watched it (the central shaft) turning slowly round and round, while a man wearing glasses appeared to be polishing it . . . Coming nearer I observed that this man was working with several queer implements.

" 'I'm trimming this to measurement,' he explained. A ribbon of steel thinner than paper was curling up from one of his implements.

" 'What do they allow you on this?'

" 'One-thousandth under; nothing over,' was the reply.

"At the point where he was working the shaft was about three feet in diameter. I was told it weighed fifty-five tons. He was trimming it to the precise measurement named in the specification—and the margin allowed him for human error was one-thousandth of an inch!

"That man remains indelibly in my memory as a figure of romance. He and his sharp eyes and steady nerves, calmly facing that margin of one-thousandth of an inch! . . .

"That man is an artist. Of the men I saw working in that cathedral of manufacture, none impressed me as a shy, modest creature. Make no mistake, they have a keen sense of the romance and adventure of work."

Going from the busy shops to a quiet little workshop in one of the laboratory buildings, we find picturesque old Julien Tournier, who had joined Edison's little group as an instrument worker in 1882. He had become an interesting "old-timer" at the Schenectady plant; a slight, white-haired, white-bearded figure, with a touch of French vivacity in his speech, he was always surrounded by an orderly confusion of tools and materials.

When Gerrit A. Beneker, the painter of men, visited Schenectady searching for types of industrial workers, he painted Tournier, and called his portrait "The Inventor." And when, a few years later, old Julien Tournier died, General Electric's current advertising space in a well-known technical journal consisted of a reproduction of Beneker's portrait of Tournier, and under it these words:

"In the life program of Julien Charles Tournier, public recognition played no part.

"He began as an instrument maker in Edison's laboratory. His forty-five years of service to electricity were completed in the same work . . . He invented and contributed improvements to switches, sockets, fuse-plugs, and attachment-plugs.

He might have retired, had he so chosen, and lived in comfort; but his love of electricity was his life, and he was content.

"We publish his picture as a tribute to him, and because he typified the thousands of men and women who have dedicated their lives to electrical development. The world will never know their names. They have no craving to be known. But their devotion is quite beyond the interest of men in ordinary business. Within the ranks of the General Electric Company are many such men. Their spirit is the best assurance that electricity will year by year find more and better ways to serve."

In 1907, TWO FIREBOATS launched upon the Chicago River by the city of Chicago, the *Graeme Stewart* and the *Joseph Medill,* were the first vessels in America to be propelled effectively by electrical energy. General Electric had not forgotten its contract with Charles G. Curtis which permitted it to use steam turbines with electric generators for driving the propeller of a ship. The Manitowoc Dry Dock Company, builders of the two fireboats, awarded to General Electric the contract for the electrical equipment of the craft. A. A. Babcock, the builders' engineer, worked with General Electric's marine engineers, particularly W. L. R. Emmet, John H. Clark, and Maxwell W. Day, over the engineering economics and operating efficiencies of so grouping the machinery that one 660-horsepower Curtis steam turbine drove both the electric generator and the water pumps.

In this same year the alternating-current transformer was helped over a hurdle. The transformer in its smaller sizes, which distributed electrical energy for local neighborhoods, had developed disconcerting electrical losses, whose only apparent remedy involved too great an expense to make their use practicable. When the prospect looked particularly dark, there came a ray of light from England. Sir Robert Hadfield, scientist, had discovered an alloy of steel and silicon, and General Electric, under a patent license, at once undertook to produce it in quantity. W. S. Moody, Chief Transformer Engineer, experimented until at last he succeeded in rolling the new steel in large tonnages. The dilemma of the small transformer was solved.

It was also in 1907 that Rice and Ord, vice presidents, recommended to the directors the purchase of seven hundred acres of land at Erie, Pennsylvania, whereon to build a new plant when times were brighter. Confident that times *would* be brighter, they sought to shift manufacturing toward the geographical center of population. The plan was amply justified; that land became the site of the Erie Works of today, the center of its electric transportation activities.

SHORTLY BEFORE 1900 a glass tube, 186 feet in length, had been placed one day in the foyer at Madison Square Garden. As night drew on this tube glowed with a brilliant white radiance. The illumination extended to all parts of the foyer. It was the first of Moore's practical gaseous lamps. Its effectiveness attracted great attention, and the test established the fact that it was more economical of electric current than the incandescent light. Within a few years a number of radiant tubes had appeared in Manhattan.

Such events were not to be ignored by General Electric, manufacturers of the lamp with the carbon filament, which Moore had once told Edison was "too small, too red, and too hot." Was that lamp to be supplanted after twenty-five years by a luminous gas?

It was possible, despite the fact that the Moore tube was cumbersome. It had to be installed by expert workmen, exhausted of its air upon the premises, and its replacement when it got out of order was a troublesome procedure. Hence, although Coffin and Rice negotiated for Moore's patent rights, they also implored Whitney to add an able man to his staff to study the elements which had promise of yielding better filaments. Whitney immediately recommended Dr. William D. Coolidge, of the faculty of the Massachusetts Institute of Technology, who had been doing original work in physical chemistry.

So Coolidge, in Boston, received a surprising offer from Whitney. But it was an offer that proved satisfactory, and early in 1905 Coolidge became a General Electric researcher.

Just as these preparations were being made, scientific men were stirred by news of a great discovery in Europe. An incandescent electric lamp had been developed which contained a filament made of the most intractable of substances, the metal known as tungsten.

37

The Taming of Tungsten

Tungsten was intractable, more brittle than dry bone, more fragile than an eggshell. Yet in 1904 men fashioned it into slender, hairlike filaments for incandescent lamps.

Two laboratory workers in a far land brought forth these filaments of tungsten. They had no funds with which to finance their work, but they summoned to their task patience and sustained, intelligent endeavor.

In 1902 Dr. Alexander Just, a laboratory assistant in the Technical High School in Vienna, began experimenting in his spare time to develop a new form of filament for incandescent lamps. He did not think at first of tungsten but tried a number of other substances. He associated with himself a colleague, Franz Hanaman, and they studied tungsten between them, experimenting for two years.

Both were men of small financial means. They paid their laboratory expenses from their humble salaries. Dr. Just's income was $55 a month. And they had set themselves a mountainous task.

Tungsten existed only as a gray-black powder of fine hard particles, or as a rough, half-fused mass. Except as an alloy in tungsten steel, it had never had any commercial value. In itself it had never been shaped into any useful form. Yet the two impoverished Austrians believed they could put this unworkable, brittle, and hitherto useless metal into incandescent lamps as thin, looped filaments.

Realizing that they could not work tungsten as ordinary metals are worked, Just and Hanaman tried various chemical treating methods, usually at high temperatures. At length they hit upon two ways of producing filaments of pure tungsten. The most satisfactory process of the two was that in which the tungsten was sintered together. The tungsten powder was first mixed with a solution of sugar and gum arabic. The thick paste resulting was squirted under high pressure through a diamond die. As it issued from the die, it was caught upon pieces of cardboard in loops. It was then treated so that the sugar and gum arabic were turned into carbon, which was removed by a further treating process, leaving pure tungsten.

In the final treating, which required a very high temperature, the tungsten, upon being freed from the carbon, underwent a curious evolution. The tiny particles became sintered, or drawn together, in a form resembling dovetailing; and so tungsten filaments of coherent mass, but of extreme fragility, were made.

At that moment was born the tungsten era in incandescent illumination, though to all intents and purposes it seemed doomed to strangulation at birth. For Just and Hanaman lacked the funds to commercialize their invention. They even lacked the funds with which to obtain a patent. In 1904 they managed to borrow $60, which enabled them to apply for British and French patents. They applied for an American patent the following year. But they lacked the further funds needed to place their invention on the market.

By that time two other European inventors, Dr. Werner von Bolton and Dr. Hanz Kuzel, in Germany, had made counter claims.

In the spring of 1906 Coffin and Rice dispatched two scouts to investigate, Dr. Whitney and John W. Howell. They went first to Berlin, and there by chance picked up the trail.

They were walking along the street one evening when they observed some unusually brilliant electric lamps shining in a store window. The shopkeeper was dazed by the rapidity of their questions. "Ach so, from the Auergeselschaft came those lamps." The Americans hastened to the plant and there heard the story of von Bolton's tungsten lamps.

Tests proved the lamps far better than any Whitney and Howell had seen. They made a bid at once for the American rights. There the plant officials told them of Kuzel's work, and also that of Just and Hanaman. Whitney and Howell went straightway to Augsburg, Budapest, and Vienna to see the other inventors and in each case to open patent negotiations. They recognized the possibility of a patent conflict. There were three inventors. But who had priority? It was impossible at that moment to determine.

General Electric paid $400,000 to Just and Hanaman alone, and it expended a total of $1,500,000 before it acquired the rights to all three patents, thus assuring the tungsten-lamp market in America, regardless of the patent outcome.

The tungsten-filament lamp was commercially introduced by General Electric in 1907. Millions of the lamps were sold yearly despite the fragile filament, because they were one hundred per cent more efficient than the tantalum lamps. The tungsten filament reduced the consumption of electric energy from two watts to one per candlepower. The tantalum lamp had yielded 370 candles per horsepower; the tungsten lamp yielded 746. It was the greatest forward step made in incandescent electric lamps.

A long leap, indeed, from Edison's first carbon lamps, consuming seven or eight watts per candlepower and yielding but 100 candles per horsepower. Yet something else as wonderful was about to happen. Coolidge, at Schenectady, had proposed that tungsten could be rendered ductile!

It was a bold adventure, along a trail many had ignored altogether. For tungsten, of all elements, seemed destined to remain untamed. It's brittleness was traditional in the scientific world. But in the face of tradition, Coolidge set to work. To decisive assertions that it could never be done, Coolidge said simply, "Let's try!"

Experiments carried him through six years, demanding more patience than would seem humanly possible. They imposed a drudgery that would kill the spirit of anyone lacking the true inventive temper. And it cost Coolidge a degree of mental concentration that lined his face for life.

In that expanding workshop where Whitney, the directing genius, made the rounds of the laboratory rooms each day with the exuberant query, "Good morning! Having good fun today?" Coolidge began wrestling with that most intractable of metals. Preoccupied from morning to night, from month to month, he worked grimly to make it ductile and pliable as wire.

Seldom was there such an unyielding subject. It permitted of being bent when heated to a very high temperature, but was as brittle as ever when it cooled. Yet Coolidge discovered that at certain temperatures he could hammer the metal and elongate it, something no one had ever before accomplished. It was enough to save him from discouragement, and it started him working in a new direction.

Coolidge now hovered incessantly around heat-treating

bottles and electric resistance furnaces, perspiring through
hot summer days in the dusty laboratory workroom. He
pressed tungsten in heated rolling mills used by jewellers.
He pressed it between hot slabs of tungsten steel. He tried
drawing it through heated dies whose diameter was no
greater than a thousandth of an inch. With larger dies the
tungsten rod invariably broke.

And then late in the fall of 1908, Coolidge first held ductile
tungsten in his hands! For the pressed tungsten filament,
drawn through one heated die after another, each slightly
smaller than the last, and itself heated and reheated, had
lost its brittleness. It could be bent without breaking, even
when cold!

Verifying his experiments, Coolidge found that tungsten
behaved in a manner that was the exact opposite of all other
metals. The longer it was worked at high temperatures the
more ductile it became; whereas other metals under this process lose their ductility and turn brittle. Peering through his
microscope he found that ductile tungsten was fibrous in
structure, while non-ductile tungsten was crystalline—which
is also the reverse of all other metals.

But Coolidge's work was by no means finished. It was one
thing to transform tungsten laboriously in the laboratory;
it was quite another to work with large quantities of the
metal on a commercial basis in the factory. It looked as if
commercial production of ductile tungsten was not to be attained. For two years more Coolidge kept at it, his hopes
almost smothered.

He could not produce the right kind of tungsten slug for
the hot-drawing process. For commercial use, a larger slug
was needed than the tiny one of pressed tungsten used in
his experiment. He pressed the tungsten powder in a mold.
When the pressed slugs were finally obtained, they were so

fragile that they could not be lifted, and a heat-treating process was developed to give them mechanical strength.

Then the slugs would shrink under the heat, break in two
or pull away from the clamps.

They were so brittle, both hot and cold, that nothing could
be done with them.

Coolidge, still unbeaten, turned to swaging machines. At
last he was able to hot-swage the slug as it came, sintered
into a coherent mass, from the treating bottle, to a diameter
of an eighth of an inch. The hot-swaging process won the
day. The slug could now be worked into smaller and smaller
diameters. Shortly before it reached the die-drawing diameter of 25 one-thousandths of an inch, the tungsten became ductile. It had become a slender gossamer wire, with
all the properties of wire—and only one-sixth the diameter
of a human hair!

Small—and marvellously strong. The more ductile it became the stronger it grew. When its diameter was measur-
able by thousandths of an inch, it attained a tensile strength
of 590,000 pounds to the square inch.

So Coolidge converted an obstinate metal, more brittle
than eggshells, into a pliable wire smaller than a hair and
stronger than any other substance known to man. It was a
transformation as extraordinary as if one were to take flour
and by some magic turn it into a wire stouter than a steel
cable.

Ductile tungsten, in recognition of the man who tamed it,
is often referred to as Coolidge metal or Coolidge wire. It
meant physical stability for the tungsten lamp. And it meant
a revolution, almost an upheaval, at the Edison Lamp Works.
Only four years before, the manufacture of the sintered filament had begun, and now, in 1911, every bit of equipment
for producing sintered filaments was scrapped.

Scores of new machines were disposed of in the junk market without being unpacked. Half a million dollars was sacrificed in replacing the old equipment with new. Another half million dollars was sacrificed in the stock of unsold sintered-filament lamps, for which there was no longer a market.

The public benefited, in reduced lamp prices, as well as in the greater efficiency of the lamp. In 1914 the volume of electric illumination utilized by the American people represented a saving of $200,000,000 a year over what its cost would have been with the metallized carbon-filament lamp. And the cost of light as a commodity was dropping while the costs of other commodities were going up.

38

The Fire of Prosecution

In 1911 GENERAL ELECTRIC was brought into court. It was the chief of thirty-four defendants in a suit instituted on March 3, 1911, by the United States government, through Attorney General Wickersham, "against what is alleged to be one of the most powerful and complete monopolies in the country."

The arraignment of the "electrical trust," and a recital of the attendant allegations, was part of the news of the day. The formal charge was a violation of the Sherman anti-trust law in the marketing of incandescent lamps. And there was a long recital of practices which the government believed to be in restraint of trade.

The attitude of the government in submitting these charges can perhaps be best understood by a brief examination of its views in the matter. The interest of General Electric in the National Electric Lamp Association was disclosed, with the intimation that competition between the different companies of the Association, both with each other and with General Electric, was artificial rather than genuine. The government in its bill of complaint pointed to the practice of requiring wholesale houses and dealers to maintain the price of lamps as fixed by General Electric, and to the patent agreement with the Westinghouse Company, which expired that year.

At first General Electric's counsel planned to make formal answer to the complaint. Indeed, such an answer was drawn, printed, and filed. It admitted the facts embodied in the practices cited, but denied that those practices constituted a violation of the law and particularly denied any intent to commit such violation. It pointed out that the National Association with its service units was fully able to compete with the Edison Lamp Works in research and experiments in all branches of lamp manufacturing, and that the stifling of competition was what they wished to avoid by financing this Association, whose management was entirely in the hands of the minority stockholders.

The bill of complaint stated that General Electric was prolonging its patent monopoly of incandescent lamps after the patents had expired. This seems to have referred especially to the carbon-filament lamp. General Electric replied that although the patents on the lamp had run out, those governing the methods of its manufacture were still in force. Every machine used in the process of manufacture was patented; most of them were essential to volume manufacture, and the processes could still be infringed upon.

The government's petition went on to charge that General Electric had bought patents and patent rights until it had a monopoly of every succeeding type of incandescent lamp that had ever appeared. This, it contended, prevented the different types—the carbon, the metallized, the tantalum and the tungsten—from competing with each other. The defence replied that the different types of lamps could not in any way be considered competitive, since each constituted an improvement and was designed to replace the preceding one.

After filing its answer to the government's charges, General Electric determined that instead of going on trial and contesting the charges, endeavoring to justify its practices before the court, it would ask permission to withdraw its answer and indicate its willingness to submit to a decree. It had never had any intention of engaging in illegal practices and was therefore willing to have the government pass judgment without pleading its case. It stipulated that it would not appeal from the Court's decision. The defendent affirmed its "desire and intention . . . to comply with each and all the provisions of the Statutes of the United States . . . and not to operate under or make or carry on any such contracts or practices as are condemned by said Act of Congress as now construed by the Court."

Judge John M. Killits, in the Circuit Court, northern district of Ohio, permitted this procedure and issued his decree on October 12, 1911. In brief, he found that most of the practices described in the government's petition were acts in restraint of trade, as embraced within the meaning of the law, particularly the method of marketing the incandescent lamp.

He ordered the dissolution of the National Electric Lamp Association, ordered General Electric to do business only in its own name, to refrain from fixing the prices at which incandescent lamps might be resold to the public, and to refrain from bringing pressure to bear in order to market types of lamps lacking any legitimate demand.

The decree raised a new problem. How could General Electric legally continue to market its incandescent lamps to the general public without risking arbitrary price manipulation by retail dealers? In the belief of General Electric only one basis existed for raising or lowering lamp prices. That

THOMAS A. EDISON AT THE AGE OF 79

ELIHU THOMSON IN LATER LIFE

basis was the rise or fall of costs—in other words, a legitimate economic basis. Artificial price changes by local dealers, according to this theory, would introduce complications resulting in an unfriendly reaction by the public toward the incandescent lamp.

To meet this situation the officials of the Company worked out the present agency plan of selling lamps by which local dealers became agents under contract of General Electric. Stocks of lamps were not sold to them outright but taken on consignment, the company retaining ownership in the lamps while they were in the agents' hands, and relinquishing ownership only when the agent sold the lamps. Thus the sale by an agent to a consumer was a first sale rather than a resale, as formerly, and General Electric could therefore legally control the price of its product to the consumer.

The company submitted this plan to the Attorney General at Washington, who declined to pass upon its legality. But feeling sure of its ground, General Electric put the plan into effect in 1912.

This practice was not passed upon by a court of law until 1926. The government again brought suit against both General Electric and Westinghouse, charging that the agency plan was only an evasion of the decree of 1911 and "intended to carry out the same evil result." The case went, on appeal, to the United States Supreme Court, which held that the agency system as practiced by General Electric was a perfectly legal method of selling a product, and that the thousands of dealers holding contracts as lamp agents were in effect in the same status as employes of the company and entitled to make first sales.

Meanwhile a radical readjustment in the National Electric Lamp Association was going on. Even before the Court's decree of 1911 was issued, General Electric had exercised its option of purchasing the remaining stock in the Association, and became sole owner.

About this time the Cleveland headquarters were moved to Nela Park, just outside of Cleveland, so pronounced in natural beauty, so impressive in man's handiwork, that it became known as one of the most remarkable institutions possessed by American industry.

The name "Nela" was coined from the initials of the National Electric Lamp Association, and so became a memorial to that organization which was dissolved by order of the Court, as were all its component companies. They were merged into General Electric; the factory at Cleveland became the National Lamp Works of General Electric; the other individual factories became simply additional plants.

Terry and Tremaine had dreamed of Nela Park long before they set to work, in 1910, to bring the dream to pass. Terry had said to his colleagues: "Let us create a center like the well-known institutions of the fine arts to stimulate morale and encourage individuality, and at the same time to make us better known before the public." The spot they finally selected was isolated amid the charm of forest and landscape. There, in 1910, they erected a group of buildings harmonious in architecture, marked by a dominant simplicity. Twelve buildings were arranged in the form of an extensive quadrangle, and have often been called "the university of light."

So emerged Nela Park, self-contained and self-maintained, yet consciously linked with the successors of Thomson and of Edison.

39

The Eternal "Why?"

IN TAMING TUNGSTEN, Coolidge had revealed an "unknown land" where scores of mysterious roads stretched away to a beckoning horizon. Both he and Whitney felt their pulses quicken as they surveyed the prospect that lay before them.

They needed new explorers. The call went out to the world of technical men, and from institutions far and near recruits flocked to the town beside the Mohawk.

By 1912 the research personnel numbered nearly two hundred. One of the new arrivals was young Irving Langmuir, who came in 1909 from Stevens Institute of Technology, once presided over by Dr. Morton, one of Edison's severest critics. The new recruit came with a fine academic record, a prolonged period of training—and an inquisitive mind. He was one of the "why" men who are ever prying into the secrets of the world's mysterious phenomena. Such men never outgrow the habit formed in childhood of continually seeking answers to their questions.

Langmuir's curiosity fitted exactly into Whitney's plan. There were a great many "whys" to be asked about the incandescent lamp. Why did the lamp bulbs sometimes show a blackening on their inside surfaces, which interfered with illumination? Why did current flow inside the bulb, between the legs of the filament, in what was known as the Edison Effect? Such questions were to Langmuir as scent is to the hound.

There were opinions and theories enough about the blackening of the bulb. It was commonly believed that minute traces of gases remained inside the bulb, and that these gases, striking the hot filament, caused it to disintegrate imperceptibly, and that the particles of tungsten from the disintegrating filament were deposited on the surface of the bulb, causing it to blacken.

Langmuir was not content with theories. He established the fact that there were gases in the supposed vacuum, and then he determined just what those gases were. Their quantities were so small that he had to invent special instruments of the utmost sensitiveness.

He found that there were five gases in the bulb, water vapor, hydrocarbon vapors, carbon monoxide, carbon dioxide, and hydrogen; but that the only gas which acted on the filament in such a manner as to blacken the bulb was water vapor. The next step was to eliminate the criminal. He tried to do this by producing a vacuum higher than any previously known; from a millionth of an atmosphere he raised the vacuum to less than a billionth. And he resorted to endless precautions to keep out water vapor.

But still the blackening went on. Why? He could think of only one other possibility—the evaporation of the tungsten in the filament.

A succession of experiments proved that the tungsten filament did lose weight; and that blackening came from its evaporation. The water vapor merely facilitated the process;

STEINMETZ DEMONSTRATES HIS MAN-MADE LIGHTNING

A FLAMING ARC CRACKLES AT PITTSFIELD

Visitors on the balcony of the High Voltage Laboratory watch electricity put through its more spectacular tricks.

the other gases, some more than others, retarded or even nullified it by reducing the rate of evaporation.

There might be one gas, thought Langmuir, which would so reduce the rate of evaporation as to increase the efficiency of the lamp. With the first experiments a new situation arose. He succeeded in retarding the evaporation of the tungsten, but the dissipation of heat from the filament through gas conduction was found to be considerable. Some gases cooled the filament so greatly that the amount of electrical energy required to maintain the proper temperature of the filament rendered them commercially impractical.

Langmuir now faced the problem of what combination of inert gas and tungsten filament would reduce the evaporation of the tungsten and overcome the dissipation of heat through the gas. It meant a study of the laws governing heat losses through convection, a subject which had hardly been touched upon.

This stage of the investigation yielded surprising information. Langmuir discovered that filaments of relatively large diameter do not suffer as large a heat loss in proportion as do smaller filaments, a fact contrary to expectations. The explanation was curious. Langmuir found that the filament, when heated in any inert gas, became surrounded by a film of hot gas. This film had a thickness independent of the diameter of the filament. If the filament was doubled in size, the film became only slightly thicker and the rate of heat dissipation did not become doubly greater. It was obvious that filaments of larger diameter would be more efficient in gases. This, unfortunately, meant a larger quantity of raw material in the filament.

Langmuir continued his experiments until he had satisfied himself that argon was the most desirable inert gas for the lamp bulb. He also found that the gas should be introduced at atmospheric pressure, rather than in a high vacuum. But the lamps he made for testing contained filaments that were relatively large, and consumed from two to six thousand watts.

One step was needed to make this the light of lights. Was it impossible to use a filament of small diameter? Anyone else would have said yes. But Langmuir discovered that a coiled filament of small diameter gave all the advantages of one of larger diameter.

Patiently he sought to discover how large a coil was desirable, how far apart the turns should be, and what would be the effect on the gas film. The outcome was an incandescent lamp which was twice as efficient as the ordinary vacuum tungsten lamp.

What did this mean? A one hundred per cent advance at a single stride! The new lamp required one-half of one watt per candle, and gave 1492 candles per horsepower. It was fourteen times as efficient as the first carbon lamps. Above all it meant that incandescent lamps of large capacity would be able to compete with the arc lamp, even with the magnetite arc! It was a marvelous illustration of what can come to pass when a trained investigator with the gift of asking questions starts to answer that enormous little word "Why?" In 1913 the first commercial gas-filled incandescent lamps made their appearance and became instantly popular.

THE YEAR 1913 saw a number of changes in the executive organization of General Electric. Charles A. Coffin, the master builder of General Electric's destiny, announced that he wished to relinquish his position as President and become Chairman of the Board. He had reached the age of sixty-nine. For twenty-one years he had been president of General Electric. During those years he had combined in his own person the positions of President of the company and Chairman of the Board, so that his action in 1913 meant virtually a division of his responsibilities. It did not deprive the General Electric Company of his counsel, nor did it decrease his keen supervision over its affairs.

E. W. Rice, Jr., was made the new General Electric President. It was just thirty years since Rice had gone to Lynn as Professor Thomson's assistant after earning his salt by cleaning castings and whitewashing walls at New Britain. Now he was the head of a great technical and industrial institution.

He entered upon his term of office under far more favorable auspices than Coffin had done, twenty-one years before. It was no longer a time of stormy financial skies and of hostile criticism. No one was attacking General Electric's methods on the ground that there could not be enough business in electrical manufacturing to pay dividends on so much capital. Yet technical problems there were in ever-greater numbers, and these Rice was supremely qualified to handle. Great as had been the accomplishments of the past, still greater and more amazing things were wrapped in the silence of the future.

Soon after the turn of the century, a tall, stalwart recruit, noticeably Scandinavian of feature, boarded a train bound for Schenectady. He had left Sweden a year or two earlier and his English was still halting. It was 1902, years before Coolidge or Langmuir had joined the research laboratory, or Hewlett had strung porcelain "dinner plates" together and called them insulators.

This recruit eagerly watched the buildings on the river flats glide into view from the train window. In his eyes there was a look of curiosity and expectancy. But what he was searching for, and how successful he would be in finding it, time alone would reveal.

For the next year or two no one heard of Ernst F. W. Alexanderson, who was bending diligently over a drafting board, then studying the construction of railway motors. His soul was there—among the armatures and field coils, the watts and torques. The world was going to hear from him.

The thing that first drew attention to his talents was the Alexanderson single-phase railway motor of 1904. Not long after, when he asked for a chance at another problem, he was assigned to the new field of radio.

Radio in those days was just plain "wireless." Embryonic, immature, firing the enthusiasm of the few, its future was ignored by the many. But the young engineer from Sweden had kept abreast of radio work from those days in 1896 and 1897 when Marconi proved to an astonished world that messages could be transmitted without wires.

Since that time General Electric had worked on radio development. It had designed and manufactured efficient spark sets working at the low frequency of five hundred cycles. This meant that the alternating current which set free those mysterious radio waves pulsated five hundred times per second. The great need of the moment was for a generator to produce alternating current of high frequency. Professor Reginald A. Fessenden had attempted to build such a generator, and finally he took his problem to General Electric. The person to attack the proposition with determination was young Alexanderson.

For two years he devoted himself to it. For two years he was a target for many a sly shot loaded with that overworked word "impossible." But like the rest of his breed, he was invulnerable. At the end of two years, the critics were converted. The first models of his high frequency alternator would generate two kilowatts of alternating current at 60,-000 cycles. Soon they reached 100,000 cycles. Inconceivable that anything in the material universe could pulsate so many times in a single second.

An alternator invented in England had a frequency of 120,000 cycles, but its output was only a fraction of a watt. Alexanderson produced an alternator of 200,000 watts. In it, precision was combined with the most delicate adjustments. The alternator when ready for the market was a ponderous affair, including a huge rotating disc that weighed tons and an array of supplementary parts which maintained exact operating regulation.

The immense rotating disc revolved in strong magnetic fields, and its periphery travelled 700 miles an hour; in four hours it could have rolled across the Atlantic. There were fearful moments in the laboratory when the first models were brought up to speed, and furtive glances toward the door. Yet for all its speed, that huge disc was not permitted to vary from its position by so much as the three-hundredth part of an inch. And the speed was kept constant, to the smallest fraction of a revolution.

This first achievement of the young Swedish inventor suggested so many possibilities that he forsook other fields of electrical endeavor. In 1906 the first installations of his pioneer achievement were made; two units were sent to the laboratory of John Hays Hammond, Jr., at Gloucester, and one to the American Marconi Company at New Brunswick.

No one could deny that Alexanderson had metamorphosed radio. The old spark set and arc generators could transmit only short distances; the new alternator created electromagnetic waves that leapt the oceans. The 200-kilowatt alternator, completed in 1918, was to become the foundation of the first great trans-oceanic radio system.

Alexanderson aspired to a complete radio transmitting system, just as Edison had once aspired to a complete electric lighting system. Soon he worked out a magnetic device for controlling the energy generated by the alternator under the impulse of the dots and dashes of a telegraph key or the sound of the human voice. He tested this magnetic modulator, as he called it, for radio telephony, but the electrical impulse coming from the microphone was so weak that the modulator would not operate. Some means of amplifying the impulse must be found.

Alexanderson turned to the Research Laboratory. Dr. Whitney once remarked that "research needs more aviators," that is, aviators in spirit. Langmuir, in the laboratory, had been "cultivating a flying spirit." And in so doing he had produced a new type of vacuum tube.

He had made this discovery in following the trail of the blackened bulbs. In solving the problem of the gases in the bulb he had invented an exhaust pump which produced a higher vacuum than ever before achieved. Formerly one molecule of air in a hundred thousand left in the bulb was thought to be a high vacuum. But Langmuir's mercury condensation pump left only one molecule in ten billion. His work with the vacuum led to another of those stimulating "Whys?" For Langmuir noted that with a certain vacuum the Edison Effect occurred, while above that range it could not be observed.

Langmuir was the latest of a brilliant succession to investigate the Edison Effect. Edison himself was the first to notice the strange blue glow within the bulb, and he proved it to be caused by the passage of current between the legs of the filament. That was thirty years earlier. Fourteen years later, in 1897, Sir Joseph Thomson, foremost scientist of his day, discovered the reason for that phenomenon when he discovered the electron, the unit of electricity. He studied particularly the electron in a vacuum, and proved that when the filament of an incandescent lamp becomes hot it throws out electrons, constituting negative electricity, and that these electrons are attracted by a wire or metallic plate connected to the positive side of the supply circuit.

Langmuir went to work at once to design a vacuum tube based on his discovery. It could work at 250 volts, whereas the old audion tube was limited to 30 volts. It could handle watts and even kilowatts, while the previous tubes were confined to small fractions of a watt. It could amplify the impulse of a microphone to any volume for radiation as electromagnetic waves from an antenna; and thus it provided the amplifier for which Alexanderson was looking.

Edison's discovery of thirty years before resulted in a new art, a new industry. Through it were assured practical radio telephony and radiobroadcasting. As Dr. Whitney once said, "In the advance of civilization it is new knowledge which paves the way—and the pavement is eternal."

Through the ages electrons had pursued their course through the world without once being detected. Into that invisible electronic world, which science now believes is identical with the material world, Langmuir was the first to enter and make those "big little things" do his bidding. He harnessed them for as long as mankind endures.

When two of Langmuir's fellows in General Electric became aware of what he had done, they applied his electronic discovery to further practical ends. One of these was Alexanderson; the other was Coolidge, the tamer of tungsten.

It was Langmuir's radiotron, the first of the high-vacuum, high-voltage tubes, which rendered Alexanderson's magnetic modulator efficient, and so permitted proper control of the energy produced by the high-frequency alternator. Alexanderson could now offer an efficient, long-distance, high-power transmitting unit. And his work from 1913–1916 was closely watched by Marconi.

Alexanderson sought to develop equipment for commercial companies. He studied the existing apparatus of commercial stations, particularly the adaptation of apparatus to his new unit, the alternator. The antenna, as Alexanderson himself once said, "corresponds to the hull of a rocking boat, with which we produce waves in the water." If the hull is heavy, greater energy is necessary to rock it because of its resistance. And Alexanderson found that the radio antennae of commercial stations possessed unduly high resistance, so that they wasted power which might otherwise have produced radio waves.

Alexanderson eliminated the waste by grounding the antenna at equal intervals producing the effect of several antennae connected in parallel, each tuned to the same wavelength. Resistance was so reduced that 200 kilowatts of energy had the same effect as 1200 kilowatts upon the former type of antenna. This was his multiple-tuned antenna, demonstrated at Schenectady in February, 1916.

Both radio telegraphy and radio telephony were now practically possible. Alexanderson immediately designed a duplex radio telephone system, and on November 24, 1916, occurred one of the earliest demonstrations of two-way wireless telephony, when men at the General Electric plant at Pittsfield talked to men at the Schenectady plant.

The Marconi wireless station at New Brunswick, however, brought the Alexanderson system to fame. It was to become one of the most notable radio stations in America during the Great War.

But before that time came, one of the most significant happenings among General Electric men was the application

208,000 HORSEPOWER

A three-unit General Electric turbine-generator set installed in a central station.

EVOLUTION OF THE INCANDESCENT LAMP

Edison's first lamp, carbon-filament lamp, tantalum-filament lamp, drawn-tungsten filament lamp with tip, gas-filled lamp with tip, vacuum lamp without tip, gas-filled lamp without tip, inside-frosted lamp.

by Coolidge of Langmuir's electronic research to Roentgen-ray work.

General Electric had manufactured X-ray equipment since Professor Wilhelm K. Roentgen, in 1895, discovered a new ray whose properties were so little known at the time as to warrant the title "X"-ray. Professor Thomson at Lynn had studied the phenomenon and designed the apparatus, which went by his name. They were the Thomson inductorium, a form of induction coil, and the Thomson Roentgen-ray transformer. The latter supplied alternating current to the tube, which contained three electrodes, two of aluminum and one of platinum.

No radical change in these tubes took place for fifteen years. Then Coolidge, fresh from ductilizing tungsten and equipped with the new knowledge of electronic behavior, began to study tungsten as an X-ray electrode, or "target," in place of platinum. X-rays of greater power were produced, as high voltages were employed.

Day after day Coolidge entered a lead-lined booth with a window of leaded glass through which he watched the action of his tubes. Lead offers an impassable barrier to the X-ray and hence constitutes a safe screen for the research worker. Outside the room was a danger zone, filled with powerful electrical emanations from the tube which was under test. But the worker in his tower was able safely to take notes of every change in the conditions governing the tube.

Finally in 1913 Coolidge brought out a tube that operated at 100,000 volts or higher; a tube in which the X-rays were created by a bombardment of electrons from the tungsten electrode; a tube which could be kept in operation for hours and whose intense rays were capable of a high degree of penetration.

YET RESEARCH WAS ONLY ONE of many departments of activity. Even as Coolidge was fashioning a new tool in therapeutics, a group of men in Hewlett's office in the Switchboard Engineering Department was talking over a control system for the mighty locks of the Panama Canal.

Here was a task fit for electricity—to make available to commerce this enormous ditch, itself one of the great engineering feats of human history. It was a task involving the movement of gates weighing four hundred tons, the largest more than seven hundred; the filling and emptying of locks a thousand feet long, three hundred feet wide; and the control of operating mechanisms scattered over fifty miles, the largest single group extending for more than a mile.

These problems were further complicated by the tropical climate. Metal parts must be made noncorroding, coils must be made moistureproof. Maximum reliability was imperative, because the Panama Canal was far removed from manufacturing centers and weeks must pass before repair parts arrived.

Edward Schildhauer, engineer of the Isthmian Canal Commission, had asked every electrical manufacturer in America to submit a bid. The rejoicing in General Electric offices over winning the contract, however, was brief; coats were taken off and sleeves rolled up, for intensive days of planning lay ahead.

No nation in the world could have asked for a more perfect test of the electrical giant at work, for if electricity could operate the Panama Canal, surely it could do anything under the sun!

It did operate the Canal—and is still doing it. Five hundred motors, rating from seven horsepower up to seventy, are on duty at the great locks, and more than five hundred others are at work at the dams, the spillways, and elsewhere along the canal—a total of over a thousand electric motors, with a combined capacity of nearly 30,000 horsepower.

And the motors were the easier half of the problem. The real task was the control system. It must be centralized at one spot for each of the locks; it must be an exact duplicate in miniature of the locks themselves, their gates, their valves, their fender chains. Everything that happened at those big locks must be repeated simultaneously on the control boards. The operators must have before them a complete record of the movement of those ponderous parts, a perfect gauge of the rise and fall of the water, accurate to one-tenth of one per cent.

Nothing short of infallibility was demanded. Errors by the operators, endangering lives and property on board vessels passing through, must be made impossible.

For previous canals there had been a large force of operators scattered along the canal-way, each charged with one control operation. Safety from error increased as the number of human beings increased. But control for each lock centered in one man's hands, and that man had to proceed without error—this was a staggering demand.

Edward M. Hewlett, designer of switches and controls, went to work over the requirements quietly. Upon Hewlett's assertion that he could make this system work, the control contract for the Panama Canal was awarded to General Electric. Now he had to live up to his promise.

First Hewlett consulted with the engineer of a concern that made interlocking railroad switch devices, to obtain a bid on that part of the work.

"You people don't know anything about interlocking devices!" exclaimed the engineer. "We know the interlocking business; you don't. You're suggesting something that can't be done at the price you require."

"Not at all," Hewlett replied with some spirit. "We were building interlocking apparatus when you were in short trousers, and what's more, we're in the business of doing things that can't be done!"

There followed weeks of reading, designing, experimenting. Within six months Hewlett had a working model of the indicating system and the interlocking system as well—the system that was accepted and operated when the canal was opened on August 15, 1914. It has been working there ever since. A system of many parts, it was yet not fundamentally complicated. It was made up of vertical and horizontal bars, two and a quarter miles of them, whose movements were governed by mechanical stops.

There was keen ingenuity in the way the movements of those bars were planned. And in the interlocking principle which ran through an intricate network of those lug-stopped rods, governing dozens of control operations, permitting only one sequence of action in the order of turning the control handles upon control boards as long as sixty-four feet. This was Hewlett's selsyn system.

PARTICIPATING LUSTILY in the work of the world, rubbing shoulders daily with cosmopolitan interests, a buyer and a seller in many markets, General Electric like other groups of humans came in for its share of controversy. Situations were continually arising which could be cleared up only by the rulings of the law courts.

On one such occasion, counsel for General Electric met its match. General Electric was in litigation with Stone and Webster of Boston, counsel for whom was Tyler and Young,

GERARD SWOPE
President of General Electric from 1922 to 1940.

OWEN D. YOUNG
Chairman of the Board of General Electric from 1922 to 1940.

and the case was handled in court by the junior member of the firm, Owen D. Young.

He was a comparative stranger in Boston, although his associates remembered vaguely that he had been born and raised a farmer's boy in northern New York. And they knew that Charles H. Tyler had given him a start upon his graduation from the law school of Boston University. Within ten years Tyler had admitted him to partnership.

The General Electric lawyers did not rate Young as a formidable opponent. He sat slouched in his chair, "his long legs lost in the shadows of the table." But when he towered before the court on those long legs, his slouch gone, head erect, they came to recognize not only his physical dominance, but his penetrating discernment and the clear-cut effectiveness of his arguments. When the trial was over, Owen D. Young was a name to be mentioned with respect among General Electric people. It reached the discriminating ears of Charles A. Coffin; and for a year or two Coffin watched him at a distance, noting the working of that keen mind, meditating upon the personality that had gotten the better of General Electric lawyers.

Coffin thought again of this display of talent and character when, in April, 1912, they brought him the news of the tragic death of Hinsdill Parsons, the brilliant lawyer who had been Vice President and General Counsel of General Electric for eleven years. During this time Young had made himself well known in and around Boston. He had, in fact, ably handled private law business for at least one of the Directors of General Electric.

So, one day, Coffin telephoned to Young and asked him to call. And he offered the young lawyer the position of General Counsel of the corporation.

Young accepted. Some years later he confided to one of

his colleagues part of what lay back of that acceptance. On Young's frequent trips from Boston to his boyhood home in New York State, his train passed close to the General Electric plant in Schenectady. Often, as he passed, he noticed the busy stir and activity. He sensed the feel of constructive effort, of building something useful. And sometimes, tired with the eternal bickering of the law courts and the litigation over affairs past and done with, he looked longingly at the Schenectady plant and wished that he could have a part in some such work, doing something truly constructive, helping to build something of lasting value. So, although Coffin's offer came as a surprise to Young, the idea was neither new nor unwelcome.

So came to General Electric this "tall rangy man of Lincolnesque height," Coffin's eventual successor as Chairman of the Board. He had come to help it grow and to grow with it.

Indeed, the growth of General Electric was so well-balanced and so healthy that it was continually able to measure up when new opportunities arose for yoking electricity. That was one reason why its salesmen and its engineers had just convinced a group of electric power prospects in the northwest that electric motors could run their trunk-line railroad.

The Chicago, Milwaukee and St. Paul Railroad extended far west of Milwaukee and St. Paul, climbed the great continental divide, penetrated the Rockies, wound upward among the Sierras, gathered its energies to cross the Cascade range, and halted only on the shores of the blue Pacific, at the northwest metropolis of Seattle. It passed through mountains that were exhilarating to passengers, but trying upon the capacities of its steam locomotives, particularly in the northwest winters.

Now electricity was to be given a chance. The inheritance of all the early traction pioneers was embodied in the electric motors that set out to conquer the Rockies. It was December, 1915, when the first electric locomotives took up their task on the St. Paul road. Nothing like them had been seen in that region before. The forty-two freight locomotives, weighing 280 tons each, were as massive as the stoutest steam hauler on the road. Each was able, through its twelve gearless motors, to haul a freight train weighing 2500 tons over steep grades at fifteen miles per hour. In 1920 electric passenger locomotives that weighed 260 tons apiece and were able to haul twelve cars weighing a total of 960 tons at twenty-five miles an hour, joined in the work. On 400 miles of mountain trackage these giant electric locomotives hauled their load with ease. One of the grades on the route extended for twenty-one miles at a rise of two per cent, but the electric giants mastered it easily.

The new locomotives worked on the principle of regenerative braking, which put a new item of economy in the budget. On the mountain divisions conditions for this type of braking were ideal. The gearless motors, the shafts of whose armatures were the axles of the wheels, after mounting those long grades, automatically reversed their action on the "down" side. Their rotation was no longer produced by the electrical impulse but by gravity. Instead of converting the electrical energy of the supply line into mechanical energy, they converted the mechanical energy created by the train's motion on the downgrade into electrical energy. And the process slowed up, or braked, the momentum of the heavy cars. Electricity produced by those generator motors constituting a saving of about twelve per cent in total power consumption, flowed back into the electrical transmission system, speeding over the distribution network as a contribution to the motive-power required by electric locomotives elsewhere on the line. A perfect operating economy—electricity helping to pay its own bills.

From the beginning automatic action had been important in electrical devices. Automatic action regulated arc lamps, kept current constant in dynamos, became the essence of the relay, the electric meter, the transformer.

When Alex Dow, President of the Detroit Edison Company, took one of his problems to General Electric engineers, they were interested at once. Dow wanted to apply the automatic idea in such a way that he could extend his lines to the outskirts of Detroit, where new homes were springing up though population was sparse.

The ordinary substation in such a district, with its payroll, would be too costly in proportion to the possible business. What Dow wanted was a station that could be controlled from a distance, through automatic action. That was what the engineers designed for him. In less than a year's time this remotely controlled substation was at work in Detroit. It was situated on Rowena Street and controlled from the generating station on Elizabeth Street, a mile away. It distributed electrical energy up to 500 kilowatts; and except for an occasional inspector, no human set foot within its walls.

Two years later the completely automatic substation appeared. An engineer in General Electric's Chicago office, Edward Taylor, designed the first of this type, which began to operate at Union, Illinois, in December 1914. It was magic —both in its working and in its effect upon operating costs. Here were machines which began working when they were needed, and stopped working when they were not.

Picture an electric car on that road running far out from

the main generating station, farther than direct current can be transmitted economically. Presently it draws near the automatic substation. At a certain point its approach actuates relays. Instantly the synchronous converters, by which alternating current is converted into direct, go into action.

In swift sequences, handled entirely by automatic control, the converters are connected through transformers to a 33,000-volt supply line, then to a 600-volt trolley line and the speeding car draws the motive power it needs. When its power is supplied from the next substation, the current in the trolley wire at the first substation drops below a certain point, causing the automatic control to shut down the converters until the next car approaches.

In less than ten years the total installed capacity of equipment of this type reached half a million kilowatts. On interurban lines especially, the cars take their power from several automatic stations in succession. The automatic generating station was to grow out of this at a later period.

Almost as marvelous was the growth of the electric generator itself. In 1902 people spoke of generators that fed 7500 kilowatts of electricity into transmission lines as "mammoth." In 1914, 20,000 kilowatts were generated by one General Electric unit. What do such capacities mean to practical folk? They mean that whereas in 1904 one generating machine could supply enough electric current to light 100,000 lamps, in 1914 it could supply 1,700,000! Only twenty-five years before, a dynamo supplying 150 incandescent lamps was thought to be wonderful. Capacities had increased eleven thousand times in a quarter century!

40

Conservatism Routed

I HAVE TONIGHT seen the greatest revelation of beauty that was ever seen on the earth," exclaimed Edwin Markham, the poet, one February evening in 1915.

"I may say this, meaning it literally," he added, "and with full regard for all that is known of ancient art and architecture, and all that the modern world has heretofore seen of glory and grandeur. I have seen beauty that will give the world new standards of art and a joy in loveliness never before reached. This is what I have seen—the courts and buildings of the Panama-Pacific Exposition illuminated at night."

The illumination which so inspired the poet was largely the work of Walter D'Arcy Ryan, director of General Electric's Illuminating Engineering Laboratory.

Ryan had tackled illuminating jobs of this magnitude before. In 1907 he had supervised the lighting of Niagara Falls —a feat that required the installation of batteries of projectors giving a combined illumination equivalent to 1,115,000,000 candles. It, too, had been a huge success. The throng that gathered on the opening night was so large that the suspension bridge swayed perceptibly and traffic had to be halted. The roar of the cataract came through the darkness, the cataract that could not be seen. Then without warning the Falls leaped out of the night, a vast, shimmering mist of plunging water, gleaming in the concentrated light. The thousands of spectators stood in awe and silence.

But Ryan encountered new difficulties when, in San Francisco, he presented his plans before the architects, designers, and color artists who were involved in preparation for the Exposition. His proposals seemed so fantastic that there was scarcely a detail which was not opposed. For Ryan's theory was founded upon the idea that to run strings of incandescent lamps along the edges of buildings so that they would be outlined by dots of light, was crude and archaic. His plan was twofold: first he proposed to throw a flood of light upon the façades of the buildings; and second, he proposed a scheme for depth, or "shadow" lighting.

A terraced tower, four hundred feet or more from a square base with broad archways, dominated the wide array of picturesque Spanish mission buildings. Ryan's idea for lighting this tower was even more fantastic. He wanted something lively and prismatic. Immediately he thought of imitation cut-glass jewels played upon by powerful searchlights. He instituted a search which finally uncovered a type of jewel made in imitation of diamonds, rubies, sapphires, and emeralds; and the glass was so cut as to possess a high index of refraction.

Many cunning hands had worked over those gems. Native workmen among the hills of Austria had kept the craft in their families for generations, treating the original uncut pieces by heat and glass-blowing methods of which they alone knew the secret. In 1913 there came from distant America an order for no less than 130,000 jewels!

The Austrian craftsmen gasped, but in time the order was filled. Ryan called the jewels "Novagems."

His laboratory workshop, crowded with color paintings of the buildings as they would appear when illuminated, color charts, and booths for demonstrating special illumination effects aroused the greatest curiosity. Some of the other specialists felt that Ryan was usurping the functions belonging to others. Upon returning from one of his trips East, Ryan found that his critics had burst into open condemnation of his plans. Someone had tried a few of his jewels upon the tower and found that they cast shadows. The architects' commission wanted to throw all the jewels bodily into San Francisco Bay.

Ryan promptly demonstrated by means of photographs that, when properly mounted, the jewels would not cast shadows, while incandescent lamps, strung up and down the tower would. Then he was told that his idea of placing heraldic banners along the avenues to add color in the daytime and to screen floodlight units at night would cheapen the exposition into a mere Coney Island spectacle because the banners would flap. Ryan replied that he intended to hang fifty-pound weighted tassels from each banner so that no ordinary breeze would disturb them.

Another outcry went up when he disclosed his plan for a steam scintillator to be played upon by a great battery of electric searchlights. He had arranged with the Southern Pacific Railroad to have a steam locomotive, painted a rich cream color, backed upon a pier on the waterside front of the exposition. Shell pits were dug and forty-eight big searchlights were placed in position, their total capacity equalling 2,600,000,000 candles. Surely "this man Ryan" was running wild! The architects' commission started a movement to have the locomotive removed.

But Ryan would not be stampeded. He stoutly defended his "fireless fireworks." The locomotive and the steam scintillator remained.

But exposition officials were secretly as fearful as the architects and designers. They hoped that Ryan was right, while they quietly consulted a local illuminating expert and had an alternate plan worked out down to the last detail, ready to be rushed into the gap should the Ryan plan fail upon trial. This alternate plan was based upon strings of incandescent lamps.

At last came the night for the trial exhibition, the night of February 15, 1915, three weeks before the date of the official opening. Upon one of the wide avenues the official party gathered. Dusk slowly began to fall. A silvery shaft leaped into the darkening sky.

Then, in a burst of glory, a scene of romantic beauty unfolded, as palaces and halls stood out richly down long thoroughfares of light. Radiance glowed from every window, as if the interiors were brightly lighted. Deep rose tints bathed the recesses in archways and columned porticoes, where forbidding shadows usually gathered. It was a city of light.

In the center rose the iridescent Tower of Jewels. And every pool and lagoon caught and reflected the glimmering tower and the fairy palaces. A 20th Century Aladdin had rubbed his lamp.

The international jury of awards of the Exposition did something never before dreamed of. It adjudged the illumination of the Exposition to be a "decorative art."

TURNING TO A FAR DIFFERENT FIELD of the electrical arts, the year 1915 also saw the battleship *New Mexico* launched.

Back in 1909 Emmet had felt that the turbine-electric drive

could be designed for sea craft. Units of 14,000 kilowatts were already a reality. He turned to the United States Navy, knowing that there he would find vessels large enough to receive maximum benefit from the turbine-electric drive, as well as financial resources sufficient to undertake so large an installation.

But the Navy was not interested in turbine-generators and electric motors for its vessels. Steam propulsion had been the traditional method for so many years, and too many naval men had been bred in the sacred belief that there could be no substitute. No one in the Navy Department at Washington took Emmet seriously. Three colliers were at that time being equipped, and preparations for installing other types of propulsion went forward without interruption. The *Cyclops* was launched, with a marine engine to propel her. A little later the *Neptune* followed, equipped with a geared turbine as her driving unit. Then Emmet, pleading fair play and an equal chance with his competitors, won a reluctant consent to the installation of a turbine-generator upon the *Jupiter*.

Naval officials did not for a minute believe the *Jupiter* could be propelled efficiently by electric motors. They even had the vessel designed so that the mode of propulsion could be altered to the marine-engine type when the anticipated breakdown of the electric drive occurred.

In this wise was the *Jupiter* built at the Mare Island Navy Yard at San Francisco, and put in commission in 1913. Her commanding officer was Commander C. S. Kernpff, and her chief engineer Lieutenant S. M. Robinson. Aside from Lieutenant Robinson, only one man on board, the chief electrician, had any conception of the nature of the electrical equipment. The apparatus was handled by enlisted men who had to be instructed from the ground up in their work.

But machinists' mates within a week's time learned how to

operate the electrical apparatus, and Commander Kernpff's report was an enthusiastic endorsement of the new method of propelling naval craft.

The report caused a stir in naval circles at Washington. The officers of the *Jupiter* were immediately replaced by others to check their sanity in expressing such enthusiasm. The new officers turned in an equally hearty endorsement.

But naval officials at Washington were not easily satisfied and accordingly they detailed two officers to serve on the *Jupiter* as inspecting officers, whose sole duty was to observe and report on the electrical equipment. Their report was even more complimentary than its predecessors.

With that, criticism temporarily subsided. Emmet, following up the advantage he had gained, recommended that turbine-generators and electric motors be provided for the battleship *New Mexico,* now under construction. The proposal immediately raised an outcry. It seemed that the new radicals would stop short of nothing. It was all very well to turn turrets, operate deck winches, revolve capstans, or hoist ammunition by electricity. And all very well to propel a vessel no larger than the *Jupiter.* But a battleship! It couldn't be done. It would require generators too large for the ship.

Emmet, undaunted, drew up a definite proposal on behalf of General Electric and submitted it to the Navy Department, but without avail. Then he interviewed the Secretary of the Navy, Josephus C. Daniels, and persuaded him to allow estimates to be prepared showing the cost of equipping the *New Mexico* for electric drive as compared with the cost of installing steam-propulsion machinery.

Emmet took his figures to the industrial engineer of the Brooklyn Navy Yard, who had been ordered to draw up the estimates. This was Admiral George E. Burd, who was fair-minded and had a passion for facts. Admiral Burd's estimate swayed the issue, for it stated that turbine-generators and electric motors on the *New Mexico* would cost a quarter of a million dollars less than either the geared turbine or the marine engine.

Emmet appeared at a conference in Secretary Daniels' office and spoke at length, drawing on his ten years' experience in designing and installing Curtis steam turbines and generators. His figures had been tested and verified, and he pointed out considerations which others had lost sight of. In the end, Secretary Daniels gave him the contract.

In 1915 the *New Mexico* was launched, a powerful floating fighting machine of 32,000 tons. She burned oil for fuel, and her dozen big tanks had a capacity of a million gallons. She required only nine boilers, while other battleships of her weight had twelve. Steam pressure on the boilers ran to 280 pounds, which meant that turbine pressures had risen 105 pounds since the Chicago turbine of 1903.

As for electrical equipment, its aggregate weight was about 600 tons. There were two main generators, each rated at 15,500 horsepower, and they supplied four propulsion motors, each with a 7000-horsepower capacity. The generators were each driven by a Curtis steam turbine, so that only two turbines were necessary, while the battleship Pennsylvania, with the geared-turbine drive, required ten.

At ten knots the *New Mexico* consumed about twenty-five per cent less fuel than the best turbine-driven ship that preceded her. And she was an all-electric ship. Electric motors operated the steering gear, boat cranes, winches, capstan, refrigerating system, laundering machines, water pumps, oil pumps; they raised anchors, revolved the turrets, hoisted ammunition, compressed air, turned the fans and blowers; they supplied the machine shop, carpenter shop, printing shop, and kitchen; and electricity heated the air, cooked toast, boiled coffee, supplied telephone systems, operated the battery of searchlights, illuminated the entire ship. It was a veritable electric home, in which 1100 men found the tasks of life amazingly simplified.

It was a triumph indeed. Yet electrical engineers admitted that the original prejudice of the Navy was no more than natural. E. W. Rice, Jr., President of General Electric, spoke later of the success to a group of Navy men.

"That electrical gear," he said, "should by any possibility prove to be more generally efficient seems a paradox . . . It is due, we believe, to the fact that in the electric drive an open air space is substituted for the teeth of the mechanical gear. Although we remove the teeth, we are able to transmit tremendous power without any mechanical connection . . . The electrical method substitutes an indestructible, infinitely elastic air space for the teeth of the mechanical gear, and obviously the air space cannot be bent, or broken, requires no lubrication, and contains nothing to rub or to get out of order."

41

A Period Ends

WAR CLOUDS OVER EUROPE brought sudden problems to the United States as April 1917 came in. In her youthful strength America was marching into the vortex of a titanic human struggle that flamed destructively across a continent.

America was separated from the scene of conflict and from all her allies by three thousand miles of ocean. She must talk continually to those allies, to her military and naval leaders, though an ocean intervened and though the enemy attacked the underwater cables.

There was but one way to do it—radio. Every army and naval radio station in the country was instantly keyed up for service. Yet few of them were equipped to span the ocean. Transoceanic radio communication was still embryonic. But now it was imperative.

In this dilemma one station alone stepped into the gap. The American Marconi Company, affiliated with the British Marconi Company, agreed to give a practical trial of the Alexanderson alternator at its large transmitting center at New Brunswick. Alexanderson had developed his 200-kilowatt alternator, and a complete unit of this size was

372

rented to the Marconi Company, replacing the old 50-kilowatt unit at the Marconi station. In January 1918 this became for the time being a United States naval radio transmitting station, operated by naval personnel.

War continued through the spring and summer of 1918. The New Brunswick station bridged the ocean daily in the transaction of government war business. But soon the operators at receiving stations both in America and Europe found themselves in a new predicament, created by the activities of the enemy.

The large German transmitting station at Nauen was "jamming the air," that is, it was sending out interfering waves for the purpose of choking incoming messages on the receiving antennae of the American and allied stations, thus preventing communication. The scheme succeeded often enough to make things disconcerting.

Radio engineers of the allied nations set to work to overcome this interference. Alexanderson soon developed his barrage receiver, which was a unidirectional system so efficient that it could eliminate the signals of a high-powered sending station operating close by. One unit of this device was sealed in the diplomatic mail of the United States government and sent to France. Another was installed in the United States government receiving station at Bar Harbor, Maine.

Meanwhile the station at New Brunswick had been bombarding Germany and her allies with a new sort of missile—radio messages and bulletins relating to the war preparations which America was making. The constant arrival of American troops in France, the launching of ship after ship, the raising of billions for waging war—all this was poured upon the air for assimilation by German stations. It was an offensive against morale, a psychological attack.

Late in October, 1918, the last great German offensive had been stopped. The attackers of heroic Verdun had again been checked, and the American divisions were steadily hammering back German lines which had been thought impregnable. The tide was slowly, surely turning. At that moment there leaped upon the air, to be picked up alike by Nauen and the allied stations, a set of call-letters from the American station at New Brunswick.

"POZ . . . POZ . . . POZ . . . de . . . NFF" buzzed the receivers. POZ was the call for the German station at Nauen, and NFF was the station at New Brunswick. The two had not been on speaking terms for a long time.

The Nauen operator replied a moment later: "Your signals are fine, old man."

Whereupon the "old man" in New Brunswick dispatched in English the first of President Wilson's statements to the German people, carrying the ultimatum that the allies would conduct no negotiations for an armistice or for peace with the German government as then constituted. In other words, Kaiser Wilhelm would have to step down.

"Thereafter," says the New York Post, "Washington was in constant communication with Berlin. President Wilson's memorable 'fourteen points' were broadcast to Germany from New Brunswick. Wireless was making history at a faster pace than all the engines of destruction. Innumerable electrical impulses, flashing back and forth across the Atlantic, were settling the war. It might have taken a month longer to negotiate the armistice if it had not been for those radio exchanges."

The war ended, but radio went on. As Alexanderson said, "It was the war which brought radio into its own. Before the war it had been interesting. With the advent of the war it became vital." Its demonstrated usefulness was only beginning.

CHARLES A. COFFIN AT THE AGE OF 80
About 11 years after his retirement as President of General Electric.

THE HOME OF G-E RESEARCH
The buildings that house the Research Laboratory, at Schenectady.

For a few months after the armistice was signed the most significant events in American radio centered around the transmitting station at New Brunswick and its peculiarly effective radio generator, the Alexanderson alternator.

Efforts to obtain customers for the high-frequency alternator had been made by General Electric before America entered the war. The government was first approached, but was already committed to the Poulsen arc. At the close of the war General Electric recommenced its efforts to sell equipment to the Marconi Company. Formerly the terms had not been agreed upon. The Marconi Company insisted upon an agreement by which it would obtain a monopoly on the Alexanderson alternator. Under this agreement they placed an order amounting to $5,000,000.

General Electric felt no hesitancy now in entering this exclusive agreement, as with one exception no other customer had been found for the costly alternator. The Swedish government planned to erect a powerful station, and the Swedish minister at Washington, W. A. F. Ekengren, had begun negotiations with General Electric.

But the Swedish government wanted only one alternator. The Marconi Company was a far larger customer, and in acquiescing to its proposal, General Electric was obliged to terminate its negotiations with Sweden. Minister Ekengren was seriously disturbed. He knew what an advantage that alternator would give to radio development in Sweden. He called upon Rear Admiral William Bullard, then Director of Communications for the Navy. Admiral Bullard became as disturbed as Minister Ekengren, but for a far different reason.

Familiar with the merits of the alternator, he knew that the American Marconi Company, despite its name and location, was dominated by the British Marconi Company. He foresaw what radio would become within a few years; and he wanted America, not a foreign country, to have control over the alternator which was at that time the most practical device for producing continuous radio waves at high power.

This was the situation in March, 1919, when E. P. Edwards, later Manager of General Electric's Radio Department, returned to Schenectady from New York with the necessary data to draw up the contract giving the Marconi Company exclusive purchasing rights to the Alexanderson alternator. As he began his work, he was called on long distance by Commander Hooper, in charge of the Radio Section of the Naval Bureau of Engineering, who besought him to delay negotiations until a conference could be arranged.

That conference, a momentous one in the history of American radio, took place on April 5, 1919. E. W. Rice, Jr., President of General Electric; Charles A. Coffin, Chairman of the Board; Owen D. Young, Vice President; Albert G. Davis, Vice President in Charge of Patents; and others, were met by Admiral Bullard and Commander Hooper.

Admiral Bullard was spokesman for the Navy. "Gentlemen," he said, "we are satisfied that the General Electric Company, through the Alexanderson alternator, has developed the most perfect system of radio communication in existence. We should like to make use of it ourselves, but we cannot secure the necessary appropriation. We know that you are negotiating with the Marconi interests, expecting to sell this apparatus exclusively to them. We are here to persuade you on the grounds of self-interest and patriotism not to do it!"

Then he pointed out what such a step would mean, in giving to Great Britain the control of world radio communication. In effect, his message was: "Save radio control for America!"

Owen D. Young, as spokesman for General Electric, replied: "You have placed a definite problem before us. You tell us that we have a wonderful system, that the Navy itself cannot buy it, and that we should not sell it to the only commercial company which is prepared to buy it.

"We realize the patriotic note in your appeal; but what do you want us to do with this apparatus? Do you want us to put it to one side, where neither ourselves nor the public will derive any benefit from it?"

"We did not come without an alternate plan," replied Admiral Bullard. "I would recommend that your company should either exploit this system directly, or should organize a subsidiary company to do so."

The appeal struck home. General Electric broke off negotiations with the Marconi Company.

Next the General Electric officials launched a new company for radio communication, rather than put their own company into a field foreign to its province. They purchased the block of stock in the American Marconi Company which was owned by British interests. Then the American Marconi Company was purchased by General Electric in behalf of the proposed new company.

The new concern was established around December 1, 1919, under the name of the Radio Corporation of America. It was to be the selling agent for General Electric's radio products.

General Electric officials now conceived of a mobilization of all American radio and communications interests behind the new company, and undertook negotiations which led to the participation in the Radio Corporation of the American Telephone & Telegraph Company, the Western Electric Company, the Westinghouse Electric & Manufacturing Company, and the United Fruit Company.

This procedure adjusted a patent dilemma which was as-

suming a gravity reminiscent of the deadlocks of 1890 and
1896. Now, in 1919, the conflict of patents held by competing companies, yet necessary for the operations of all, would
have crippled radio communication in all its aspects. Such
an outcome would have been calamitous, for radio was directing the public mind to technical innovations in a manner
without precedent.

The marvels which electricity was producing were meeting with far less prejudice and a far readier welcome than
did those of three decades ago. People had become electrically minded!

As STEINMETZ ENTERED the high-studded laboratory room,
with its wide windows and its maze of apparatus, conversation ceased. Heads turned in his direction, attention was
riveted on that impressive figure, diminutive in stature, yet
suggestive of a power beyond physical strength.

"Good morning! Good morning!" he exclaimed. "How are
you?" Then, to his adopted son, J. LeRoy Hayden, he added,
"What's new?"

It was the greeting with which he had opened the day at
office and laboratory for nearly thirty years. But on this
morning, Steinmetz knew better than anyone else what was
"new." He was about to demonstrate his famous lightning
generator.

For weeks he had been investigating lightning with this
strange device. His purpose was to discover new knowledge
which he could pass on to the designers of lightning ar-
resters, so that these watchdogs of transmission systems might
be made more reliable. As he picturesquely termed it, they
are the traffic officers; lightning is the criminal of these
systems.

In the study which he had been making, the lightning

NIAGARA FALLS AS ILLUMINATED BY GENERAL ELECTRIC
IN 1925

GENERAL ELECTRIC BUILDING, 570 LEXINGTON AVENUE, NEW YORK,
FLOODLIGHTED WITH FLUORESCENT AND MERCURY LIGHTS, 1940

generator was but a means of an end. Yet it was spectacular in itself.

There were many who wanted to see, on this winter's morning of 1922. And what they saw were rows of large glass panes, connected by wires to a group of glass tubes and by other wires to a circuit, or "discharge path," in which was placed a small tree limb. The glass plates were the condenser, which stored up electricity as does a thundercloud until the point was reached when it could hold no more and electricity was discharged in a quick flash—that was the artificial lightning-bolt. The lightning "flashed," the thunder "roared," and the tree limb was split into fragments. It was a perfect imitation, in miniature.

"We get a discharge," said Dr. Steinmetz, "of 10,000 amperes at 120,000 volts; that is, over one million horsepower, lasting for a hundred thousandth of a second. This gives us the explosive, shattering effect of real lightning."

According to his calculation, natural lightning might represent as little as 3000 amperes but with a hundred million volts behind it, or five hundred million horsepower.

This was the most spectacular of many deeds which General Electric men performed in these later years of the great electrical enterprise. General Electric was more than a manufacturing concern. It was an institution of science and of engineering, of vocational training and of character building, an institution of wide social and economic influence. Through its scientists, engineers, workmen, and salesmen it had become what it was.

A few months before Steinmetz manufactured lightning, the General Electric laboratory at Pittsfield transmitted electric current at a million volts. This was achieved by Guiseppe Faccioli and Frank W. Peek, Jr., upon the spot where the famous SKC trio had pitted their confidence against the electrical conservatism of the early nineties. The plant manager at Pittsfield at that very moment was Cummings C. Chesney, last of the SKC men.

As for the manufacture of the incandescent lamp, hardly a hand operation now remained. One by one machines had taken over these intricate, patience-wearing operations.

In 1918 William R. Burrows, Howell's resourceful associate, was still looking for more economical methods of manufacturing the lamp. He reflected that there were six or eight major processes, each located in a different department. Some machines produced more rapidly than others, so that surplus parts had to be stored between operations. Burrows and his staff soon reduced the number of basic machines to four, which were placed next to each other. The work was fed in sequence from one to the next. A balance of production was .thereafter maintained, in which there were no surplus parts. Production costs dropped down, as did the price to the consumer. Within thirty months General Electric reduced its lamp prices five times, the total reduction amounting to thirty-seven per cent.

A further economy was the tipless lamp. For forty years no one had been able to eliminate that little glass tip, which was a liability for it increased the breakage hazard. The tip was caused by the method of exhausting the air from the bulb, through a glass tube welded to the top of the bulb, which in being sealed off left a protuberance. In 1929 two foremen of the National Lamp Works of General Electric at Cleveland, Loris E. Mitchell and Arthur J. White, contrived to exhaust the lamp through the base of the bulb. This new method abolished one step of manufacture, and production cost and the market price dropped again.

THE PIONEERS OF THE COMPANY, the men who had brought the organization through its earlier years, grew older. Inevitably, younger shoulders assumed the heavier burdens of management.

In January, 1919, General Electric segregated its export business, which up to that time had been handled by a foreign department. The foreign business had increased threefold during the preceding five years. It needed separate attention—attention of a kind different from that accorded domestic affairs. So it was decided to set up a new company, to be called the International General Electric Company.

To head that new company, a man was chosen from outside the organization, a vice president of the Western Electric Company, who had built on a background of engineering training a reputation for merchandising ability and a keen grasp of the fundamentals of business. That man's name was Gerard Swope. Strictly speaking, he was returning to the fold. But probably few were aware that he was the same "G. Swope, helper, per day $1" who had been on the Company's payroll at the Chicago World's Fair of 1893, when he was a student at Massachusetts Tech and General Electric was only a "million a month" concern.

For almost two years Swope traveled constantly in the foreign countries in which General Electric was doing business. He reorganized the scattered personnel of the various foreign offices, he worked out standard and consistent contracts with foreign business firms, he developed a smooth-running organization to handle the large amount of business which had all but swamped the previous staff.

The duties of Owen D. Young, as General Counsel, had been at first largely in giving legal advice and handling strictly legal affairs. But gradually he was called on to be arbitrator in other matters. All sorts of questions were brought to him, and he showed an uncanny faculty for coming to a quick decision, but a decision that the passage of time showed to be as wise as though it had been the result of long and laborious discussion. When matters reached an impasse, it became a habit to take them to Mr. Young.

In the organizing of the Radio Corporation, too, Young had taken a leading part. As Chairman of the Board of that company, he had already, by 1922, shown his ability in guiding the new venture through the hazards and pitfalls of its earliest years.

In the spring of 1922, the industrial world learned of important executive changes in the General Electric organization. The directors had elected Gerard Swope as President of General Electric, and Owen D. Young as Chairman of the Board. Edwin W. Rice, Jr., whom Swope succeeded as President, became Honorary Chairman of the Board.

And so Coffin, the great leader, retired. He kept his desk in the suite of offices at 120 Broadway, New York, where the executive heart of the Company had long been centered. He came regularly to his office. Visitors there met with the same kindly reception, the same quiet humor that had smoothed the deliberations of so many executive and directors meetings. But his day-by-day interests were now more personal, confined largely to innumerable philanthropic activities that had been one side of his life for a long span of years.

In honor of the first President, the Charles A. Coffin Foundation awards were added to a long and growing list of activities in which General Electric had long been pioneering—again leading the way that others would eventually follow. This was the field of employee relations, which General Electric was exploring by establishing plans contributing to employee security. A pension plan had been set up in 1912; a mutual benefit association to provide benefits in case of sickness, death, or hospitalization had been established in 1913; a profit-sharing system in 1916; a life-insurance plan in 1920; a savings plan in 1922. A suggestion system, whereby employees were paid for suggestions helpful to the operation of the Company, had been established as far back as 1906, and through the intervening years one plan after another had been added to protect employees against the vicissitudes of life, and to provide opportunity and a measure of security.

In the spring of 1926 a young General Electric man, William W. Trench, called upon Charles A. Coffin at the latter's office in New York. It was one of the last interviews in Mr. Coffin's career of which there is a record. Mr. Trench describes it as follows:

"That May morning found him full of the exuberance of youth. Just in from his home on Long Island, he was full of the beauty of the country—had time to discuss two child poets whose works aroused his enthusiasm, to speak glowingly of the notable men who had been attracted to General Electric by the fascination of the industry, possessing, as it does, no known bounds of service or accomplishment.

"The conversation touched on the extraordinary contributions of young men to the advancement of the industry. Mr. Coffin remarked on the age at which Edison did his revolutionary work—at which Langmuir and Coolidge brought forth their first great discoveries. His thoughts turned to the possibilities of making greater use of youth in other fields of activity. He deplored the program of several young men he knew who were still pursuing their studies at twenty-eight, with the realm of actual life yet unexplored—he looked with some hope at ways and means of aiding youths to acquire wisdom as well as knowledge during the early vital years of their lives.

"As in the case of any discussion with Mr. Coffin, one left the room stimulated—aroused. One felt a greater interest in the manifestations of nature—in the beauty of cultural things —in the possibilities of building and training youth for larger activities—in the part America should play in world affairs."

Mr. Coffin was then in his eighty-second year. Two months later he passed away.

The Second Generation

WITH THE DEATH OF Charles A. Coffin the first great era in General Electric history came to a close. During his administration he had launched a new industrial art and established it firmly as an essential part of mankind's way of living. Now, under the leadership of Owen D. Young and Gerard Swope, a new era in the Company's history began. Before them lay the task of bringing a frontier organization to industrial maturity, of refining the rough-hewn policies that had served the pioneer period. There was plenty of pioneering yet to be done, but it was pioneering of another sort. The struggle to overcome the skepticism that had confronted the early efforts of the pioneers was largely won. Now came the task of moulding the giant force of electricity to human needs; of applying it to bring new comforts and conveniences, higher living standards for the nation; of fitting a new industry to take its place beside the older industries to help build a greater America.

It was to this task that Owen D. Young and Gerard Swope now applied themselves. They early worked out a division of responsibilities that was to continue as long as they held office. As Mr. Young described it, "One of us shall act as captain of the ship, the other as navigator." Mr. Young would concern himself with policy, Mr. Swope with production, research, engineering, and sales.

In the 18 years of their leadership, the teamwork of these two men produced many marvels, but none of more lasting significance than their common effort on behalf of labor. For years the Company had been in the forefront of American industry in providing fair compensation and good working conditions for employees, but these were to be supplemented by many employee benefit plans. Many of these plans had been inaugurated before Mr. Coffin retired, but under Mr. Young and Mr. Swope they were expanded and welded into a unified program for the employees' welfare. Since 1916 there had been in effect supplementary compensation and profit-sharing plans for the employees, and Mr. Swope and Mr. Young applied themselves to the perfecting of these plans. Together they further developed the pension plan which had operated since 1912, and the mutual-benefit associations which provided sickness, hospitalization, and death benefits. They established life insurance plans; a savings plan; the suggestion system, whereby employees reap the benefits from their suggestions for improving methods and working conditions; vacations with pay; a plan to adjust employee earnings automatically as variations occur in the cost of living; loan funds; a plan to assist employees in acquiring homes; and year by year additional methods were worked out to protect employees against the vicissitudes of life, and provide opportunity and a measure of security. Employee representation was instituted, unemployment insurance was put into operation, and educational and recreational facilities for employees developed.

These efforts on behalf of labor, described as "liberal" and

PHILIP D. REED
Chairman of the Board of General Electric.

CHARLES E. WILSON
President of General Electric.

even as "radical" by many of their contemporaries, sprang from a new conception of their responsibilities as leaders of the General Electric Company. Up to the time the electrical industry was founded most businesses had been managed by their owners directly. As the years passed and large corporations came into being, there came about a separation of management and ownership—now represented by stockholders—but management still considered itself the agent of the owners, working in their interests. It was this conception of management that prevailed throughout the business world at the time Mr. Young and Mr. Swope succeeded to the Board Chairmanship and Presidency of General Electric. They were among the first to recognize a new conception of management's responsibilities—a conception of management, not as an agent of the owners, but as a trustee of all groups vitally interested in industry—owners, employees, and the general public, including customers. It was their determination to guard the interests of all three groups.

This conception of their responsibilities had a profound influence on the General Electric Company. No serious labor disturbance occurred during their entire administration, even though that period saw the nationwide struggle which accompanied the union movement in America.

Another field in which this, the second generation of General Electric administrators, was outstandingly successful was the field of public relations. Mr. Coffin had been of a retiring nature. He himself said, "A company's job is simply to make goods and sell them. The less said about personalities, the better." As a result of this reticence, many considered General Electric an "interest," controlled by "Wall Street." Under the direction of Mr. Young and Mr. Swope, the public began to get better acquainted with General Electric. The introduction of home appliances, together with the appliance advertising, helped; the public relations program that they instituted was instrumental in bringing it about; and they themselves, rapidly growing to the stature of internationally known figures, became widely recognized as the leaders of General Electric. The emphasis which Mr. Young placed on this phase of the Company's activities is illustrated by his admonition to a group of employees:

"Everyone," he said, "has had mornings when he hates to hear the telephone ring, or to see the office door open. I beg of you, gentlemen, when next you meet such a morning, take a stick of dynamite and blow up one of our plants. But do not take it out on a customer of the General Electric. We can replace the plant you have destroyed; we know its value; we have a reserve from which we can rebuild. But we cannot measure the goodwill you have destroyed, and we can never know if we have replaced it."

Consideration for the public and public opinion directed several important policy changes during the early years of their administration. General Electric's ownership of the Electric Bond and Share Company, giving it an influential interest in a goodly number of public utilities, was a potential source of public criticism, and Mr. Young and Mr. Swope soon advocated taking the Company out of this business. "We can't carry water on both shoulders," said Mr. Swope; "it is wrong to our own customers." Even against the advice of Mr. Coffin they urged this step to their Board of Directors, and in December 1924 they disposed of General Electric's holdings in the Electric Bond and Share Company by distributing its stock to General Electric's stockholders.

In another direction, too, this new concept of their management responsibilities began to be felt. On behalf of the general public additional emphasis was placed on making electricity more useful, and less costly so that everyone could afford its advantages. When they took control, lamps and' fans were about the only General Electric products sold to the general public—in fact, few electric appliances of any sort were on the market. General Electric products consisted principally of huge turbines and generators, motors, and other apparatus, sold largely to industry, railroads, public utilities.

Between 1925 and 1930 General Electric devised and put into production many new electrical appliances, designed to help banish drudgery from the home. Electric refrigerators, radios, washing machines, vacuum cleaners, and many smaller appliances were placed on the market. Air-conditioning equipment was developed; electric ranges, water-heaters, electric ironers, and garbage-disposal units took their place beside the others. At first these devices were crude and costly, but as sales volume increased and improved methods of production were worked out, the selling prices were steadily reduced. At the same time, vast improvements were made in the products themselves—they lasted longer and consumed less electricity, so that each year millions more families were able to afford them. It was not many years before the manufacture of electrical products for the home began to be almost as large a part of General Electric's business as the large apparatus which had previously accounted for most of the Company's sales. In creating these new comforts and conveniences for the home, contributing directly to the benefit of the public, General Electric also assisted in creating a whole new branch of the electrical industry, providing new employment for thousands of people in the factory, thousands of salesmen all over the country, and a host of workers in other industries providing the raw materials from which these appliances are made.

Nor was General Electric idle in the field of industrial

equipment. Under the leadership of Mr. Young and Mr. Swope, General Electric's scientists, engineers, and workmen were busy fitting electricity and electric apparatus to the needs of the world. They were revolutionizing methods of production throughout industry by creating electrical methods for doing existing jobs, and for making possible new operations which could not be done before. In every factory and shop, electricity was being put to work to enable many industries to produce goods by the thousands at lower cost, so that millions of people could enjoy them.

By constant improvement of the apparatus for generating, transmitting, and distributing electricity, General Electric was making it possible for the power and light companies to expand the areas they served, and helping them to reduce the cost of electricity year by year so that more people could enjoy its benefits. The steam turbine has been so improved that today twice as much electricity is produced for each pound of coal consumed as was produced in 1922. Hydrogen cooling was developed for large generators, further increasing their efficiency. Transformers have been vastly improved, new steels developed for the cores which have greatly reduced power loss in the transformers, and a new method developed in which the cores of distribution transformers are wound, producing better transformers at less cost. Research in lightning has been carried forward and expanded, and many new protective devices developed to minimize lightning damage.

Throughout the whole range of electric apparatus employed in making and distributing electricity, constant improvement has resulted in making electricity more readily available to everyone. In this field, General Electric is still seeking new and better ways. Research and development on the mercury turbine, direct-current transmission, and hundreds of other experiments give promise of the progress yet to come.

To help industry provide in abundance the thousands of articles in common use, General Electric has developed hundreds of new electrical devices. Arc welding has enabled industry to fabricate giant machines for the factory, as well as smaller products for the home. Bridges, buildings, ships, and hundreds of industrial products are made more easily, more quickly, and at less cost than would be possible without arc welding.

Electric heat, in the form of huge electric furnaces and small elements, is employed in melting, annealing, hardening, and enameling metal products. Many industrial processes would be practically impossible without electric heat.

New motors—more compact, more flexible, more adaptable—give vast amounts of mechanical power to help industry do its many tasks. Small motors—fractional horsepower—have been applied to bookkeeping machines, electric appliances, air-conditioning equipment, and hundreds of other useful applications. Electric control has been applied to hundreds of machines, making them capable of doing things that would be impossible by hand. In many fields, electric control governs the processes of converting raw materials to useful finished products.

In mining operations and in the oil industry, electricity has made possible improved methods, and today electricity operates the drills, pumps oil through electrically welded pipe lines to electrically operated oil refineries, and operates the gasoline pumps at the service stations. In every industrial endeavor electricity has been applied to enable men to produce more with less effort.

In the field of transportation, electricity has made vast improvement possible. General Electric played an important role in electrifying the Pennsylvania Railroad from New York to Washington and Harrisburg—the world's largest main-line electrification project. High-speed electric locomotives have won new passenger revenue for the railroads. Auxiliary equipment for air-conditioning trains has made travel more comfortable. General Electric has developed a new, more powerful, steam-electric locomotive, which carries its own steam turbine to produce the electric power it uses to drive its wheels.

For urban transportation, General Electric has developed trolley coaches, streamlined street cars, and oil-electric buses. Faster, smoother, more comfortable transportation has been furnished hundreds of American cities. On the high seas, electricity has made ships faster, safer, more comfortable. Turbine-electric and geared drives have revolutionized methods of ship propulsion. And in dozens of other ways, electricity has contributed to passenger, freight, and naval vessels alike.

In the air, General Electric superchargers have become almost standard equipment on commercial and military airplanes. Airplane instruments, airport lighting, radio beacons, all owe their efficacy to electricity.

In the constant war against disease, electricity has been placed at the aid of the physician and surgeon in countless ways. The X-ray, developed by Dr. W. D. Coolidge of the General Electric Research Laboratory, has proved invaluable in diagnosis, and in the treatment of disease. The electro-cardiagraph, for analyzing heart conditions; the artificial fever machine for treating several painful, crippling diseases; electro-surgical apparatus; diathermy; ultraviolet radiation; infrared radiation; ionic radiation; surgical ionization; and other remedial measures have been provided by electricity.

Through research and engineering developments, the incandescent lamp has been vastly improved and reduced in cost. The "Science of Seeing" has been developed, aiding and safeguarding the sight of millions of people. The lamp has invaded the field of photography, and street and highway lighting have made our streets safer after dark. New light sources of ever greater efficiency have been developed—sodium lights, fluorescent lights—all are opening up new fields of usefulness. Sealed-beam headlamps for automobiles are making night driving safer and more comfortable.

Another achievement of vast importance in the home has been the radio. Dr. Irving Langmuir's development of the high-power vacuum tube made radiobroadcasting possible, and General Electric's own radiobroadcasting stations have pioneered in making radio entertainment available to almost everyone. Today, General Electric has regular broadcasting stations at Schenectady, Denver, and Oakland; has two shortwave stations at Schenectady and one at San Francisco broadcasting to South America, Europe, and the Orient in several languages; has television stations at Schenectady and at Bridgeport; and has a frequency-modulated station at Schenectady.

In still another field General Electric has been pioneering—the new field of plastics, already important, and promising vast benefits for the future. As an outgrowth of the early nonmetallic gears, the present list of plastic products ranges from heels for ladies shoes to radio cabinets, from pencils to parts for machines. In any forecast of the future, plastic products must be given a leading place.

This then, was the picture of General Electric that Mr. Young and Mr. Swope could look back upon as 1939 drew to a close. Behind them lay a period in which General Electric had made electricity of service to mankind, contributing to greater comfort of living for millions of people. Behind them lay a period of post-war collapse, an unprecedented period of business boom, followed by a decade of devestating depression. Yet through it all General Electric had made steady progress in applying electricity to the needs of civilization, creating "More Goods for More People at Less Cost." Mr. Young was just past 65, Mr. Swope was 66. They had long advocated the retirement of General Electric employees at 65; now they faced the task of turning over to others the responsibilities they had discharged so well.

At the Board of Directors meeting on November 17, 1939, Mr. Young read the statement that he had written on his scratch pad a week before, "We took up these offices together and we wish to lay them down together."—January 1, 1940. Listening to his words were two men who had entered the room a few minutes before as the Assistant to the President and Executive Vice President, respectively, but who were to leave a few minutes later as Philip D. Reed, Chairman of the Board of Directors, and Charles E. Wilson, President.

So ended the second period of General Electric history; so started the third. What lies ahead none can know, but if the history of the past can be taken as a guide, the future holds in store possibilities as vast and as promising as any that have gone before.

APPENDIX

Statement of

OWEN D. YOUNG

to the

Temporary National Economic Committee

Regarding the Formation of Capital

of the

General Electric Company

WASHINGTON, D. C.
May 17, 1939

THIS IS AN EFFORT to draw an over-all picture of the material growth of the General Electric Company and to show the origin and development of its capital. The statement does not deal with the adventures and the accomplishments of the Company in the field of science, nor with its experience in welding together great numbers of human beings of widely diversified capacities and skills into an organized and effective service.

Even in the material field, the attempt to reflect the story truly and briefly is a daring one. None will understand that better or make more charitable allowance than the group for which this memorandum is prepared.

The corporate age of the General Electric Company is 47 years, but as it sprang from the consolidation of the Edison and Thomson-Houston Companies, it is perhaps more correct to say that its present age is sixty years.

At the close of its sixtieth year on December 31, 1938, we find its material resources are carried on its books at the net value of $322,739,000, classified as follows:

Net working capital (current assets less current
liabilities) $155,023,000
Affiliated companies and other investments, (including International General Electric Co.,
and manufacturing, selling, real estate and
other companies, $105,585,000) $141,528,000
Plant and equipment 40,148,000
Other assets 10,022,000

$346,721,000
Less: other liabilities and miscellaneous reserves $ 23,982,000
Total capital investment 322,739,000

This capital was accumulated as follows:
From retained earnings, now carried as surplus and
general reserve $142,452,000
From issue of capital stock 180,287,000

This capital stock was issued:
For properties $ 37,784,000
For cash 75,379,000
In exchange for bonds of the Company 17,334,000
As dividends 49,790,000

$180,287,000

Representing this stock there is now issued and outstanding 28,845,927 shares, held by 208,580 stockholders. There
are no bonds and no preferred stock outstanding. In a word,
the two hundred thousand-odd stockholders own the Company, not an equity in its assets.

This picture, which is one of affluence in the foreground,
might well be misleading unless we can see in the background the rough and dangerous road on which the pioneers
set out, with confidence and courage, more than a half century ago. In that great caravan were scientists and inventors
to originate, engineers to apply, manufacturers to make, com-

mercial men to sell, people with savings to finance, entrepreneurs and administrators to develop and manage, and a vast army of conscientious and skillful men and women doing their respective jobs with pride in a new art and enthusiasm in the creation of a new industry.

In looking for the beginning of the road it is necessary for us to recall what has been earlier stated, that the progenitors of the General Electric Company were the Edison General Electric Company and the Thomson-Houston Electric Company. Let us speak of the latter first, not because it is the more important of the two, but rather because, in typical American fashion, it arose out of the unknown.

If we exclude the telegraph, it is fair to say that in 1878 the electrical manufacturing industry was not only nonexistent, but the art as a practical one was unknown. The men who created, financed and managed the Thomson-Houston Company were likewise relatively unknown. At that time Edison was well enough known through his inventions so that his initial adventure into the electrical industry was financed by a group of prominent New York capitalists. Not so with the Thomson-Houston group. There were no prior inventions, there were no names of great capitalists, and there was very little money.

Elihu Thomson and Edwin J. Houston were teachers in the Philadelphia Central High School. They built a dynamo, induction coils and an arc lamp. Thomson showed the contraption to his friend, Thomas H. McCollin, a commercial photographer in Philadelphia. McCollin asked his cousin, George A. Garrett, to see a demonstration. Thomson, then 26 years old, said, "I can build a better machine than this, one that will run any number of lights you want." Garrett, with enthusiasm replied, "Let's build a four-lighter. I'll stand the expense." That was America speaking in 1879!

The first installation was in an all-night bakery, the second in a brewery. When the brewery caught on fire one of the firemen who was holding the hose said, "What the dickens kind of a light is that? You pour water on her and she won't go out!" That was news in America sixty years ago.

At the same time, Mr. Edison, having incorporated the Edison Company with the backing of J. P. Morgan and a capital of $300,000, was receiving considerable well-deserved publicity in the New York press.

Thereupon, Frederick H. Churchill of New Britain, Connecticut, seeking a new industry for his town, invited Thomson and Houston to settle there. When they accepted, Churchill circulated a prospectus in New Britain which, after describing the new company as "a rare opportunity for the upbuilding of a successful business enterprise," ended with the following sentence: "Such an industry would have within it a capacity for expansion and growth such as is furnished by but few of the business opportunities that today present themselves to the business world."

Churchill died in 1881 and the New Britain venture failed; not, however, before one of its installations had been made in an armory in Lynn, Massachusetts. A Lynn newspaper proprietor, Silas A. Barton, became interested in the possibility of a second installation in that city and visited New Britain. Learning that the business was for sale, he suggested the idea of purchase to a group of Lynn shoe manufacturers, among whom was Charles A. Coffin, then under forty years of age. The upshot was that Coffin and his associates purchased a controlling interest in the company, moved it to Lynn and changed its name to the Thomson-Houston Electric Company.

The members of the Lynn syndicate were successful shoe manufacturers. Initially they were primarily interested in bringing a new industry to their town. That business soon captured the imagination of Charles A. Coffin, and from that time until his retirement in 1922 he was its leader through bad times and good.

It is necessary for us to remember that in 1882 the problem which faced both the Thomson-Houston Company and the Edison Company was not only the origination, development and manufacture of electrical machines. That was only half the task. Broadly speaking there were no buyers. New customers had to be created to buy the new machines. This led to the creation of local light and power companies. The sponsors were usually made up of local capitalists and politicians, for it was necessary to have a franchise and some money.

For the most part they were motivated by civic pride and the promotion of local development. The capital of the companies was proverbially inadequate. This forced the manufacturing companies to accept in part payment for the new equipment the bonds and stocks of the new customer companies. The Edison Company, through a somewhat different technique—that of issuing exclusive licenses against securities of local operating companies—ultimately faced the same necessity of accepting additional securities in part payment for its products.

Leaving now the Thomson-Houston Company at Lynn, with Charles A. Coffin and his associates in charge, let us look at the development of the Edison Company.

In 1879, while Thomson, the high school teacher, was tinkering with his arc light system, Edison, still under 35, had already established a modest position as an inventor. One of his earlier inventions, relating to the electric telegraph, had been the subject of patent litigation. Grosvenor P. Lowrey, a prominent New York lawyer, had defended

Edison's interests and as a result became one of his most faithful and staunch supporters. Lowrey, having confidence in Edison's ability and knowing of his interest in developing an incandescent lamp, approached Mr. J. P. Morgan and other influential financiers of his acquaintance. The result was the organization of the Edison Electric Light Company. The capital stock amounted to $300,000, of which $250,000 was issued in payment for equipment and the remaining $50,-000 was subscribed for, with 80 per cent paid in in cash. That, too, was America speaking in 1878.

Edison's immediate problem was the discovery of some material for a filament that would stand incandescence for a considerable period without disintegration.

On October 21, 1879, his experiments were crowned with success at Menlo Park, when his carbonized cotton filament burned continuously for forty hours. Truly a historic demonstration!

To successfully operate an incandescent lighting system, however, it was necessary for Edison, in addition to the lamp, to develop a completely new set of mechanisms to generate and transmit the electric current. This was the kind of staggering task which only a great genius could master. It soon made Edison's facilities at Menlo Park inadequate. In 1880, therefore, he organized the Edison Machine Works in New York City to manufacture generators, and the Edison Lamp Works near Newark, N. J., to manufacture lamps.

In 1886, Edison decided to move the Edison Machine Works out of the metropolitan area. He became interested in an unused plant at Schenectady, and made an offer which was refused by the owners.

An impasse threatened. But civic pride burned bright in the breasts of some, at least, of Schenectady's citizens. They grasped what it would mean to the town to have a plant of the famous Edison. A meeting was called, and eventually by local subscription a fund was raised which made up the difference between "bid and asked" prices.

So it was that the Mohawk Valley became the center for manufacturing the generating equipment required by the growing number of Edison licensee operating companies.

These were stirring times. The formative period of electric development was approaching its height. The Edison system, as an organization for manufacturing, licensing and selling electric light systems, was beginning to sprawl. Greater integration seemed desirable, and in 1889 a merger of the individual Edison enterprises was consummated through the formation of the Edison General Electric Company.

At the same time that the Edison Machine Works was established at Schenectady and the Thomson-Houston Company was getting under way at Lynn, another idea was germinating in the minds of several competent and creative engineers, notable among whom were Charles J. Van Depoele and Frank J. Sprague. In 1887 and 1888 these two, working independently, had demonstrated the practicability of using electricity to propel streetcars.

This opened almost at once a vast new field for the electrical manufacturers. Larger power units had to be made, longer transmission was necessary, and cars needed to be equipped with motors. The old horse railways had to be transformed, franchises modified or enlarged and additional capital provided. As in the lighting field, the problem of financing was difficult but imperative. It invited the manufacturing companies to extend their limited credit further in order to enlarge their business.

The rapidity of the development of the Edison and Thomson-Houston Companies is shown in the following statement of their condition in 1891:

	Edison General Electric	*Thomson-Houston*
Capitalization	$15,000,000	$10,400,000
Gross business	10,940,000	10,304,500
Profits	2,098,000	2,700,000
Number of employees	6,000	4,000
Factory space, sq. feet	400,000	340,000
Customers	3–4,000	3–4,000
Central stations	375	870
Isolated installations	2,300	very few
Street railways equipped	180	204
Street railway cars	2,230	2,760

The Thomson-Houston Company, springing from the unknown, is catching up with the great Edison Company and in points surpassing it. With two-thirds the capital and two-thirds the number of employees, Thomson-Houston is equalling Edison in gross business and exceeding it in profits. It has a larger number of central lighting stations, more street railways and more streetcars equipped. The Edison Company, in its annual report for that year, said that it "could have done a much larger business if it had been willing to accept securities in payment for orders; but . . . a strict rule was adopted of declining all such and doing business exclusively on a cash or short credit basis."

The Thomson-Houston Company had been rediscounting its customers' notes with its banks and pledging operating company securities as collateral for its loans. Finally the banks became hesitant, particularly in accepting securities as distinguished from customers' notes, and in 1890 Charles A. Coffin organized the United Electric Securities Company. The purpose was to transfer to it large blocks of securities of utility operating companies and to sell to the public its own debentures, and so obtain longer term money to bolster the waning treasury of Thomson-Houston. The Thomson-Houston Company kept the common stock of the United Electric Securities Company.

The public, however, was hesitant too. It soon became apparent that debentures could not be sold in sufficient quantities to finance the rapidly increasing amount of utility securities which the manufacturing company was obliged to take. The Edison Company was drawing in its horns as a matter of business policy. The Thomson-Houston Company was doing the same thing from necessity.

Perhaps at this point we should remind ourselves that there were several other companies operating at this time in the electrical manufacturing field; notable among them was the Westinghouse Company. They were all more or less in the same condition with the same problems and the same difficulties.

Under such circumstances, what could be more natural than to combine the Edison and Thomson-Houston Companies, giving the consolidated concern the business leadership of Charles A. Coffin, the inventive genius of Edison and Thomson, eliminating patent conflicts which were threatening both concerns, and bringing together the financial interests in Boston which had supported Thomson-Houston with the great prestige of Mr. Morgan and his associates in New York?

So it was that the General Electric Company was incorporated on April 15, 1892, and began active business on the first day of June in that year. Charles A. Coffin was made President, and the contest began for the market of electrical manufactures between the Westinghouse Company led by George Westinghouse, the brilliant and imaginative engineer, and Charles A. Coffin, the daring and equally imaginative man of business.

The first board of directors of the General Electric Company reflected its distinguished and substantial backing; F. Lothrop Ames, Charles A. Coffin, T. Jefferson Coolidge, Jr., and Henry L. Higginson, all of Boston, Thomas A. Edison, Charles H. Coster, Frank S. Hastings, General Eugene Griffin, Darius O. Mills, H. McK. Twombley, and J. Pierpont Morgan of New York.

The directors made their first report to stockholders on April 11, 1893, covering the eight months from June 1, 1892, to January 31, 1893. At that time it stated its capital investment to be $45,688,755, against which it had issued $10,000,-000 of bonds, $4,236,900 of preferred stock and $30,426,900 of common stock with a surplus of $1,024,955. It had 3,272 stockholders. There were then 1,277 central station lighting companies using Edison and Thomson-Houston apparatus, supplying 2,500,000 incandescent and 110,000 arc lamps. Of the lighting companies, the report says:

"The growth of these companies has been phenomenal, and it is very satisfactory to note that those which have been established longest are making the most rapid increase in size of plant and volume of business.

"During the past year there has been a very marked appreciation in the value of the securities of local companies, especially in the larger cities, testifying to the increased confidence of investors in such properties."

It is interesting to note, at this time, the growth in two years of the electrification of street railways. On February 1, 1891, there were 151 roads operating electrically or under contract; on the same date in 1893 there were 435. On February 1, 1891, there were 1,578 electric cars; on the same date in 1893 there were 8,386. On February 1, 1891, there were 1,252 miles of electric railway in operation; at the same date in 1893 there were 4,927 miles.

In its first eight months of its existence, the Company did $11,728,000 of business, at a profit of $2,996,011 of which $1,971,056 was distributed in dividends and $1,024,955 was carried to surplus.

The prestige of the Company enabled it to sell $454,300 par value of the preferred stock of the United Electric Securities Company for a price in excess of $408,000. It was still necessary for the Company, however, to endorse and discount customers' notes, because such notes unendorsed were not acceptable to the banks. On January 31, 1893, these amounted to $3,787,312.69. In addition it had outstanding $10,000,000 of five per cent bonds.

In such a condition the new General Electric Company faced the panic of 1893. It will be interesting to see what happened during the next few years.

The first shock of the depression was dramatically told in the second annual report of the Company issued under date of January 31, 1894:

"It is needless to say that the past year has been a most trying one to all corporations. It has been especially so to companies like your own, dealing with local enterprises situated in all parts of the United States, and largely dependent on normal conditions for their success and development. During the summer of 1893, even old and strong customers were obliged to ask for leniency in paying their accounts and notes. Under these circumstances, your Company found itself with its own obligations to meet, but unable at that time to collect the money with which to meet them. The difficulties thus presented were carefully considered by your Board and were met by selling to a syndicate certain of the Company's assets consisting of claims against, and stocks and bonds of, local lighting and railway companies, the same being of a class of which your Company sold several million dollars in 1892 and which your Directors, in their last report, said they intended to continue to sell from time to time as heretofore 'through the ordinary channels.' The channels through which your Company usually made such sales having become unavailable owing to the panic, your Directors adopted a plan used on several occasions in the earlier days of the Thomson-Houston Company, and made the sale of assets above described to a syndicate which paid over $4,000,000 in cash. Although the transaction involved a large shrinkage from book valuations, the sale was at a price high under the conditions then prevailing. Few of the securities sold were listed on any exchange or commonly dealt in, and it was not possible to effect a ready sale except in bulk to a syndicate. These assets were placed in a trust known as 'The Street Railway and Illuminating Properties.' After the financial stringency had subsided, the right to subscribe to them was offered to the Stockholders of your Company.

"The depreciation in value of the assets thus sold applies equally to those still on hand. Holders of stocks and bonds of almost every kind find them quoted today much lower than a year ago, and this Company, as a holder of electrical stocks and bonds, is no exception to the rule. In fact, the shrinkage in values of electrical securities has been greater than in most others. The last year has been characterized by shrinkage in every direction, and your Company has suffered severely from it."

The officers of the Company were making a titanic effort in their race with receivership. By January 31, 1894, the debt had been reduced by $6,750,000. The cash had dwindled from $3,871,000 on January 31, 1893, to $591,000 on January 31, 1894. The directors stated:

"While the liquidation of the debt has been going on, the Company has also readjusted its basis for sales, either to cash or to short credits to desirable customers. In view of the extreme depression and the uncertainty as to the early future, your Directors have not felt justified in any other course than that of adhering strictly to sales on this basis. It is believed that your Company has lost little legitimate business in consequence of its curtailment of credit to customers. It intends to confine its business to this basis, and to accept smaller profits."

The capital investment of the Company dropped in that year from $45,000,000 to $32,000,000 and its surplus from $1,000,000 in the black to $12,000,000 in the red. Such was the first impact of the panic on the capital structure of the new concern.

It is interesting to note that the red figures in the surplus continued at substantially the same figure until 1898, when it was wiped out by a reduction of capital stock of $14,000,000. In January 1899, the surplus was in the black to the extent of $156,000, and it has remained in black continuously ever since. The directors further said in their report of January 31, 1894:

"Your Directors do not believe that it will be possible for some time to come to do as large a business as was done by the Company prior to the panic, although a gradual improvement has been apparent during the last two months. The street railway business, which to a considerable extent was formerly done through syndicates and promoters, many of whom have become embarrassed, promises to be smaller than during the previous year. Arc lighting business is also reduced, largely because of the inability of local companies to secure capital with which to extend their business for the purpose of carrying out municipal contracts. The business of the Company, with respect to incandescent lighting, which is to a great degree performed by strong and conservatively managed local companies, is in a more healthy condition, and has not suffered so severely."

In the third annual report, as of January 31, 1895, to cover additional losses the directors "arbitrarily charged $2,000,000 to Profit and Loss Account."

During that year, however, they were busy dealing masterfully with their debt. Of it they say:

"In the last report, your Directors expressed the opinion that they could, out of the then unliquidated assets, pay off the balance of your floating debt and also provide all necessary working capital. These expectations have been realized, and in addition thereto the Company has purchased and cancelled $1,250,000 of its own Debentures at an average cost of less than 89 per cent."

In the fourth report as of January 31, 1896, the Directors make the following statement:

"In their last report, your Directors referred at some length to the liquidation of old assets, and stated that the sum of $2,000,000 had been charged to Profit and Loss for the purpose of providing for all shrinkages which could then be anticipated in the liquidation of old matters.

"Much has been accomplished in the year just closed in liquidating old and slow assets, and the condition of the assets of like character which still remain on the books of the Company is such as to enable your officers to more definitely fix their proper values. Information regarding these matters will be found in the report of the Second Vice-President, to which particular attention is invited. There have been charged against the $2,000,000 item above referred to the sums of $530,152.16, representing the shrinkages which have accrued from the liquidation so far as completed, leaving $1,469,847.84 still standing to provide for possible shrinkages in the future. It is the belief of your Directors that this amount is sufficient to cover all the purposes for which the above sum of $2,000,000 was originally set apart."

The purge continued, but signs of health were reappearing.

"The business secured by your Company for the fiscal year just closed was less than ten per cent greater in value of sales than for the year previous. The *actual* increase in output of factories, based upon capacity of machines and number of articles produced, is more than thirty per cent greater than for the previous year. While the selling prices as thus shown have been materially reduced, there has been a corresponding curtailment in manufacturing and other expenses and lowering in costs, largely due to improved designs and methods of manufacture."

The gross business was still running around $12,000,000. Even in 1897 the business had not increased. In that year, however, the directors referred again to the $2,000,000 that had been set aside in 1894 to provide for shrinkage in assets.

"The business of your Company has suffered during the past year, in common with that of all manufacturing enterprises, from the disturbed financial and political conditions which have prevailed during a considerable portion of the time. These conditions have curtailed the amount of capital ordinarily available for the establishment and extension of Power and Lighting Plants, and have enforced the practice of great economy on the part of its customers. As a result, the shrinkage in orders received by your Company was very marked, especially during the latter half of the year. This shrinkage is not shown by a material falling off in shipments, as given in the Profit and Loss Statement on page 17 of this report, but the amount of work in progress and unfilled orders on hand is considerably less than a year ago.

"With a return to normal commercial conditions, a corresponding revival in the business of your Company may be expected. The volume of business secured by it for the first three months of the current year is slightly in excess of that for the same period in either of the three previous years.

"On January 31, 1895, the sum of $2,000,000 was set aside, as shown in the Annual Report of that year, to provide for shrinkage in assets, the exact values of which it was then extremely difficult to fix. During the past year your Directors have been able to value these items with substantial accuracy, and the $2,000,000 fund has been found sufficient and has been used to provide for the proper adjustment of all accounts and other assets for which it was created."

In opening the sixth report as of January 31, 1898, the President said:

"The past year witnessed a revival in business which increased rapidly in activity and volume during its latter months."

He was there referring to orders taken rather than sales billed. The latter remained at substantially $12,000,000. The clouds were lifting—the sum was beginning to shine. For five years the depression had continued. The struggle for survival was over at last.

A reduction of forty per cent in the share capital of the Company was made, bringing the common stock from $30,-460,000 to $18,276,000 and the preferred stock from $4,252,-000 to $2,551,200.

In 1898 the Company was clearing the way for dividends. The surplus went into the black, as heretofore stated, to $156,000. The business jumped to $15,500,000. In the report to stockholders for that year there appears the following significant statement:

"The Company has no Note Payable, nor is there under discount any paper bearing the Company's endorsement or guaranty.

"It has not borrowed any money, nor has the Company's credit been used during the year either by issuing notes, endorsing customers' paper for discount or lending its name in any way; but by adhering to the policy of the previous four years and maintaining sales on a basis of cash or short credit to desirable customers, all purchases have been paid for in cash."

By 1898 the volume of business had grown to more than $22,000,000, and the market was beginning to take securities, which the Company was selling at prices substantially in excess of their book value after the drastic write-downs of the depression years. The Company was off to a new start and was to participate profitably in the truly amazing developments of the next thirty years.

By the turn of the century, then, the capital investment of the Company as shown by the report of January 31, 1901, was $32,114,681 (in contrast with the $46,000,000 with which it had started eight years before) and was represented by $1,534,000 in bonds, $2,551,200 of preferred stock, $21,400,300 of common stock, and $6,629,181 of surplus. The sales billed for that year were approximately $28,000,000.

The two succeeding years were very profitable ones, especially due to the liquidation of securities above the then book values, and the surplus had risen to $15,000,000. All the preferred stock and about $1,000,000 of bonds were converted into common. About $2,000,000 of new bonds were issued. The Company restored the stock reduction which had been made in 1898, which brought its capital stock to approximately $42,000,000.

During the next four years it was able to find new capital with which to carry on its rapidly increasing business by issuing its common shares to stockholders for cash at par to the extent of approximately $20,000,000.

So the Company faced the critical year of 1907 with a capital investment of $81,000,000 represented by $2,000,000 of bonds, $64,000,000 of common stock, and $15,000,000 of surplus. Its volume of business had grown to approximately $60,000,000.

As a result of the panic of 1907 the directors said in their report of January 31, 1908:

"Late in the year there was a sudden and severe shrinkage in the value of all merchandise and materials used by your Company, notably copper. All said materials, whether raw, manufactured, or in process, which were on hand January 31st, 1908, were inventoried at the prevailing lower prices. The book value of such inventories was thereby reduced by about $2,000,000."

The stockholders having subscribed for only $1,500,000 of common stock in 1907, the Company issued $13,000,000 of 5% ten year debenture bonds convertible into stock at par on and after June 1, 1911. The financial pressures had forced the use of convertible debentures to maintain an adequate capital structure, but fortunately by this time the resources and credit of the Company enabled it to withstand the shock of the short depression of 1907.

During the year 1911, $12,000,000 of the bonds were converted into common, bringing the common capital to $77,-000,000. In 1912 the Company declared a stock dividend of 30% out of surplus for the purpose, as stated in the report, "of recouping the stockholders in part for dividends passed or reduced during the years 1893 to 1902." During that same year the Company authorized an issue of $60,000,000 of forty year debentures to be sold from time to time as required, and they sold, in 1912, $10,000,000 of such bonds bearing a rate of 5% per annum.

So, at the end of 1912, the capital investment stood at $125,000,000, with bonds of $12,000,000, surplus of $12,-000,000 and common stock of $101,000,000.

During the war years, 1917, 1918 and 1919, there were substantial temporary borrowings, increases of capital and surplus, the detail of which throws little light on the normal and progressive capital development of the Company.

The year 1920 brought another crisis. The orders for that year were $318,000,000, more than eighty millions in excess of the previous year. Inventories and receivables had increased, so when the sudden and severe decline in market prices came, the Company wrote off of inventory some $18,-

000,000. During the year it made short term loans of $45,-000,000, but between January and April of the succeeding year, $42,000,000 of such loans had been repaid. The common capital, however, was increased in excess of $50,000,000 during the two years 1920 and 1921 ($40,000,000 being for cash and property and the balance as stock dividends) bringing the total capital investment up to $298,000,000, consisting of $176,000,000 of common stock, $38,000,000 of bonds and $84,000,000 of surplus and general reserve.

In 1922 a special stock was created having no preference over the common except a limited dividend rate of 6%. For the next several years this special stock was issued as stock dividends, and no further dividends in common stock were issued. The last dividend paid in special stock was in 1926, and the total amount issued was $43,000,000.

In 1923 the Company called and paid off $15,000,000 of its bonds. In 1925 it called $15,000,000 more, and it had acquired enough in the market in the meantime so as to reduce its funded debt to $2,000,000. In 1935 the Company called this remaining $2,000,000 of bonds and retired all of its $43,000,000 of special stock.

The Company had in the year 1935 $180,000,000 of common stock, $136,000,000 of surplus and general reserve, making a total capital investment of $316,000,000.

From the above brief sketch of capital growth, I have only drawn attention to the major changes and the problems which faced the management. The résumé of the source of capital was shown at the beginning of this statement.

When one looks at the growth of the volume of sales of the General Electric Company, he finds it remained stationary at $12,000,000 for the first five years of its life, but at the turn of the century it reached more than $25,000,000. At 1910 it was $70,000,000; at 1920 it was $275,000,000; and at

1929 it reached its high point of $415,000,000. In 1933 it dropped to $136,000,000; in 1937 it recovered to $350,000,-000 and in 1938 it was $260,000,000. The enormous growth in the two decades after 1910 needs to be accounted for by anyone who wishes to understand the background of the capitalization of the electrical industry.

I wish now to go back to the trying year of 1893, when the General Electric Company transferred reams of utility securities to the Street Railway and Illuminating Properties in order to raise $4,000,000 in cash, and thereby saved itself from bankruptcy. The Street Railway and Illuminating Pool, as it was then called, was strictly a liquidating concern. It had no intention of entering the utility business as such. It had no particular interest in or knowledge of management of such properties. In order to make its securities marketable, it was obliged in many instances, if not indeed in most, to reorganize the operating units through receivership by reducing the prior lien bonds and preferred stocks. It thereby threw larger equities in the new common. The new bonds and preferred were sold to the public to the extent and at such prices as the market would take them. The new common shares remaining in the liquidating pool were, for the most part, not marketable through then established channels. Something new needed to happen and it did.

For the ten years preceding the turn of the century, the glamour of the new electrical art had attracted many of the most brilliant young men of the time into the field of electrical engineering. Most of them took a post-graduate course with the manufacturing companies known as "The Test." Thereafter, some of them remained in manufacturing, but many others went out to the lighting and railway companies. A few of them started in business on their own account, first as expert advisers to existing companies, and later as experts in management. It was to this last group that liquidators like the Illuminating Pool went for the purpose of creating, through expert management and engineering skill, values in common shares. The usual procedure was to turn over to such management groups a small block of the common shares at a rather nominal figure and install the engineering organization as manager. To spur the management, it was usually customary to grant options on additional blocks to be taken up in specified periods at increasing prices.

So the young engineers came into positions of management and later control of operating public utilities. They replaced the nominees of the old politician and the local capitalist who, with little knowledge, had endeavored to operate in the early days and whose influence was much diminished and in many cases entirely eliminated by the purge of the panic of 1893.

So we find at the beginning of the twentieth century groups of highly trained young engineers, able and ambitious to develop utilities, with an opportunity open to them not only to render great service to the community, but to acquire a competence for themselves. At the same time in the manufacturing organizations their contemporaries were coming into positions of influence. For the first time the manufacturers had competent and appreciative buyers, and conversely these young managers of utilities were stimulating and urging the electrical producers to make more efficient and more economical equipment.

Here then were producers and users venturing into a new field unafraid of new things. The rate of technical advance was tremendous. Human brains alive and at work everywhere were enlarging the field of electrical service and materially reducing the costs. Values began to be reflected in these common stocks and then the public itself began to buy them, in limited quantities to be sure, but nevertheless a market was emerging. Soon the old liquidating concerns had finished their task, usually with great profit to the stockholders who had dared to invest their money in the dark days of the panic.

But when the utility common shares became valuable the new managers did not wish to sell them, although they could do so at a profit, because they might lose control of the companies which they had really made. As energetic Americans, however, they were ambitious to extend their management operations and achieve the added economies that such extension promised.

To meet this situation the utility holding company was invented, which enabled these ambitious young managers not so much to sell their original common shares at a profit as to obtain some funds against them through the issue of holding company securities, and thereby enable them to enlarge their operations in the communities which they served or to acquire an interest in other properties and so extend their management program. Then, too, the holding company was a better medium for the investor. Instead of taking common shares in an individual operating company, he was able to invest in a diversified group of shares, and if he took preferred stock of the holding company he would gain some security through the equity margin represented by the common.

This, broadly, is the story of utility holding companies before the great war. If holding companies have, in these later days, fallen under criticism, we must ever remember the service which they performed in the rapid expansion of electrical services to the public. As an effective instrument for providing capital it made possible the rapid development and use of the steam turbine, not only in great centers of population but in power plants serving large numbers of rural communities through networks of transmission systems. In no other way could the small communities have received such high character of service at such low cost.

This mechanism was developing during the period from 1900 to 1910, during which time the business of the General Electric Company trebled. But even so, the full effect was not felt until the next two decades when the business of the Company rose from $70,000,000 to more than $400,000,000. This tremendous increase was not experienced alone by the General Electric Company, but by the entire electrical manufacturing industry. Indeed, General Electric's percentage of the industry business has remained through the years at between twenty and twenty-five per cent.

There is another aspect, however, of this co-operation between the engineers of the utilities and the engineers of the electrical manufacturers. As I have suggested before, it was difficult for the manufacturers to keep pace with the demands of their own customers for new things. To do so, the General Electric Company in 1901 established a research laboratory and called to it men of great vision and ability to explore the unknown. Those men had no specified jobs. To improve what we had was the work of the engineers. The research men were to move out into an unknown land, and they were supported on their adventure in the hope that they would bring back among their discovered treasures a few at least that would be of practical advantage to the electrical industry. One might well have criticized in those days a corporate management which gambled stockholders' money on such remote chances. Yet I suppose no venture has been more profitable to the General Electric Company, to investors and operators in utilities and to the public served by them than these research laboratories.

The drive for economy and efficiency in the production of electrical power so urgently demanded by the utility engineers was supported by the work of the research laboratories and the engineers of the manufacturers. Indeed, the profits of the utility operating companies became so large as not only to attract investors, but to precipitate constantly calls from customers for reduced rates. In the beginning, municipalities endeavored to regulate rates, but the utility rapidly outgrew the municipality. Then State Commissions were charged with that responsibility, but the utilities in some cases overran State boundaries and so the Federal government found its justification for a limited entry into the field of utility regulation.

I should like to say in passing that in the political debates incident to the entrance of the Federal government into the field of regulation, there has been criticism of the incompetence not only of local regulating bodies, but frequently of State commissions. I should like to take the opportunity of saying here that by and large I think those criticisms are unfair and unwarranted. The fact is that the research laboratories and the engineers in the electrical industry made such rapid progress in efficiencies and economies that regulating bodies were unable to keep up with them. As a consequence, by the time the rather cumbersome machinery of regulation established a rate, the efficiencies introduced meanwhile frequently kept the profits on the new rate as high as they were on the old ones. This fact led customers to criticize the regulating boards. Such criticism to my mind was unjustifiable. Indeed, on the whole, I think the fact that the utility companies were highly prosperous during the early days was of great public advantage. Their earnings were largely turned back into their properties and so supplemented the capital which they were able to get from the public and which in amount would, I think, have been inadequate to have provided for the rapid expansion of facilities which took place between the years 1910 and 1930.

I have spoken of the part which the engineer managers of the electrical utility companies played in the development of the business, and consequently the capital formation of the General Electric Company. To complete the picture it is now necessary to speak of the major adventures of the General Electric Company itself in the utility field.

I have already told how essential it was in the earlier days for the Company to accept public utility securities in part payment for its apparatus and how large blocks of such utilities were sold in the panic of 1893 to save the Company's life. Attention has also been called that prior to the organization of the General Electric Company, Charles A. Coffin had organized the United Electric Securities Company of Boston as a medium through which, by the issue of its debentures and preferred stock, he could find an indirect market for the securities of operating companies which he wished to take. The United Electric Securities Company was continued in existence as a subsidiary of the General Electric Company and was used from time to time for the purpose of liquidating in part the utility securities of the General Company. Its headquarters were in Boston and its securities were largely sold in that market.

In 1904 the General Electric Company caused to be organized the Electrical Securities Corporation in New York for the purpose of doing a similar business in New York and thereby widening the opportunity of the General Electric Company to aid in the financing of utilities. The common stock of this company too was held by the General Electric Company. Many years later, to save overhead and simplify the organization, the United Electric Securities Company of

Boston was liquidated by a transfer of its assets in the domestic field to the Electrical Securities Corporation, and in the foreign field to the International General Electric Company, which is the subsidiary of the General Electric Company doing its foreign business, except in Canada. It is unnecessary to speak of the United Electric Securities Company further than to say that it served a useful purpose for more than forty years with satisfactory returns to its investors and the General Electric Company and that it had rendered a substantial service to the financing of utilities during periods when the market was not ready to supply capital demands.

The Electrical Securities Corporation still exists, but it no longer issues its securities to the public, all of the outstanding ones having been called and retired. It had developed through many years a highly specialized management and it is today, practically speaking, only an incorporated Securities Department of the General Electric Company. It too, as a financing mechanism to protect utility credits, had served a useful purpose.

These two companies were investment companies. They were not in any sense management companies although at infrequent times they were compelled as investors to participate as directors, and occasionally as managers. Such activities, however, were purely incidental.

I shall now speak of another adventure of the General Electric Company into the utility field which did not originally contemplate, but which ultimately eventuated, in management and in a "holding company." I speak of the Electric Bond and Share Company. It was natural that the two investment companies above referred to should take the securities of the larger public utility operating companies. It was, of course, the ambition of the engineer managers, of whom I have spoken, to operate initially in the larger communities. Even after the turn of the century, the utilities operating in the smaller communities were finding it difficult to get adequate capital and particularly equity capital. Prior lien securities, such as bonds and preferred stocks of the smaller companies could only be sold on a high interest basis and when adequate capital for common stock was not available, the senior securities often could not be sold at all.

Under these circumstances, the General Electric Company, again under the leadership of Charles A. Coffin, conceived the idea in 1905 of organizing the Electric Bond and Share Company for the purpose of aiding the smaller utilities in raising junior capital and in selling their senior securities at a better price. The development of the utility business in serving many communities from centralized power plants through the use of long transmission lines practically forced the Electric Bond and Share Company, through the normal evolution of its business, into a large holding and management company. Meantime, other operating units, through holding companies and otherwise, were extending their lines to serve not only small cities, but small villages and hamlets; indeed, they were reaching out for the farms. As these operating units became larger and the general trend of the utility business was profitable, the Bond and Share Company was well able to handle financing and to provide its own capital requirements without help from the General Electric Company. Accordingly, on December 30, 1924, the General Electric Company decided to divest itself of ownership of the Electric Bond and Share Company by distributing the common stock of that Company to its own stockholders as a dividend. Such stock at the time of its distribution was valued on the books of the General Electric Company at $25,000,000.

In 1919, after the close of the great war, the General Electric Company, at the suggestion of the President of the United States, undertook to secure the co-operation of all American concerns interested in wireless in the creation of a unified organization to develop and protect the communication interests of the United States throughout the world. The story of radio and its rapid development need not be repeated here. It is only referred to because the Radio Corporation of America was organized for the above purposes in 1919 and as the result of a decree of the Federal Court, the common stock of the Radio Corporation which the General Electric Company held was distributed in 1933 to the stockholders of the General Electric Company as a dividend. The value of that stock as carried on the books of the General Electric Company was approximately $26,500,000 and that amount was deducted from surplus in that year.

While speaking of dividends, perhaps I should say at this point that in addition to the Electric Bond and Share and the Radio Corporation dividends of $51,000,000, the General Electric Company has, during the forty-eight years of its life, paid cash dividends to its stockholders of $655,662,000 and an additional $47,000,000 to retire its special stock issued as stock dividends. During this same period the Company has sold approximately $7,000,000,000 worth of electrical products and it has paid to its employees in wages and salaries something over $2,700,000,000.

Now we are back to the point where I started. The enterprise has been profitable, but it took the vision and daring of genius to create it. It took confidence, persistence and courage to develop it and carry it through its earlier days. It remains only for us at this time and for those who come after us to so administer this great concern that it may continue to render a service in the future comparable to the past.

Index

A

Adams, Thomas E.
Brush-Adams lamp invented 69
Addison, Dr. Thomas H. G-E
representative on West Coast 200
Alexanderson, Ernst F. W.
alternator on trial at New Brunswick, 372; duplex radio telephone system, 354; single-phase railway motor, 350; high-frequency alternator, 351; magnetic modulator, 352; multiple-tuned antenna, 354; two-way wireless telephony, 354
Alteneck, inventor of Siemens dynamo 7
American Electric Company
organized, 33; bought by Lynn Syndicate, 54
American Marconi Company
Alexanderson alternator tested, 372; purchased by G. E. Co., 377
American Telephone & Telegraph Company
part in organizing RCA 377
Ames, F. L.
financial supporter of Thomson-Houston Co., 147; Director of G. E. Co., 195, 406

Andrews, William S.
Edison lighting installation, Sunbury, Pa., 59
Arc lamps
Brush type, 7, 8; displayed at Dr. Longworth's residence, 27; first installation, Wanamaker's store, 13, 30; automatic regulator, 15, 19; street, first installation, 27; Jenney type, 71; luminous, 310
Asmussen, Oscar, friend of Steinmetz 169
Association of Edison Illuminating Companies
organized, 97; renewing customer's lamps, 265

B

Babcock, A. A., turbine-electric ship propulsion 330
Baltimore & Ohio Railroad, tunnel electrification 254
Barton, Silas A.
General Manager of Thomson-Houston Co., 164; organizer of Lynn Electric Lighting Co., 52
Batchelor, Charles
came to Schenectady, 149; Edison's model maker, 22

Farmer, Moses G., inventor incandescent lamp 182
Fireboats, first electrically propelled 330
Fish, Frederick P.
Counsel for Thomson-Houston Company, 193; General Counsel of G. E. Co., 197
Fiske, Lieutenant Bradley A. 251
Fiske Street Station, Chicago, to begin operation 279
Folsom Falls, California, electric power plant 250
Force, Martin, Edison's laboratory assistant 22
Fort Wayne Electric Company purchased interest in Wood's arclight system, 164; reorganized, 225; Slattery alternating-current system, 215–216
Fort Wayne Electric Corporation organized, 226; purchased by G. E. Co., 284
Fort Wayne Electric Light Company 71, 143
Foster, W. J., three-phase induction motor tests 209
Franklin Institute of Philadelphia, tested dynamos 10, 12, 23
French Thomson-Houston Company 168
Fuller Bakery, Philadelphia, Thomson-Houston dynamo installed and tested 14, 400
Fuller-Wood Co., Wood's dynamo 18

G

Gardner, George P., financial supporter of Thomson-Houston Co. 147
Garfield, E. I., first Secretary of G. E. Co. 197
Garrett, George S., witnessed demonstration, Thomson's inventions 13
Gary, Indiana, steel mill, electric drive 320

Gaulard and Gibbs system 107, 177
"Gem," incandescent lamp developed 315
General Electric Co.
broadcasting stations, 393; Comptroller, first, 198; consolidation announcement to employees, 195; cooperation with labor, 387; Department Heads, first, 198; Directors, first, 195, 406; District Offices established, 176, 198; Electric Bond and Share Co. stock distributed to stockholders, 388; Engineering Committee formed, 221; Erie Works, land purchased, 331; Executive Committee formed, 220; executive officers, first, 197; exhibits, World's Fair Chicago, 1893, 215; financial reports, 221, 397–398, 406–415; frequency-modulation station, 393; Home Office transferred to Schenectady, 226; incorporation date, 193, 405; Manufacturing Committee formed, 221; Moore's gaseous lamp patents obtained, 332; Mutual Benefit Association, established, 383; new title beginning date, 195; Niagara power plant plans, 235; patent agreement with Curtis, 276; patent agreement with Westinghouse, Tesla type polyphase induction motor, 287; patents held, 272; Pension Plan established, 383; Pittsfield Works started, 177; profit-sharing system established, 383; progress of industry since 1922, 385–394; purchase Cooper Hewitt Electric Co., 310; Research Laboratory organized, 299, 314; River Works, Lynn, new plant, 287; Sales Committee formed, 221; Schenectady Works, history of buildings, 150, 242–243, 305, 313–314; sales, 1892–1938, 415–416; stockholders and shares issued, 398; tantalum lamp manufacture, 316; tungsten filament, commercially introduced, 335; tungsten filament patent purchased, 335; Young, Owen D.,

Paine, Sidney B.
electric lighting in textile mills, 63; electrical salesman, 210
Panama Canal control system 356
Panics, effect on G. E. Co.
1893 221, 407
1907 413
Parker, William, President American Electric Co. 33
Parshall, Horace F.
Manager, Calculating Department of G. E. Co., 200; designed generator, 214; designed motor, 211; engineer, Niagara plant, plans, 235; engineer, Sprague Co., 154
Parsons, Hinsdill, Vice-President and General Counsel, G. E. Co. 359
Patents
agreements, Brush and Telegraph Supply Co., 9; consolidations, 192; Patent Control Board, 272; lamp monopoly, 340
Peabody, S. Endicott, financial supporter of Thomson-Houston Co. 147
Peach, Benjamin F., Jr. Treasurer of G. E. Co., first 197
Peek, Frank W., Jr. transmission million volts of electricity 380
Pelton impulse water wheels 232
Pevear, Henry A., organizer of Lynn Electric Lighting Co. 53
Polyphase system, first in world 231
Polyphase transmission 218
Porter, Charles T., designed steam engine 44
Potter, William B.
engineer, Railway Department of G. E. Co., 257; selling experiences, 144
Pratt, Charles E., designer elevator motor 289
Protective equipment, for transformers 108

Radio Corporation of America organized, 376; distribution of stock held by G. E. Co., 424
Railway motors, Brush, Sprague, Thomson-Houston compared 142
Reed, Philip D. Chairman of the Board, G. E. Co., elected 394
Regenerative braking
electric trains, 361; first time used, 85
Reist, H. G.
generator design for steam turbine, 279; three-phase induction motor work, 209
Resistance welding
principle discovered, 12; Thomson's method, 50
Rheostats, railway motor demonstration 85
Rice, E. W., Jr.
personal interest in young experts, 166; steam turbine interest, 275; work on Niagara power plant plans, 235; superintendent at Lynn, 87; Thomson-Houston organization plan, 102; Technical Director of G. E. Co., first, 197; Vice-President in charge of Engineering and Manufacturing, 247; President G. E. Co., 349; Honorary Chairman of the Board, G. E. Co., 382
Rohrer, Albert H.
assistant engineer at Lynn, 87; entertains President Villard, Edison G. E. Co., 191
Rotary converter Bradley type, first used 238
Ryan, Walter D'Arcy
Illuminating Engineer, 266; illumination installations supervised, 364; designed Tower of Jewels, Panama-Pacific Exposition, 367; scientific basis for illumination, 265

R

Rach, Christian, foreman 150, 243
Radio, trans-oceanic system, first 351

S

San Francisco, headquarters Pacific Coast territory 200

TYPOGRAPHY, PRINTING, AND BINDING IN THE U. S. A. BY
KINGSPORT PRESS, INC., KINGSPORT, TENNESSEE

2/97